# CURRENT RESEARCH
# ON OPTICAL MATERIALS,
# DEVICES AND SYSTEMS
# IN TAIWAN

**SELECTED TOPICS IN ELECTRONICS AND SYSTEMS**

*Editor-in-Chief:* **P. K. Tien**

# CURRENT RESEARCH ON OPTICAL MATERIALS, DEVICES AND SYSTEMS IN TAIWAN

Editors

## S. Chi
National Chiao Tung University,
Taiwan

## T. P. Lee
National Science Foundation,
USA

**World Scientific**
Singapore • New Jersey • London • Hong Kong

*Published by*

World Scientific Publishing Co. Pte. Ltd.

P O Box 128, Farrer Road, Singapore 912805

*USA office:* Suite 1B, 1060 Main Street, River Edge, NJ 07661

*UK office:* 57 Shelton Street, Covent Garden, London WC2H 9HE

**British Library Cataloguing-in-Publication Data**
A catalogue record for this book is available from the British Library.

**CURRENT RESEARCH ON OPTICAL MATERIALS, DEVICES AND SYSTEMS IN TAIWAN**

ISBN 981-02-3297-7

Printed in Singapore by Uto-Print

# INTRODUCTION

During the last quarter of a century, the economy in Taiwan has transformed from a basically agricultural economy into an industrial one. Consumer electronics and personal computers have replaced rice and textiles as the leading export products. The people in Taiwan have enjoyed a standard of living that is unprecedented in Chinese history. The success of the industrialization in Taiwan can be attributed to a combination of factors: a sound government policy, a dynamical local industry, and, to a large extent, a well-educated and motivated work force.

Since the mid-1980's, the electronics industry in Taiwan has shifted its emphasis from customer-based electronics to information-based electronics products. Taiwan is now enjoying 65% of the world market for PC motherboards and keyboards, 64% in scanners, and 57% in PC-monitors. The electronic information products amount to 46% of the electronics exports at a total value of $35 billion in 1995.

Among information-based electronics, a sub-group in optoelectronics is starting to grow. In addition to the PC-monitors and the visible light-emitting diodes for displays that have already established a large world market share, other technologies such as optical storage, optical signal processing, optical switching and transmission are emerging. Focused research efforts in various universities and research institutions are strongly supported by the National Science Council, the Ministry of Economic Affairs, and the Ministry of Telecommunications.

A Photonic/Taiwan'96 Seminar was held on December 12–13, 1996, in the Industrial Technology Research Institute in Hsinchu, Taiwan. The seminar was co-sponsored by the Optical Engineering Society of the Republic of China, IEEE/LEOS Taipei Chapter, SPIE Taiwan Chapter, and the National Science Council. A total of 166 technical papers were presented that encompassed broad subject areas which included:

(1) group III-IV semiconductor materials including nitrides,
(2) organic materials and optical thin films,
(3) semiconductor lasers and optical amplifiers,
(4) photodetectors and photodiode arrays,
(5) optical fiber communications,
(6) optical measurements,
(7) optical pattern recognition and signal processing,
(8) optical computing,
(9) nonlinear optics and optical memory,
(10) guided-wave optical devices,
(11) display technology,

(12) optical storage devices,

(13) ultra-fast optics, and

(14) solid-state lasers.

Prof. Sien Chi, the guest editor, has invited authors who have participated in the seminar mentioned above to contribute to this volume. He has selected subject areas that are representative to that covered in the seminar. The first two papers deal with epitaxial growth in InP and InGaAs multiple quantum wells by MOCVD and MBE techniques respectively. A high quality InP epitaxial layer that was obtained by using flow-rate-modulation MOCVD is reported by M. K. Lee, and a large absorption edge shift, that was observed in the MBE-grown InGaAs MQW at 1.3 micron wavelength, is presented by C. T. Lee and T. E. Nee. In the third paper, C. C. Yang *et al.*, present a comprehensive view of passive mode-locking techniques of lasers. A mode-locked laser produces very short optical pulses that are essential for very high-speed time-division-multiplexed optical systems such as soliton communication systems. Numerical simulations of a nonlinear polarization mode-locked laser, a nonlinear coupling mode-locked semiconductor laser and an additive-pulse mode-locked fiber laser are also discussed. The following three papers deal with guided-wave devices. Y. T. Huang *et al.* discussed dual antiresonant reflecting optical waveguide (ARROW) devices in both $SiO_2/TiO_2$ and InP/InGaAsP systems. The ARROW concept can be applied to power dividers, hybrid couplers, wavelength filters, polarization beamsplitters, and pressure sensors. W. S. Wang, Y. P. Liao and C. H. Yang introduce a nickle-indiffusion waveguide for the TE-TM mode splitter in lithium niobate, and show improved performance with a much simplified process. A numerical analysis of nonlinear directional couplers is presented by C. H. Lai, H. C. Chang, and J. P. Pang using the segmentation method that produced more accurate results compared with the simple coupled-mode theory and its improved version. In the seventh paper, a theoretical model of a quantum-mechanical energy band filter with resonant semiconductor superlattices is presented by H. H. Tung and C. P. Lee. The analysis uses a quantum-mechanical wave impedance (QMWI) matching method that is analogous to the familiar circuit theory. Based on the QMWI method a structure for a perfect energy pass-band filter is proposed. The method is also used to analyze the scattering process in a resonant tunneling diode. The eighth paper, presented by Y. K. Su and C. T. Lin, discussed the performance of HgCdTe photoconductors with a simple photo surface treatment to reduce the $1/f$ noise. A surface recombination velocity as low as 300 cm/sec and a detectivity as sensitive as $3 \times 10^{10}$ cmHz$^{1/2}$/W have been obtained.

In the ninth paper, C. L. Pan *et al.* demonstrated an accurate, non-contact and compact electro-optical characterization technique for measuring both the amplitude and the phase of microwave standing waves in a GaAs microstrip transmission line. The voltage standing wave ratio and the reflection coefficient as well as the dispersion characteristics were determined up to 16 GHz. A general review of the real-time shift-invariant optical pattern recognition is given by Y. S. Cheng in the tenth paper. In the eleventh paper, a read-only holographic memory for digital data storage is experimentally demonstrated by C. P. Yang *et al.* The performance of the memory and the techniques for improving its bit error rate are presented. Finally the last paper by Y. K. Chen, S. K. Liaw, and S. Chi described an experiment of a high-speed SONET wavelength-division-multiplexing self-healing ring network using optical power limiting amplifiers. A constant channel power, a small inter-channel power variation and a low noise figure with a large dynamic range are achieved.

This volume of collected papers by no means covers the breath and depth of the optical research that has been carried out in Taiwan; it simply represents a snap shot of a small sample of the work that is in progress. Evidently, some of the research results will lead to further development for commercial products that will be successful in the marketplace in the near future.

We are most grateful to the authors of this volume who have committed a good deal of their time and effort. We would also like to thank Dr. P. K. Tien, the Editor-in-Chief of IJHSES, for his suggestions, enthusiasm, encouragement, and patience. Sincere thanks also go to the editorial staff of World Scientific Publishing Co. for the resourceful support throughout the preparation of this volume.

Sien Chi
Professor
Institute of Electro-Optical Engineering
National Chiao Tung University
Hsinchu, Taiwan
R.O.C.

Tien Pei Lee*
Chief Scientist and Director
Optoelectronic Technology Research
Bell Communications Research (Bellcore)
Red Bank, New Jersey 07701-5699
U.S.A.

*Dr. Lee retired from Bellcore in February 1997. He is currently the Program Director at the National Science Foundation, Arlington, Virginia.

**Sien Chi** was born on July 6, 1936, in Huaiying, Jiangsu, China. He received a B.S.E.E. degree from National Taiwan University and an M.S.E.E. degree from National Chiao Tung University, Taiwan, ROC, in 1959 and 1961, respectively. He obtained his Ph.D. degree in electrophysics from the Polytechnic Institute of Brooklyn, Brooklyn, NY, in 1971.

In 1971, he joined the faculty of National Chiao Tung University, where he is currently a Professor of Electro-Optical Engineering. From 1972 to 1973, he was the Chairman of the Department of Electrophysics. From 1973 to 1977, he was the Director of the Institute of Electronics. From 1977 to 1978, he was a resident visitor at Bell Laboratories, Holmdel, NJ. From 1985 to 1988, he was the Principal Advisor of Hua-Eng Wires and Cables Company, the first manufacturer of fibers and fiber cables in Taiwan, for developing fiber making and cabling technology. From 1988 to 1990, he was the Director of the Institute of Electro-Optical Engineering.

He is a Fellow of the Optical Society of America and the Photonics Society of Chinese-Americans. He was the Symposium Chair of the International Symposium on Optoelectronics in Computers, Communications and Control 1992, which was co-organized by National Chiao Tung University and SPIE. From 1993 he has been a recipient of the distinguished Research Award sponsored by the National Science Council, ROC. His research interests are in the area of optical solitons, optical fiber amplifiers and nonlinear fiber optics.

**Dr. Tien Pei Lee** is presently the Program Director of the National Science Foundation, in Arlington, Virginia. He was the Chief Scientist and the Director, Optoelectronic Technology Research, Bell Communications Research (Bellcore), Red Bank, New Jersey. He has published more than 200 technical articles and 10 book chapters on LEDs, photodiodes, and semiconductor lasers for optical fiber communications. He holds seven US patents and five foreign patents. Dr. Lee is the recipient of the Distinguished Member of Technical Staff Award, Bell Laboratories, 1983. He is a Fellow of IEEE, the Optical Society of America, and the Photonic Society of Chinese Americans. He served as the Guest Editor, *IEEE Transactions on Electron Devices*, April 1983, and the Associate Editor of the *IEEE Journal of Lightwave Technology*, 1986–88. He is now the Co-Editor-in-Chief of the *International Journal of High Speed Electronics and Systems*.

# CONTENTS

International Journal of High Speed Electronics and Systems, Vol. 8, No. 4 (1997) 575–586

# HIGH QUALITY InP EPITAXIAL GROWTH USING FLOW RATE MODULATION METALORGANIC CHEMICAL VAPOR DEPOSITION

M. K. LEE and C. C. HU

*Department of Electrical Engineering, National Sun Yat-sen University,*
*Kaohsiung, Taiwan 80424, R.O.C.*

The characteristics of modified flow rate modulation metalorganic chemical deposition is studied. From observation with the atomic force microscope, the flatness of a InP homoepitaxial layer is improved to atomic scale by phosphine modulation metalorganic chemical vapor deposition. The full width at half maximum 5.6 meV of photoluminescence at 77 K can be achieved under optimum growth conditions. The satellite peak around the near band emission can also be reduced to a negligible quantity under optimum growth conditions. Also, MFME can improve the electrical characteristics of the epilayer with higher electron mobility and lower compensation ratio.

## 1. Introduction

The conventional flow rate modulation epitaxy (FME)[1–3] is a variance of MOCVD in which sources are alternatively supplied into the reactor. It shows a significant improvement in the heterointerface abruptness.[4] But the growth interruption will enhance the impurity incorporation. The modified flow rate phosphine modulation epitaxy (MFME)[5,6] can offer a superior InP crystal quality. The basic difference between MFME and FME is that the group V source is switched periodically on and off, while the group III source is always kept on. During the off time of the group V source, MFME can create a metal surface on the growth front. The metal atom has a wider electron distribution than that of the III–V molecule and group V atom,[7] so it is a physical adsorption instead of a chemical adsorption for the metal adatom on the growing surface. Thus, the metal adatom has a higher surface mobility than that of the III–V molecule and group V atom and can move to a more proper position for the crystal growth. On the other hand, lower surface mobility of InP molecules would nucleate locally and produce a large number of clusters in conventional MOCVD. These clusters will form steps on the growth front and cause roughness of the growing surface and defects of the epilayers. Therefore, MFME can provide a more homogeneous nucleation on the growth front for the following growth, and it is believed that such a modified FME, compared to conventional FME and MOCVD,[8,9] would reduce both clusters and defects. The metal surface will be transformed into crystals when the group V source is switched on. The growth is repeated during each cycle of the MFME.

The formation of one metal monolayer on the growth surface is crucial for the MFME. The growth temperature, flow rates of group III and V sources and the on/off time of the group V source are important parameters for MFME. If the off time of the group V source is improper, there is an insufficient or excess coverage of one metal monolayer which would result in defects and degrade the crystal quality owing to the non-stoichiometry growth.[8,9] The growth temperature also determines the crystal quality in MFME. Higher growth temperature will result in group V outgassing during the off time of group V source. Lower growth temperature cannot offer sufficient thermal energy for the metal surface mobility. And, the flow rates of groups III and V have a certain relationship with the on/off time of the group V source. However, there exists a wide range of the MFME growth conditions,[6] in which the crystal quality is superior than that of the conventional MOCVD.

## 2. Experimental

The InP homoepitaxial layers were grown in a vertical low pressure MOCVD system. The reactor pressure is 100 torr. The hydrogen main flow rate is 2 l/min. Trimethylindium (TMIn, kept at 5°C) and phosphine (PH$_3$ 5% in H$_2$) were used as source reactants. Silane (500 ppm diluted in H$_2$) was used as $n$-type dopant. Fe-doped [100] InP was used as substrate. The gas flow sequence of TMIn, PH$_3$ and SiH$_4$ in MFME are shown in Fig. 1. The high quality InP epilayers are grown under

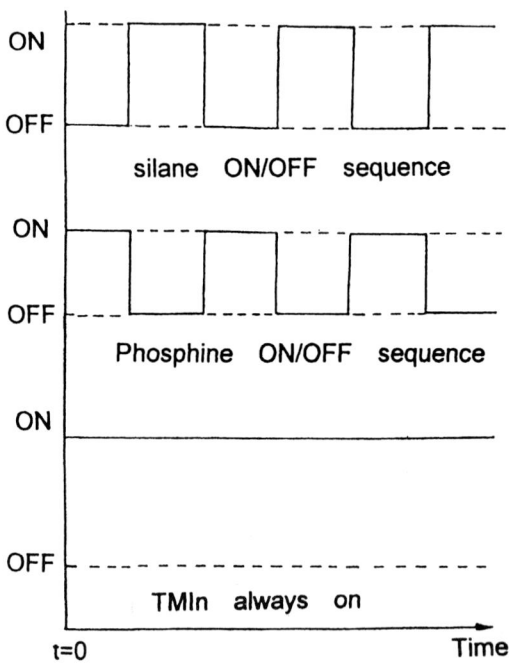

Fig. 1. On/off time sequence for TMIn, PH$_3$ and SiH$_4$ in MFME.

the growth temperature 565°C, V/III ratio 226, and phosphine on/off time kept at 20/2 seconds in MFME. Conventional MOCVD growth occurs under growth temperature 585°C and V/III ratio 380. Growth rate is controlled at about 0.45 $\mu$m/hr confirmed by scanning electron microscope (SEM). Under such a growth rate, a monolayer of metal on the growth front is expected during the switching off time of phosphine source in MFME. The optical quality of epilayer was examined by 77 K photoluminescence (PL) full width at half maximum (FWHM). The crystallinity of epilayers was examined by the single-crystal X-ray diffractometry technique. The mobility and carrier concentration were examined by Van der Pauw Hall measurement.

In order to achieve further observation of surface flatness, the atomic force microscope (AFM) was used. The epilayer thickness of samples under observation are 0.45 $\mu$m. The AFM resolution (2 nm) is limited by the tip. The scanning are is 400 nm$^2$. All the samples are kept clean before AFM observation.

### 3. Results and Discussion

The basic growth parameters of MFME studied include the V/III ratio, growth temperature, and phosphine on/off time. The PL FWHM as a function of V/III ratio is shown in Fig. 2. A PL FWHM of 5.6 meV is achieved by the MFME at the optimal V/III ratio of 226. When the V/III ratio is lower than 226, insufficient phosphorus would degrade the epitaxial quality by the formation of phosphorus vacancies. When V/III ratio is higher than 226, the excess phosphorus is introduced into crystal to induce defects and the PL quality becomes worse. While in conventional MOCVD, PL FWHM remains unchanged as the V/III ratio increases larger than 380. Figure 3 shows PL FWHM as a function of PH$_3$ on time at a fixed off time 2 s. Figure 4 shows PL FWHM as a function of PH$_3$ off time at a fixed on

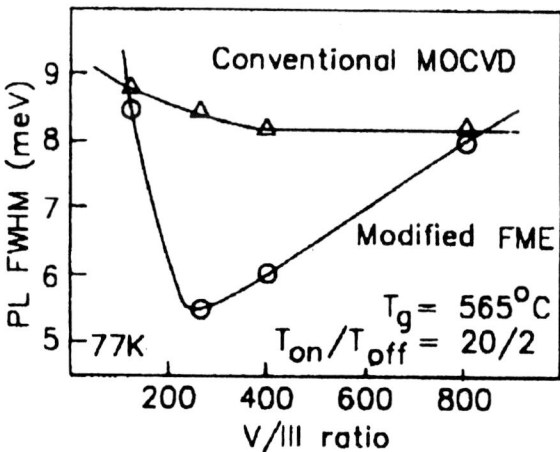

Fig. 2. PL FWHM as a function of V/III ratio for the MFME and the conventional MOCVD.

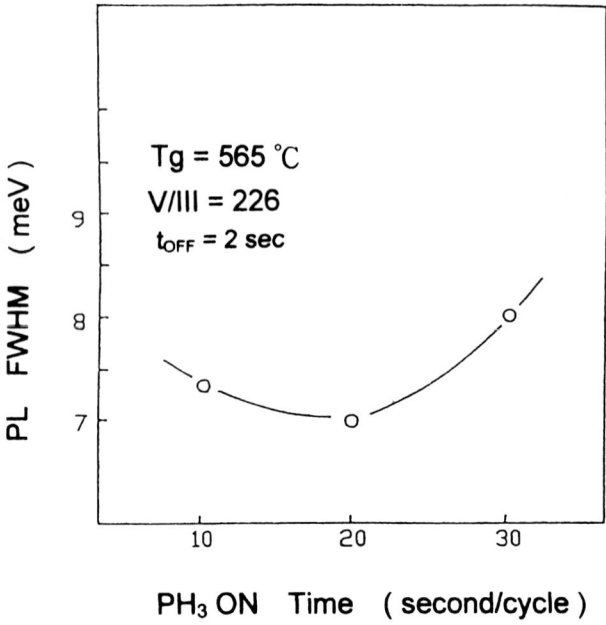

Fig. 3. PL FWHM as a function of PH₃ on time at a fixed off time for the MFME.

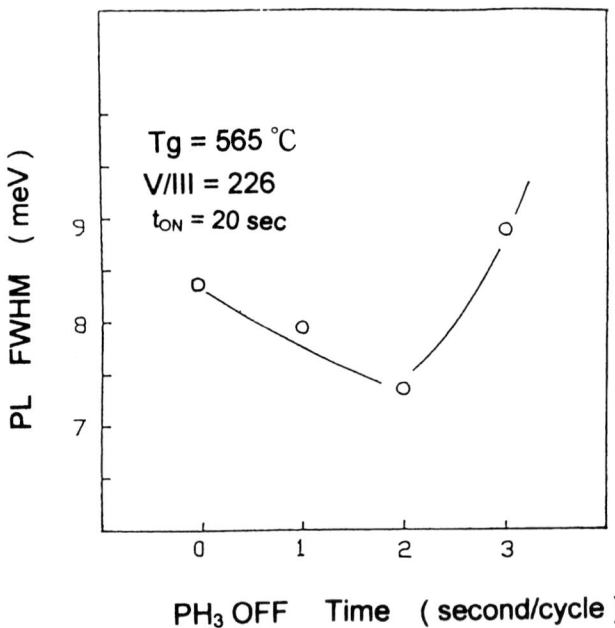

Fig. 4. PL FWHM as a function of PH₃ off time at a fixed on time for the MFME.

time 20 s. They show that the best optical quality can be obtained when PH$_3$ on time ($T_{on}$) is 20 s in which PH$_3$ off time ($T_{off}$) is kept at 2 s. When $T_{on}$ is shorter than 20 s, the quality is degraded by phosphorus outgassing caused by insufficient PH$_3$; and when $T_{on}$ is longer than 20 s, PL FWHM is degraded by defects caused by excess phosphorus and defect-related impurity incorporation. It is the same situation for $T_{off}$. It is believed that the MFME is very sensitive to the amount of phosphorus, either excess or insufficient phosphorus would affect the crystal quality significantly.

Figure 5 shows the optical quality as a function of the growth temperature. PL FWHM becomes better as the growth temperature increases when the growth temperature is below 565°C for the MFME and 585°C for the conventional MOCVD. On the other hand, PL FWHM becomes worse as the growth tempera-ture is further increased from 565°C for the MFME and 585°C for the conventional MOCVD. In the lower growth temperature region, the optical quality improvement as the growth temperature increased is from the enhancement of the migration of either In atoms (in FME) or InP molecules (in conventional MOCVD). The higher surface mobility of In atoms than that of InP molecules lowers the optimum growth temperature, and higher crystal quality can be obtained for the MFME. In the higher temperature region, PL FWHM becomes worse as the growth temperature increases, which results from the sublimation of phosphorus in both the conventional MOCVD and the MFME, and the MFME is more sensitive than the conventional MOCVD (from the slopes of solid and dashed lines). Since, in the MFME, the pyrolysis of phosphine is more efficient as the growth temperature

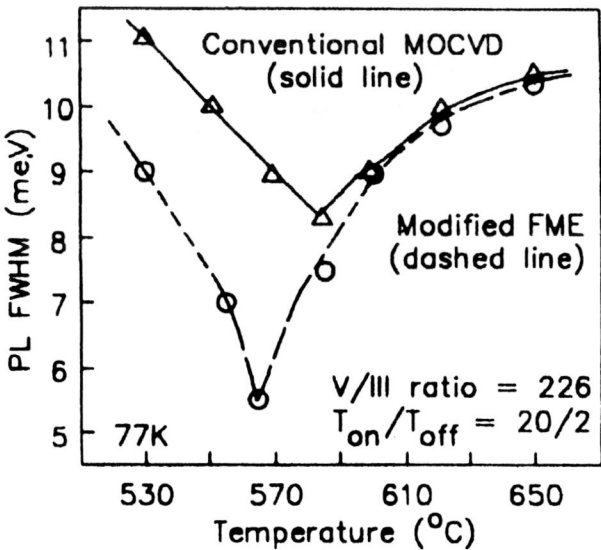

Fig. 5. PL FWHM as a function of the growth temperature for the MFME and the conventional MOCVD.

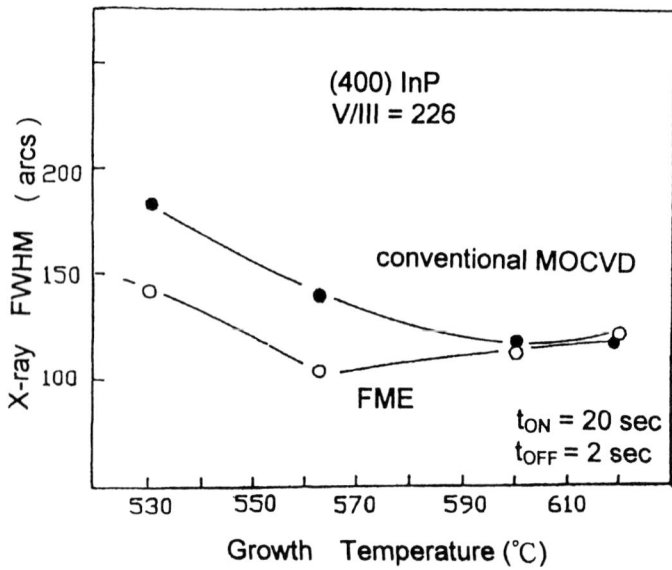

Fig. 6. X-ray FWHM as a function of the growth temperature for the MFME and the conventional MOCVD.

increases and causes sufficient phosphorus to be sustained in the boundary layer in the $T_{off}$ time, more InP molecules and fewer In atoms coexist on the growing surface. Owing to the lower surface mobility of InP molecules, the degradation of crystal quality grown by the MFME is a stronger dependence on the growth temperature in the higher growth region, and this is also caused partially by the sublimation of phosphorus. The corresponding X-ray examination is shown in Fig. 6. The result is similar to the observation of Fig. 5. From the results of PL and X-ray examination, it can be concluded that MFME grows better crystal quality than conventional MOCVD at lower growth temperature.

If In surface mobility would be enhanced by MFME, it would give a flatter surface. It is examined by AFM. Figure 7(a) shows the AFM image of InP epilayer prepared by conventional MOCVD under optimum growth conditions in which the growth temperature is 585°C. Figures 7(b), (c), and (d) show the AFM surface images of the InP epilayers prepared by MFME. The phosphine off time varies from 1 second to 3 seconds. The corresponding surface roughness measured by AFM were shown in Fig. 8. From Fig. 7(a), we can observe a rough surface caused by three-dimensional growth of conventional MOCVD. From Fig. 7(b) to Fig. 7(d), the surface roughness is much improved by MFME. But Fig. 7(b) only shows a slight improvement, when the off time is 1 s. The In adatom has sufficient high surface mobility in MFME, it can reach a proper position during the phosphine 1 s off time. Because the growth rate is kept at 0.45 $\mu$m/hr, complete coverage of one In monolayer cannot be obtained in 1 s. The clusters still exist on the growth

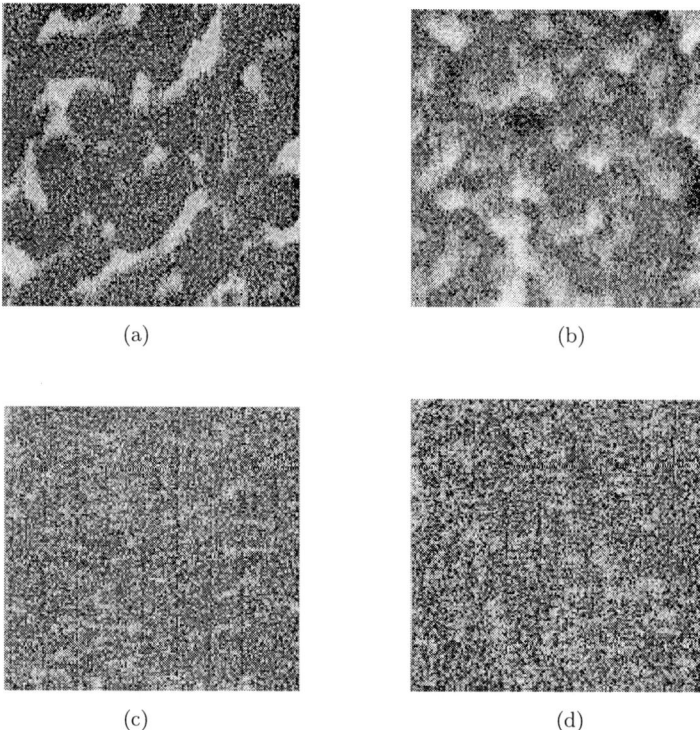

(a)

(b)

(c)

(d)

Fig. 7. AFM surface images of InP epilayers by (a) MOCVD and by MFME with different phosphine off times (b) 1 sec (c) 2 sec and (d) 3 sec.

surface and the surface roughness is shown in Fig. 7(b). When the off time is 2 s, complete coverage of one In monolayer removes clusters, and the surface becomes very smooth as shown in Fig. 7(c). As the off time is as long as 3 s, the In atom accumulation is more than one monolayer during the phosphine off time, and the surface is still smoother than that of conventional MOCVD as shown in Fig. 7(d).

The optimum PL FWHM of the conventional MOCVD is 8.3 meV and the V/III mole ratio is 380 and the growth temperature is 585°C. The PL FWHM of 5.6 meV can be obtained by MFME, which indicates the epilayer has a very smooth initial growth surface, and the V/III ratio is as low as 226. MFME can reduce the phosphine flow rate by 40%, it comes from the metal catalysis on the growth front and a metal-rich surface takes up group V atoms much more efficiently.[10]

From 77 K PL examination, there is always a satellite peak (900 nm) around the peak of near band emission (880 nm) of InP epilayer grown by conventional MOCVD under our optimum growth conditions, and the same phenomenon observed in conventional FME.[5] It was attributed to an acceptor related transition and could be from phosphorus-related antisite defects and a low incorporation of unintentional shallow acceptor impurities.[11,12] However, it can be reduced to a negligible quantity by MFME under the optimum growth conditions. Obviously,

7

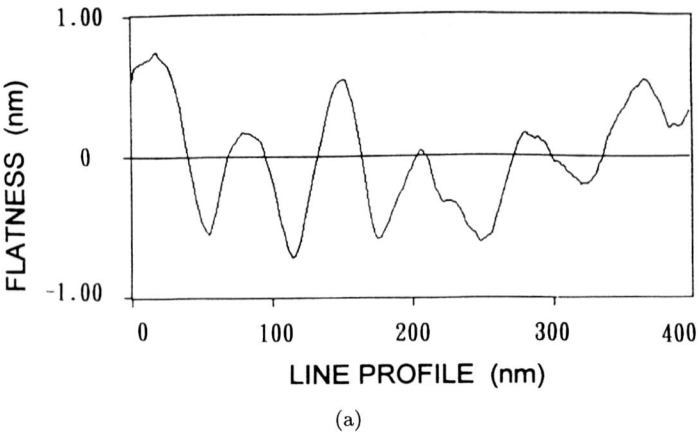

(a)

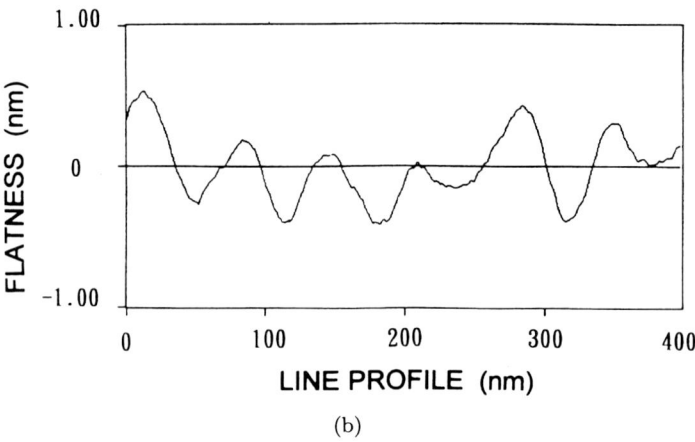

(b)

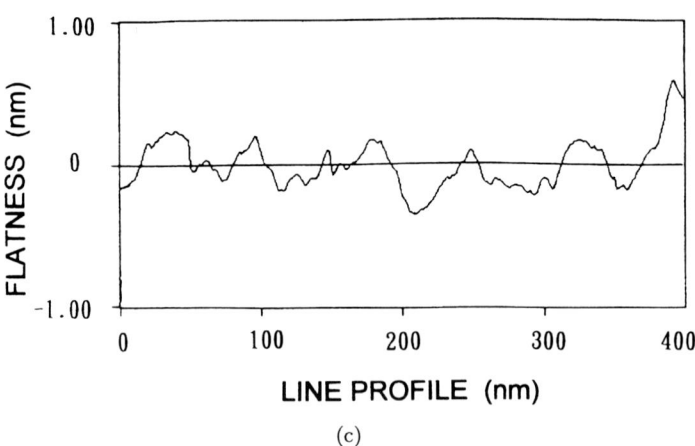

(c)

Fig. 8. Surface roughness by AFM measurement corresponding to Fig. 7.

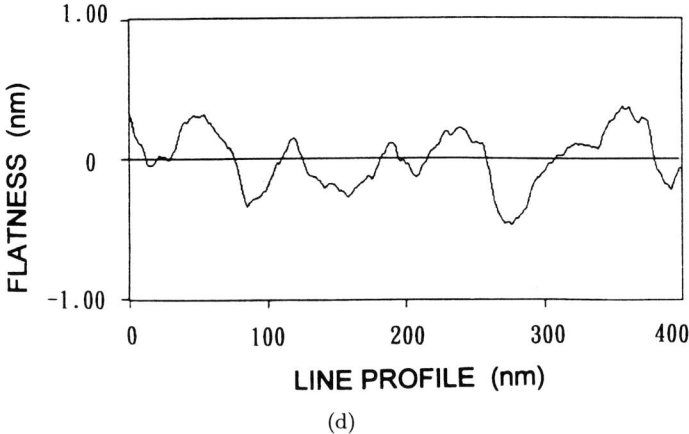

(d)

Fig. 8. (*Continued*)

the very flat surface could reduce the adsorption sites on the surface and hence reduces the impurity incorporation,[13] and the intensity of the satellite peak.

On the other hand, we check the function of the growth temperature on the PL peak intensity with the fixed on/off time at 20/2 s. Figure 9 shows the 77 K PL peak intensity as a function of the growth temperature of the MFME. As the growth temperature is higher than 565°C, P would outgas during the phosphine off time. As the growth is lower than 565°C, the thermal energy is not sufficient for the In adatom surface mobility. Both cases would result in defects and clusters and induce the PL satellite peak. At the optimum growth temperature of 565°C, not only the near band emission is the best, but also the satellite peak can be reduced to a negligible quantity. The two-dimensional initial growth of MFME will improve the flatness and defects simultaneously.

The conventional Van der Pauw Hall measurement is used to measure the electron carrier concentration and mobility. An electron concentration of up to $2.3 \times 10^{18}$ cm$^{-3}$ is obtained. The electron concentration is an approximately linear relation with the silane flow rate in MFME. The graphs of 300 K electron mobility versus carrier concentration of Si-doped epilayer prepared by MFME and conventional MOCVD is shown in Fig. 10. The solid lines in the figure are the theoretical mobilities for different compensation ratios.[14] The compensation ratio is about 0.2 for the MFME which is better than 0.4 for the conventional MOCVD. In conventional MOCVD, Si will bond to In and P simultaneously. A certain amount of Si–P bonds are formed and therefore a higher compensation ratio is expected. In the MFME environment, TMIn and SiH$_4$ are introduced at the same time during the phosphine off time. In and Si atoms will compete on the growing front. There is less chance for the formation of the Si–P bond. On the other hand, flatness-related defect and defect-related acceptor impurity incorporation is reduced in MFME.

9

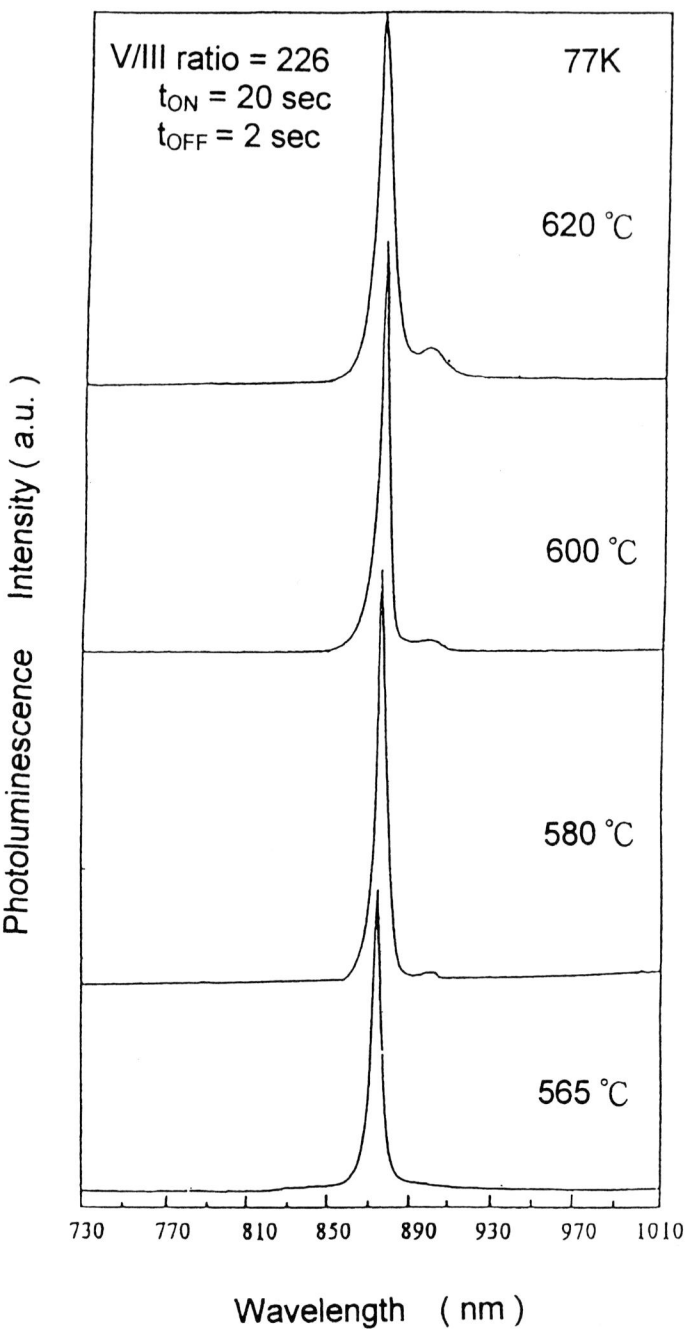

Fig. 9. PL peak intensity as a function of the growth temperature of InP by MFME.

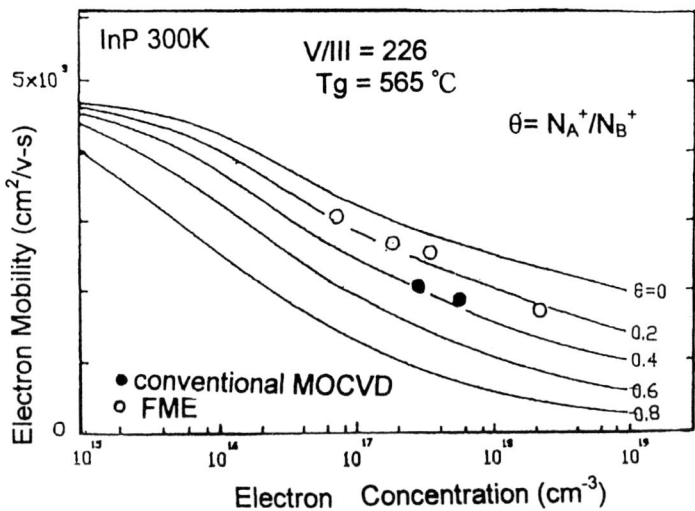

Fig. 10. 300 K electron mobility as a function of carrier concentration in Si doped InP epilayers.

MFME can improve the characteristics of the epilayer with higher electron mobility and lower compensation ratio.

## 4. Conclusion

In conclusion, the basic characteristics of MFME has been presented. The surface flatness of InP is much improved by MFME. The three-dimensional growth of conventional MOCVD is observed. While in MFME, the two-dimensional initial growth can provide a smoother surface and more perfect crystal. From PL examination, the satellite peak is attributed to the flatness-related defects which can be reduced to a negligible quantity by the MFME technology. Moreover, MFME can improve the electrical characteristics of the epilayer with higher electron mobility and lower compensation ratio. It is very important for device applications.

## Acknowledgment

This work is supported by National Science Council of Republic of China under the contract number NSC-84-2215-E110-012.

## References

1. N. Kobayashi, T. Makimoto, and Y. Horikoshi, "Flow-rate modulation epitaxy of GaAs", *Jpn. J. Appl. Phys.* **24** (1985) 962–964.
2. T. Makimoto, N. Kobayashi, and Y. Horikoshi, "Modulation doped *n*-AlGaAs/GaAs heterostructure grown by flow-rate modulation epitaxy", *Jpn. J. Appl. Phys.* **25** (1986) 513–515.

3. Y. Yamauchi, T. Makimoto, and Y. Horikoshi, "Optimal growth conditions of AlGaAs/GaAs quantum wells by flow-rate modulation epitaxy", *Jpn. J. Appl. Phys.* **28** (1989) 155–158.

4. R. P. Schneider, Jr. and B. W. Wessels, "InPAs/InP strained single quantum wills grown by atmospheric pressure organometallic vapor phase epitaxy", *Appl. Phys. Lett.* **57** (1990) 1998–2000.

5. A. J. Neuhalfen and B. W. Wessels, "Electronic and photoluminescent properties of InP prepared by flow modulation epitaxy", *J. Appl. Phys.* **71** (1992) 281–288.

6. M. K. Lee, C. C. Hu, and M. H. Lin, "Metalorganic chemical vapor deposition of InP using phosphine modulation", *Appl. Phys. Lett.* **62** (1993) 1245–1247.

7. S. Munnix, R. K. Bauer, D. Bimberg, J. S. Harris, Jr., R. KohrBruck, E. C. Larkins, Ch. Maierhofer, D. E. Mars, and J. N. Miller, "Growth kinetics, impurity incorporation, defect generation, and interface quality of molecular-beam epitaxy grown AlGaAs/GaAs quantum wells: role of group III and group V fluxes", *J. Vac. Sci. Technol.* **B7** (1989) 704–709.

8. M. D. Pashley, K. W. Haberern, W. Friday, J. M. Woodall, and P. D. Kirshner, "Structure of GaAs (001) (24)-c(28) determined by scanning tunneling microscopy", *Phys. Rev. Lett.* **60** (1988) 2176–2179.

9. P. K. Larsen and D. J. Chadi, "Surface structure of As-stabilized GaAs (001): 24, c(28), and domain structures", *Phys. Rev.* **B37** (1988) 8282–8288.

10. A. Y. Cho, "Growth of III-V semiconductors by molecular-beam epitaxy and their properties", *Thin Solid Films* **100** (1983) 291–317.

11. E. Kubota, Y. Ohmori, and K. Sugii, "Electrical and optical properties of Mg-, Ca-, and Zn-doped InP crystals", *J. Appl. Phys.* **55** (1984) 3779–3784.

12. S. J. Bass, C. Pickering, and M. L. Young, "Metal organic vapour phase epitaxy of indium phosphine", *J. Cryst. Growth* **64** (1983) 68–75.

13. M. Kondo, C. Anayama, T. Tanahashi, and S. Yamazaki, "Crystal orientation dependence of impurity dopant incorporation in MOVPE-grown III-V materials", *J. Cryst. Growth* **24** (1992) 449–456.

14. W. Walukiewicz, J. Lagowski, L. Jastrzebski, P. Rava, M. Lichtensteiger, C. H. Gatos, and H. C. Gatos, "Electron mobility and free carrier absorption in InP; determination of the compensation ratio", *J. Appl. Phys.* **51** (1980) 2659.

International Journal of High Speed Electronics and Systems, Vol. 8, No. 4 (1997) 587–598

# ELECTROABSORPTION OF UNSTRAINED InGaAs/InAlGaAs MULTIPLE QUANTUM WELL STRUCTURE GROWN ON GaAs SUBSTRATES

CHING-TING LEE and TZER-EN NEE

*Institute of Optical Sciences, National Central University,*
*Chung-Li, Taiwan, R.O.C.*

Large electroabsorption was observed in InGaAs/InAlGaAs multiple quantum well structures grown on GaAs substrates operating near 1.3 $\mu$m. The molecular beam epitaxy (MBE) growth of these structures was incorporation of a carefully designed InAlAs multistage strain-relaxed buffer. The optical absorption spectra as a function of the reverse bias at room temperature are shown. The good characteristics of the optical modulators fabricated on this structure have indicated its potential for practical applications of high-speed modulation.

## 1. Introduction

There is considerable interest in external modulation for optical-fiber transmission systems, as well as for interconnect and signal processing systems. Especially for high-bit rate, long-haul optical-fiber communication systems, the external modulators operating in the long-wavelength region have been intensively investigated owing to the modulation speed limitation and wavelength chirping of the directly-modulated lasers.[1] The reason can be attributed to the fact that the frequency broadening associated with high-speed direct laser modulation causes a dispersion penalty.

The titanium indiffused lithium niobate (Ti:LiNbO$_3$) modulators have found extensive applications of external modulation.[2,3] Various configurations and electro-optical (E-O) devices based on the LiNbO$_3$ crystal have been reported recently.[4-8] However, for the development of monolithic electro-optical integrated circuits (EOIC), the III-V compounds materials may eventually replace LiNbO$_3$, because the III-V materials can offer versatile advantages of monolithic integration of active/passive photonic and electronic devices. Furthermore, because of the significant improvements in growth of high quality III-V epilayers in recent years, EOICs based on III-V materials have been demonstrated.[9-13]

Surface normal quantum well modulators and quantum well self-electro-optic effect devices (SEEDs) are the most widely researched optoelectronic devices.[14] These devices are used for both communication systems and optical processing applications and can perform Boolean logic. In recent years, various configurations and excellent performances of those optoelectronic devices have been reported. Those include resistor-biased SEEDs,[15] diode-biased SEEDs,[16,17] transistor-biased SEEDs,[18,19] symmetric SEEDs,[20,21] and multistate SEEDs.[22,23] However, the basic concept of the SEEDs is the change of the optical absorption induced by changing an electric field perpendicular to the thin semiconductor layers in quantum well material.[24] For practical applications of different wavelengths, various III-V compound material systems are used and demonstrated.[25–30]

The InGaAs/InAlGaAs system is a promising configuration for MQW structures operating in the long-wavelength region. Since there is a considerable lattice mismatch between the InGaAs/InAlGaAs MQW's structure and GaAs substrate, a properly designed strain-relaxed buffer layer is desirable.[31] This strain-relaxed or so-called metamorphic buffer layers must be able to not only accommodate the large lattice mismatch between the guiding layer and the GaAs substrate by the formation of misfit dislocations, but also confine these misfit dislocations in the lower regions of the buffer and prevent them from propagating into the guiding and cladding layers.

In this work, the electroabsorption characteristics of the InGaAs/InAlGaAs MQW on GaAs operating wavelength of 1.3 $\mu$m were grown and demonstrated in waveguide geometry. Furthermore, its optical modulator operating at low voltages was also shown.

## 2. InGaAs/InAlGaAs Multiple Quantum Well Structure and Material Growth

The structure of the InGaAs/InAlGaAs multiple quantum well (MQW) used in this study is shown in Fig. 1. The MQW structure consists of ten periods of 7 nm thick undoped $In_{0.3}Ga_{0.7}As$ well and 25 nm thick undoped $In_{0.3}(Al_{0.15}Ga_{0.85})_{0.7}As$ barrier as shown in Fig. 1(a). Its associated energy band diagram is shown in Fig. 1(b). Owing to a large lattice mismatch between the MQW's structure and GaAs substrate, a strain-relaxed buffer layer has to be properly designed. This kind of buffer layer must be able to not only accommodate the lattice mismatch and confine misfit dislocations in the lower regions of the buffer layer, but perform the $p^+$ or $n^+$ layer of the required structure of MQW $p$-$i$-$n$ diode. Both step-graded and linear-graded buffer layers are widely used to achieve strain-relaxed function.[32,33] The InGaAs and InAlGaAs materials are chosen as the strain-relaxed buffer layer. However, high leakage current is reported for the associated devices used those buffer layers.[34] Since InAlAs has a higher band gap and exhibits better strain-relaxed buffer performances than those of InGaAs.[35] Therefore, step-graded InAlAs buffer layers are used in this work.

The structure of the InGaAs/InAlGaAs MQW $p$-$i$-$n$ diode used in the paper is shown in Fig. 2(a). Its associated energy band diagram is shown in Fig. 2(b). The structure was grown on (100)-oriented Si-doped GaAs substrate. Three-stage

| In₀.₃(Al₀.₁₅Ga₀.₈₅)₀.₇As | 0.6μm |
|---|---|
| In₀.₃Ga₀.₇As | 7nm |
| In₀.₃(Al₀.₁₅Ga₀.₈₅)₀.₇As | 25nm |
| In₀.₃Ga₀.₇As | 7nm |
| In₀.₃(Al₀.₁₅Ga₀.₈₅)₀.₇As | 25nm |
| In₀.₃Ga₀.₇As | 7nm |

●
●
●
●
●

| In₀.₃(Al₀.₁₅Ga₀.₈₅)₀.₇As | 25nm |
|---|---|
| In₀.₃Ga₀.₇As | 7nm |
| In₀.₃(Al₀.₁₅Ga₀.₈₅)₀.₇As | 25nm |
| In₀.₃Ga₀.₇As | 7nm |
| In₀.₃(Al₀.₁₅Ga₀.₈₅)₀.₇As | 0.6μm |

(a)

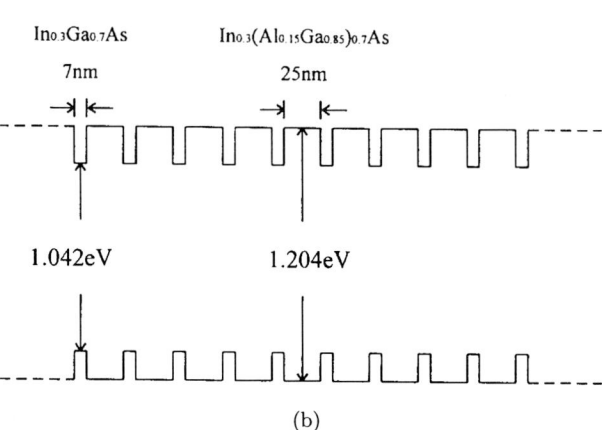

(b)

Fig. 1. (a) The MQW structure consists of ten periods of 7 nm thick undoped $In_{0.3}Ga_{0.7}As$ well and 25 nm thick undoped $In_{0.3}(Al_{0.15}Ga_{0.85})_{0.7}As$ barrier. (b) Its associated energy band diagram.

| | | | |
|---|---|---|---|
| $p^+$ | $In_{0.3}Al_{0.7}As$ | $0.2\mu m$ | $1x10^{18}$ |
| p | $In_{0.3}Al_{0.7}As$ | $1.5\mu m$ | $3x10^{17}$ |
| i | $In_{0.3}(Al_{0.15}Ga_{0.85})_{0.7}As$ | $0.6\mu m$ | |
| i | $In_{0.3}Ga_{0.7}As/In_{0.3}(Al_{0.15}Ga_{0.85})_{0.7}As$ | MQW | |
| i | $In_{0.3}(Al_{0.15}Ga_{0.85})_{0.7}As$ | $0.6\mu m$ | |
| n | $In_{0.3}Al_{0.7}As$ | $1.5\mu m$ | $3x10^{17}$ |
| $n^+$ | $In_{0.2}Al_{0.8}As$ | $0.2\mu m$ | $5x10^{18}$ |
| $n^+$ | $In_{0.1}Al_{0.9}As$ | $0.2\mu m$ | $5x10^{18}$ |
| $n^+$ | GaAs        Substrate | | $5x10^{18}$ |

(a)

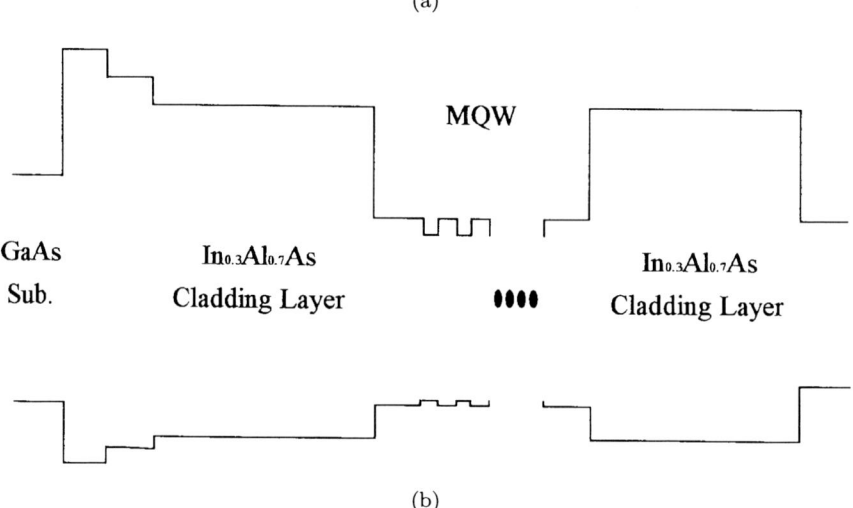

(b)

Fig. 2. (a) Schematic structure of 1.3 $\mu m$ unstrained InGaAs/InAlGaAs multiple quantum well structure grown on GaAs substrate. (b) Its associated energy band diagram.

step-graded Si-doped $In_{1-x}Al_xAs$ buffer layers with $x = 0.9, 0.8, 0.7$, respectively, were grown on the GaAs substrate for strain-relaxed buffer layer and n region of the p-i-n diode, sequentially. The MQW layers were sandwiched between two 0.6 $\mu m$ un-doped $In_{0.3}(Al_{0.15}Ga_{0.85})_{0.7}As$ barrier layers. A Be-doped $In_{0.3}(Al_{0.15}Ga_{0.85})_{0.7}As$ layer with thickness of 1.5 $\mu m$ and concentration of $3 \times 10^{17}$ cm$^{-3}$ for p region of p-i-n diode and Be doped $In_{0.3}Al_{0.7}As$ with thickness of 0.2 $\mu m$ and concentration of $1 \times 10^{18}$ cm$^{-3}$ for ohmic formation were grown subsequently.

This device studied was grown in a Riber 32P MBE system. The beam equivalent pressure ratio of As$_4$/III was maintained at about 20. To grow the multistage step-graded strain-relaxed buffer and particular chemical compositions shown in Fig. 2(a), various growth interruptions were employed to change the temperatures of both the substrate and the effusion cells. Streaky $(2 \times 1)$ reflection high energy electron diffraction (RHEED) patterns, indicating two-dimensional growth, were observed throughout the growth. The MQW *p-i-n* structure was grown on the step-graded strain-relaxed buffer layers at a substrate temperature of about 520°C. This temperature was chosen so that the growth was in a two-dimensional-growth mode while In loss was negligible. Using standard photolithographic processes, the *p-i-n* diodes are fabricated. The samples were then polished by a Logic PM4 machine to a thickness of about 80 $\mu$m. The *p* and *n* ohmic contact materials are Au/Au-Zn and Au/AuGeNi metals, respectively.

## 3. Multiple Quantum Well Electroabsorption and Modulators

At low temperature in bulk semiconductor materials, their associated absorption spectra exhibit smooth variation starting at bandgap energy and rising smoothly for increasing photon energy. When a photon is absorbed in bulk materials, a bound electron-hole pair (exciton) is created. Therefore, the absorption spectrum exhibits exciton peaks. When an electric field is applied, the absorption spectrum near the bandgap changes due to the Franz–Keldysh effect.[36] However, the equivalent temperature energy is larger than the. bounded energy of the electron-hole pair, while the excitonic phenomena in the absorption spectrum are not exhibited at room temperature.

A quantum well consists of a thin well material bounded on both sides by a thick barrier material. The bandgap energy of the barrier is higher than that of the

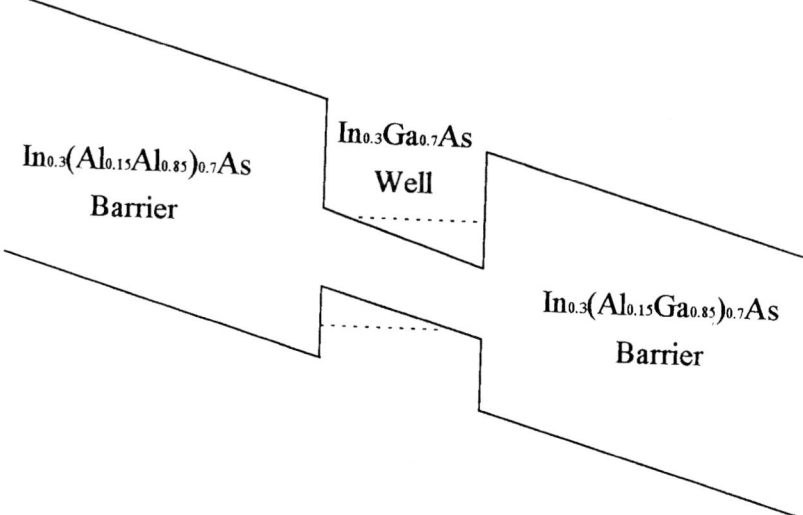

Fig. 3. When an electric field is applied perpendicular to the plane of the quantum well structure, the electron and hole tend to move toward the opposite sides of the well.

well. In the quantum well structure, the electron and hole energies are quantized in the conduction band and valence band, respectively. The exciton in the well region is confined by the barriers and keeps intact until the carriers escape from the well. Therefore, several strong peaks in the absorption spectrum are observed even at room temperature. When an electric field is applied perpendicular to the plane of the quantum well structure, the electron and hole tend to move toward the opposite sides of the well as shown in Fig. 3. Since the exciton is still confined by the barriers, it remains intact. This prevents rapid field-ionization of the exciton. However, the separation between the associated quantized energies of electron and hole in the well region is decreased with the applied electric field. Therefore, the photon energy required to create the electron and hole is reduced. A red shift in the absorption spectrum of quantum well structure is observed when an electric field is applied. The value of red shift depends on the applied electric field. This effect is called the quantum-confined Stark effect (QCSE).[37,38]

The designed InGaAs/InAlGaAs MQW's are stacked by ten periods of undoped InGaAs well and undoped $In_{0.3}(Al_{0.15}Ga_{0.85})_{0.7}As$ barrier. When the barriers are thick enough and have a large enough energy bandgap compared to the wells, the wells act independently. The Stark effect of having multiple wells is to multiply the electroabsorption of a single quantum well by the number of wells. This is the reason that a MQW structure is employed in the work. The electroabsorption measurements of the designed MQW $p$-$i$-$n$ diode shown in Fig. 2(a) were performed by illuminating this diode with chopped light perpendicular to the MQW layers from a tungsten filament lamp dispersed by a monochromator. Figure 4(a) shows the optical spectrum at room temperature. A clear step-like absorption edge of 1.3 $\mu$m was observed. In addition, a sharp peak are also observed at the absorption

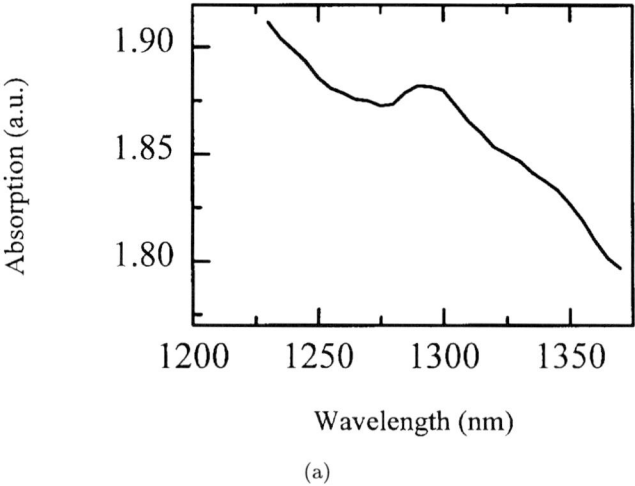

(a)

Fig. 4. (a) The optical spectrum at room temperature. (b) When an electric field is applied perpendicular to MQW layer, electro-optical spectra for various applied voltage.

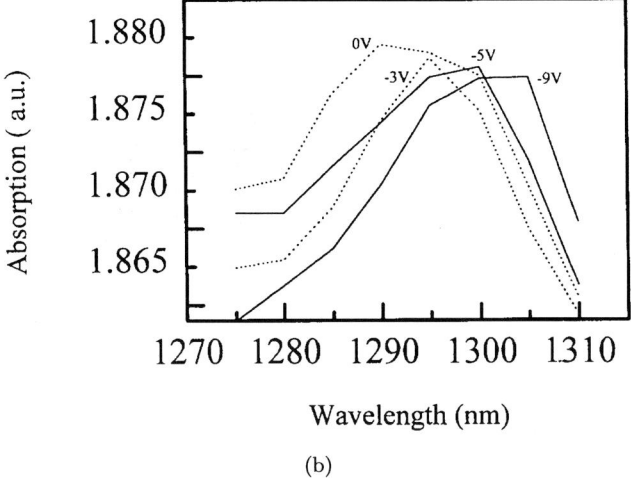

Wavelength (nm)

(b)

Fig. 4. (*Continued*)

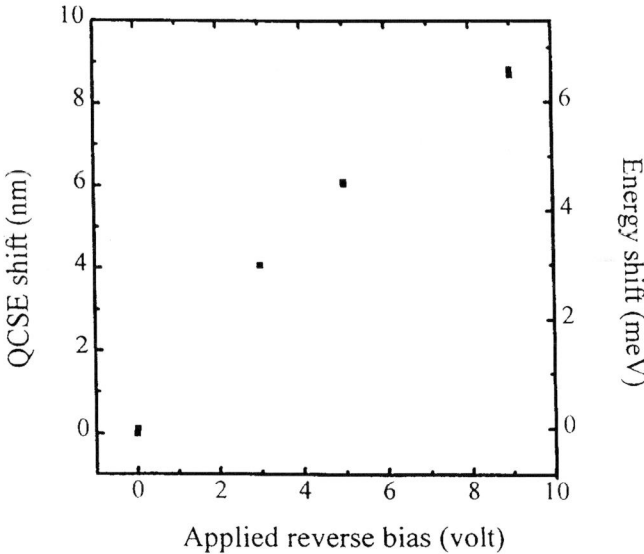

Applied reverse bias (volt)

Fig. 5. The QCSE shift and correspondent energy shift varied with applied voltage.

edge, corresponding to two-dimensional density of states and excitonic transition. Moreover, sharp exciton resonance width is generally associated with high quality material. When an electric field is applied perpendicular to MQW layer, electro-optical spectra for various applied voltage were shown as in Fig. 4(b). It can be seen that the red shift of the absorption edge is exhibited in the absorption spectra. The QCSE shift and correspondent energy shift varied with applied voltage are shown in Fig. 5.

19

We have performed a variational calculation of the energy shift of the ground-state exciton transition as a function of applied field.[39–41] In this calculation, we take into account only the single-particle electron and hole states and neglect both the residual strain effects and the change of exciton binding energy with field.[26,41] The theoretical zero-field peak position has been adjusted to agree with the experimentally determined value. Furthermore, we have taken the total band-gap discontinuity to be divided between the conduction and valence bands in the ratio 66/34 account to the results of J. L. Shieh *et al.*[42] and have estimated the electron and heavy hole effective masses for the quaternary by linear interpolation between the values for InAlAs and InGaAs. Consequently, the calculated QCSE are in good agreement with experimental results. As far as the red shift is concerned, the absorption edge is 1298 nm at −3 V and increases to 1303 nm at −9 V. Since the electric field was assumed to drop uniformly over the intrinsic MQW waveguide layer, the corresponding energy shift, i.e. QCSE, is 6.5 meV at an electric field of $6 \times 10^4$ V/cm. The QCSE studied in this work were comparable to reported results.[43–45] From the above comparison, it is known that we have overcome the difficulty of high-quality MBE growth of InGaAs with sufficiently high In content for 1.3 $\mu$m operation and have demonstrated a considerably large QCSE MQW structure, which serves as the active layer in an effective transmission electroabsorption modulator.

The device was operated as a modulator by tuning the laser to a fixed incident wavelength above the zero-field absorption edge. Therefore, the modulator was illuminated from a pigtailed laser diode and the output light from the modulator was coupled to a cone-shaped front fiber connected to a HP70951A optical spectrum analyzer. Figure 6 shows that the relative power of the modulator for wavelength of

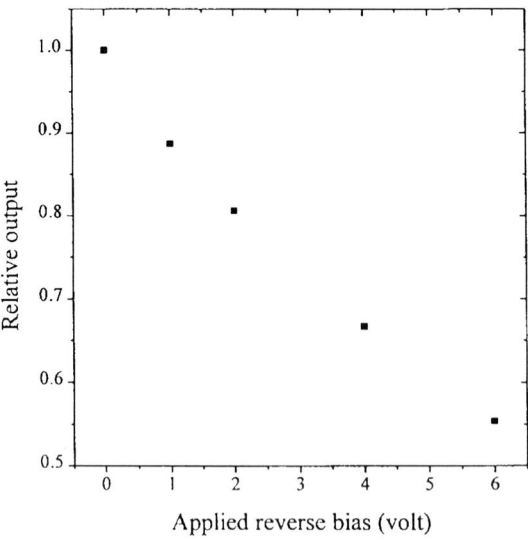

Fig. 6. Relative output intensity as a function of applied voltages.

incident light, i.e. 1.3 $\mu$m, is reduced by 45% between 0 and $-6$ V applied voltage. For the considerable fact that unguided light passes through the transparent GaAs substrate without absorption in the active layer is coupled directly to the optical spectrum analyzer, the modulation efficiency of the devices demonstrated in this study, therefore, is believed to be good enough for applications in optoelectronic devices.

## 4. Conclusion

We have demonstrated a large QCSE operating wavelength around 1.3 $\mu$m in InGaAs/InAlGaAs MQW *p-i-n* diode on a metamorphic InAlAs buffer with a GaAs substrate. Moreover, the electroabsorption modulator based on this structure exhibits good characteristics. The theoretical results are well consistent with the experimental ones. These results indicate that high quality InGaAs/InAlGaAs materials can be obtained via a carefully designed strain-relaxed structure under proper growth conditions. Therefore, it has application in high-speed optoelectronic devices. This work has shown the existence of another feasible way in progress on the integration of monolithic devices with different lattice constants. Such a modulator could also potentially be monolithically integrated with monolithic microwave integrated circuits on a GaAs substrate.

## Acknowledgment

The authors thank the MBE laboratory of the National Central University for the growth of the material used. The research was financially supported by the National Science Council of the Republic of China under Grant NSC-85-2215-E008-021.

## References

1. F. Devaux, S. Chelles, A. Ougazzaden, A. Mircea, and J. C. Harmand, "Electroabsorption modulators for high-bit-rate optical communications-comparison of strained InGaAs/InAlAs and InGaAsP/InAlAsP", *Semiconductor Sci. Technol.* **10** (1995) 887–901.
2. C. T. Lee, H. C. Lee, and L. G. Sheu, "The reduction of harmonic and intermodulation distortions with a cascaded Mach-Zehnder modulator", *Opt. Rev.* **3** (1996) 341–344.
3. P. S. Jiang and A. C. O'Donnell, "LiNbO₃ Mach-Zehnder modulators with fixed negative chirp", *IEEE Photon. Technol. Lett.* **8** (1996) 1319–1321.
4. C. T. Lee, H. C. Lee, H. H. Lai, and L. G. Sheu, "Complementary optical bistable operation with integration of two-directional couplers on LiNbO₃ crystal", *Jpn. J. Appl. Phys.* **35** (1996) 2686–2689.
5. C. T. Lee and L. G. Sheu, "Analysis of Nd:MgO:Ti:LiNbO₃ waveguide lasers with nonuniform concentration distributions", *J. Lightwave Technol.* **14** (1996) 2268–2276.
6. E. L. Wooten, R. L. Stone, E. W. Miles, and E. M. Bradley, "Rapidly tunable narrowband wavelength filter using LiNbO₃ unbalanced Mach-Zehnder interferometers", *J. Lightwave Technol.* **14** (1996) 2530–2538.
7. K. Kintaka, M. Fujimura, T. Suhara, and H. Nishihara, "High-efficiency LiNbO₃ waveguide second-harmonic generation devices with ferroelectric-domain-inverted gratings fabricated by applying voltage", *J. Lightwave Technol.* **14** (1996) 462–468.

8. L. Thylen, "Integrated optics in LiNbO₃: recent developments in devices for telecommunications", *J. Lightwave Technol.* **6** (1988) 847–861.

9. M. Auki, M. Suzuki, H. Sano, T. Kawano, T. Ido, T. Taniwatari, K. Uomi, and A. Takai, "InGaAs/InGaAsP MQW electroabsorption modulator integrated with a DFB laser fabricated by band-gap energy control selective area MOCVD", *IEEE J. Quantum Electron.* **29** (1993) 2088–2096.

10. R. M. Lammert, G. M. Smith, J. S. Hughes, M. L. Osowski, A. M. Jones, and J. J. Coleman, "MQW wavelength-tunable DBR lasers with monolithically integrated external cavity electroabsorption modulators with low-driving-voltages fabricated by selective-area MOCVD", *IEEE Photon. Technol. Lett.* **8** (1996) 797–799.

11. D. V. Phant, A. Z. Shang, M. R. Otazo, D. R. Rolston, B. Robertson, and H. S. Hinton, "Design, modeling, and characterization of FET-SEED smart pixel transceiver arrays for optical backplanes", *IEEE J. Quantum Electron.* **32** (1996) 1391–1398.

12. W. S. Lee and S. A. Rosser, "Monolithically integrated long wavelength optical receiver OEICs using InAlAs/InGaAs heterojunction MESFET's (HFET's)", *Electron. Lett.* **28** (1992) 365–367.

13. P. Berthier, L. Giraudet, A. Scavennec, D. Rigaud, M. Valenza, J. I. Davies, and S. W. Bland, "GaInAsP channel HFET's on InP for OEIC applications", *J. Lightwave Technol.* **12** (1994) 2131–2138.

14. D. A. B. Miller, "Quantum-well self-electro-optic effect devices", *Opt. and Quantum Electron.* **22** (1990) S61–S98.

15. D. A. B. Miller, D. S. Chemla, T. C. Damen, A. C. Gossard, W. Weignann, T. H. Wood, and C. A. Burrus, "Novel hybrid optically bistable switch — The quantum well self-electro-optic effect device", *Appl. Phys. Lett.* **45** (1984) 13–15.

16. D. A. B. Miller, J. E. Henry, A. C. Gossard, and J. H. English, "Integrated quantum well self-electro-optic effect device — 2 × 2 array of optically bistable switches", *Appl. Phys. Lett.* **49** (1986) 821–823.

17. G. Livescu, D. A. B. Miller, J. E. Henry, A. C. Gossard, and J. H. English, "Spatial light-modulator and optical-dynamic memory using a 6 × 6 array of self-electro-optic effect devices", *Opt. Lett.* **13** (1988) 297–299.

18. P. Wheatley, P. J. Bradley, M. Whitehead, G. Parry, J. E. Midwinter, P. Mistry, M. Pate, and J. S. Roberts, "Novel-nonresonant optoelectronic logic device", *Electron. Lett.* **23** (1987) 92–93.

19. D. A. B. Miller, M. D. Feuer, T. Y. Chang, S. S. Shunk, J. E. Henry, D. J. Burrows, and D. S. Chemla, "Field effect transistor self-electro-optic effect device: integrated photodiode, quantum well modulator and transistor", *IEEE Photon. Technol. Lett.* **1** (1989) 62–64.

20. F. A. P. Tooley and S. Wakelin, "Design of a symmetric self-electro-optic effect device celluar-logic image processor", *Appl. Opt.* **32** (1993) 1850–1862.

21. L. M. Loh, J. L. LoCicero, and A. L. Lentine, "S-SEED switching characteristics", *J. Lightwave Technol.* **12** (1994) 2122–2130.

22. A. L. Lentine, D. A. B. Miller, J. E. Henry, J. E. Cunningham, L. M. F. Chirovsky, L. A. D'Asaro, R. F. Kopf, and J. M. Kuo, "Multistate self-electro-optic effect device", *IEEE J. Quantum Electron.* **25** (1989) 1921–1927.

23. A. L. Lentine, S. J. Hinterlong, T. J. Cloonan, F. B. McCormick, D. A. B. Miller, L. M. F. Chirovsky, L. A. D'Asaro, R. F. Kopf, and J. M. Kuo, "Quantum well optical tristate device", *Appl. Opt.* **29** (1990) 1157–1160.

24. D. A. B. Miller, D. S. Chemla, and S. Schmitt-Rink, "Electroabsorption of highly confined system — theory of the quantum confined Franz–Keldysh effect in semiconductor

quantum wires and dots", in *Optical Nonlinearities and Instabilities in Semiconductors*, ed. H. Haug (Academic Press, San Diego, 1988) pp. 325–360.

25. G. D. Boyd, D. A. B. Miller, D. S. Chemla, S. L. McCall, A. C. Gossard, and J. H. English, "Multiple quantum well reflection modulator", *Appl. Phys. Lett.* **50** (1987) 1119–1121.

26. I. Bar-Joseph, C. Klingshirn, D. A. B. Miller, D. S. Chemla, U. Koren, and B. I. Miller, "Quantum-Confined Stark-Effect in InGaAs/InP quantum well grown by organometallic vapor-phase epitaxy", *Appl. Phys. Lett.* **50** (1987) 1010–1012.

27. T. Ido, S. Tanaka, M. Suzuki, M. Koizumi, H. Sano, and H. Inoue, "Ultra-high-speed multiple-quantum-well electro-absorption optical modulators with integrated waveguides", *J. Lightwave Technol.* **14** (1996) 2026–2034.

28. L. Shen, H. H. Wieder, and W. S. C. Chang, "Electroabsorption modulation at 1.3 $\mu$m on GaAs substrates using a step-graded low temperature grown InAlAs buffer", *IEEE Photon. Technol. Lett.* **8** (1996) 352–354.

29. K. K. Loi, I. Sakamoto, X. B. Mei, C. W. Tu, and W. S. C. Chang, "High-efficiency 1.3 $\mu$m InAsP-GaInP MQW electroabsorption waveguide modulators for microwave fiber-optic links", *IEEE Photon. Technol. Lett.* **8** (1996) 626–628.

30. X. R. Huang, S. K. Cheung, A. N. Cartwright, A. L. Smire, and W. T. Tseng, "An interdigital stacked p-i-n multiple-quantum-well modulator", *IEEE Photon. Technol. Lett.* **8** (1996) 1172–1174.

31. T. P. Chin and C. W. Tu, "Heteroepitaxial growth of InP/In$_{0.52}$Ga$_{0.48}$As structures on GaAs (100) by gas source molecular beam epitaxy", *Appl. Phys. Lett.* **62** (1993) 2708–2710.

32. P. Win, Y. Druelle, A. Cappy, Y. Cordier, J. Favre, and C. Bouillet, "Metamorphic In$_{0.3}$Ga$_{0.7}$As/In$_{0.29}$Al$_{0.7}$As layer on GaAs — A new structure for high-performance high electron-mobility transistor realization", *Appl. Phys. Lett.* **61** (1992) 922–924.

33. J. C. P. Chang, J. Chen, J. M. Fernandez, H. H. Wieder, and K. L. Kavanagh, "Strain relaxation of compositionally graded In$_x$Ga$_{1-x}$As buffer layers for modulation-doped In$_{0.3}$Ga$_{0.7}$As/In$_{0.29}$Al$_{0.7}$As heterostructure", *Appl. Phys. Lett.* **60** (1992) 1129–1131.

34. K. Inoue, J. C. Harmand, and T. Matsuno, "High quality In$_x$Ga$_{1-x}$As/InAlAs modulation-doped heterostructures grown lattice - mismatched on GaAs substrates", *J. Cryst. Growth* **111** (1991) 313–317.

35. J. I. Chyi, J. L. Shieh, C. S. Wu, R. M. Lin, J. W. Pan, Y. J. Chan, and C. H. Lin, "Characteristic of In$_{0.3}$Ga$_{0.7}$As/In$_{0.29}$Al$_{0.7}$As heterostructures grown on GaAs using InAlAs buffer", *Jan. J. Appl. Phys.* **33** (1994) L1574–L1576.

36. J. I. Pankov, *Optical Processes in Semiconductors* (Prentice Hall, NJ, 1971, p. 29).

37. D. A. B. Miller, D. S. Chemla, T. C. Damen, A. C. Gossard, W. Wiegmann, T. H. Wood, and C. A. Burrus, "Band-edge electroabsorption in quantum well structures-The quantum-confined Stark-effect", *Phys. Rev. Lett.* **53** (1984) 2173–2176.

38. D. A. B. Miller, J. S. Weiner, and D. S. Chemla, "Electric field dependence of linear optical-properties in quantum well structures-wave-guide electroabsorption and sumrules", *IEEE Quantum Electron.* **22** (1986) 1816–1830.

39. R. L. Greene and K. K. Bajaj, "Binding-energies of Wannier excitons in GaAs-Ga$_{1-x}$Al$_x$As quantum well structures", *Solid State Commun.* **45** (1983) 831–835.

40. J. A. Brum and G. Bastard, "Electric field induced dissociation of excitons in semiconductor quantum well", *Phys. Rev.* **B31** (1985) 3893–3901.

41. G. Bastard, E. E. Mendez, L. I. Chang, and L. Esaki, "Variational calculations on a quantum well in an electric field", *Phys. Rev.* **B28** (1983) 3241–3245.

23

42. J. L. Shieh, J. I. Chyi, R. M. Lin, and J. W. Pan, "Band offsets of $In_{0.3}Ga_{0.7}As/In_{0.29}Al_{0.71}As$ heterojunction grown on GaAs substrate", *Electron. Lett.* **30** (1994) 2172–2173.
43. R. P. Leavitt, J. L. Bradshaw, and J. T. Pham, "Superlattice-equivalent InGaAs/InAlAs as quantum wells with large Stark shifts in the 1.3 $\mu$m spectral electroabsorption on room temperature region", *Appl. Phys. Lett.* **66** (1995) 1803–1805.
44. K. Wakita, Y. Kawamura, Y. Yoshikuni, and H. Asahi, "Excitons in InGaAs/InGaAlAs multiple quantum well structures", *Electron. Lett.* **21** (1985) 339–340.
45. S. M. Lord, B. Pezeshki, and J. S. Harris Jr, "Electroabsorption modulators operating at 1.3 $\mu$m on GaAs substrate", *Opt. and Quantum Electron.* **25** (1993) S953–S964.

International Journal of High Speed Electronics and Systems, Vol. 8, No. 4 (1997) 599–619

# PASSIVE MODE-LOCKING TECHNIQUES OF LASERS

C. C. YANG, DING-WEI HUANG, CHIH-WEI HSU, SHENG-YAU LIANG,

CHOONG-WEN LAY, and MING-SHAN LIN

*Institute of Electro-Optical Engineering and Department of Electrical Engineering,*
*National Taiwan University, 1, Roosevelt Road, Sec. 4, Taipei, Taiwan, R.O.C.*
*E-mail: ccy@cc.ee.ntu.edu.tw*

In the frequency domain, mode-locking of a laser is to "lock" the relative phase of various longitudinal modes in order to form pulses. In many applications, passive mode-locking is superior to active mode-locking because the former does not need any external active sources as required for the latter. For passive mode-locking, we only need certain nonlinear effects to produce pulse compression mechanisms in laser systems. When the compression mechanism is balanced with some broadening effects, such as group-velocity dispersion, stable pulses can be obtained. In this paper, we first review several passive mode-locking techniques by explaining the pulse compression mechanisms. These techniques include saturable absorption mode-locking, colliding-pulse mode-locking, additive-pulse mode-locking, Kerr-lens mode-locking, nonlinear polarization mode-locking and nonlinear coupling mode-locking. Then, we review some of our research results related to nonlinear polarization mode-locking, nonlinear coupling mode-locking and additive-pulse mode-locking. These results come from the experimental, theoretical and numerical studies of fiber and semiconductor lasers.

## 1. Introduction

Mode-locking is the most important technique for producing ultrashort optical pulses from a laser system. Its fast developments since early 1980's had led to many accomplishments in ultrafast optics. Ultrashort pulses with durations in the picosecond and femtosecond ranges have proved useful in many application areas, including medical diagnostics and treatments, communications and basic research, etc. Ultrashort pulses manifest their useful characteristics including not only the temporal resolution but also the high peak power and broad bandwidth. Nowadays, pulses as short as a few tens of femtoseconds with wavelengths ranging from UV through mid-infrared are available for various applications. Such achievements should be attributed to the successful developments of laser mode-locking techniques.

Laser mode-locking techniques can be classified into two categories: active and passive mode-locking. In active mode-locking, usually an electro-optic or acousto-optic component is required for controlling the periodic gain and forcing the laser to oscillate in the pulsed mode. Such an extra component would usually add to the complexity and cost of the laser system. On the other hand, passive mode-locking does not require such an external source. It simply needs an appropriate design of the laser system so that an optically nonlinear mechanism can exist to compress pulses inside the laser cavity. With such a pulse compression mechanism, after it has been balanced with some pulse broadening mechanisms, such as group-velocity dispersion (GVD), periodic pulses with pulse repetition rate equal to the free spectral range of the laser cavity would emerge. Various passive mode-locking techniques have been applied to different laser systems, including solid-state lasers, semiconductor lasers, fiber lasers and liquid lasers.

In this paper, we review various passive mode-locking techniques in different laser systems. Mode-locking implies "locking" the phases of various frequency modes in a multiple modes laser. Without phase locking, the randomly distributed phases of those modes would lead to a noisy cw laser output. After the phases have been arranged in order by mode-locking, the superposition of those modes would lead to a pulse. When the phases of those modes are all the same, we can obtain the shortest pulse. Such a pulse is called transformed-limited. In understanding a mode-locking mechanism, it is, however, easier to consider the problem in the time domain, instead of considering those modes in the frequency domain. In Sec. 2 we will describe briefly the operation mechanisms of different passive mode-locking techniques. Then, we will review some results of our experimental, theoretical and numerical research in the related topics. In Secs. 3, 4 and 5, the results of nonlinear polarization mode-locking, nonlinear coupling mode-locking and additive-pulse mode-locking are to be presented, respectively. Finally, conclusions will be made in Sec. 6.

## 2. Passive Mode-Locking Techniques

As mentioned earlier, a passive mode-locking technique requires a certain nonlinear optical mechanism. Before we review various passive mode-locking techniques, let us discuss briefly optical nonlinearities.

Nonlinear optics covers very broad areas. For the applications of passive mode-locking, we can simply categorize into two kinds: fast and slow nonlinearities. The most widely used fast nonlinearity is the Kerr effect which implies that the refractive-index, $n$, of a material is linearly dependent on the applied optical intensity as

$$n = n_L + n_2 I \,. \tag{1}$$

Here, $n_L$ is the linear refractive-index, $n_2$ is the nonlinear refractive-index and $I$ is the optical intensity. The nonlinear refractive-index $n_2$ can be positive or negative. The Kerr effect is usually regarded as instantaneous. Since the response and decay times of the virtual electronic transition in many materials (such as fiber) and two-photon transition in semiconductors are believed to be in the sub-100 femtosecond range, they can be classified as having fast nonlinearity characteristics. In the time domain, a pulse propagation in a Kerr medium will experience self-phase modulation due the self-induced refractive-index change. The time dependence of the nonlinear phase $\phi_{NL}$ is given by

$$\phi_{NL}(t) = \frac{2\pi}{\lambda} n_2 I(t) z. \qquad (2)$$

Here, $\lambda$ is the wavelength, $z$ is the propagation distance and the time dependence is explicitly shown. Hence, the phase distribution of the pulse follows the pulse intensity. In the spatial domain, a laser beam in a Kerr medium may induce self-focusing or self-defocusing depending on whether $n_2$ is positive or negative. When $n_2$ is positive, the central part of the beam with a higher intensity induces refractive-index increase and effectively focuses the beam. When $n_2$ is negative, the other way occurs.

The slow optical nonlinearities are related to real electron transition. They include absorption saturation and gain saturation. The decay time of absorption or gain saturation is in the range of a few hundred picoseconds to a few nanoseconds and is much longer than the Kerr effect. The commonly used materials for absorption saturation include semiconductor and dye. Gain saturation can be observed in semiconductor optical amplifiers. In the steady state, absorption (gain) saturation can be expressed as follows:

$$\alpha = \frac{\alpha_0}{1 + \frac{I}{I_s}}, \quad g = \frac{g_0}{1 + \frac{I}{I_s}}. \qquad (3)$$

Here, $\alpha$ ($g$) is the absorption (gain) constant, $\alpha_0$ ($g_0$) is the small-signal absorption (gain) constant and $I_s$ is the saturation intensity. Because the refractive-index near the band gap in a semiconductor depends on the carrier density, the refractive-index changes with absorption or gain saturation. Hence, absorption or gain saturation also induces nonlinear phase changes.

In the following, we review conceptually several passive mode-locking techniques, including saturable absorption mode-locking, colliding-pulse mode-locking, additive-pulse mode-locking. Kerr-lens mode-locking, nonlinear polarization mode-locking and nonlinear coupling mode-locking.

### *Saturable absorption mode-locking*

Mode-locking using saturable absorption has been widely used to mode-lock various laser systems. In such a laser system, we place a saturable absorber besides the gain medium inside the cavity. The basic idea is shown in Fig. 1 in which both gain and absorption as functions of time are shown. In most of the time period in an oscillation round-trip, the absorption is always higher than gain, including the most portion of gain and absorption saturation, except in a short window in which net gain exists. This net gain is produced because the decays of gain and absorption in saturation have different slopes. This window can be as short as a few hundred femtoseconds or even shorter. Hence, a transient signal can evolve into a short pulse of about this period. The passive mode-locking technique based on saturable absorption has been applied to almost all kinds of mode-locked lasers, such as Nd:YAG, Nd:YLF, Nd:glass lasers[1,2] and semiconductor lasers.[3,4]

27

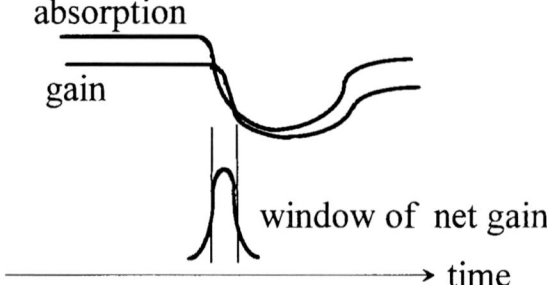

Fig. 1. Schematic diagram showing the relative strength of gain and loss in a mode-locked laser using a saturable absorber.

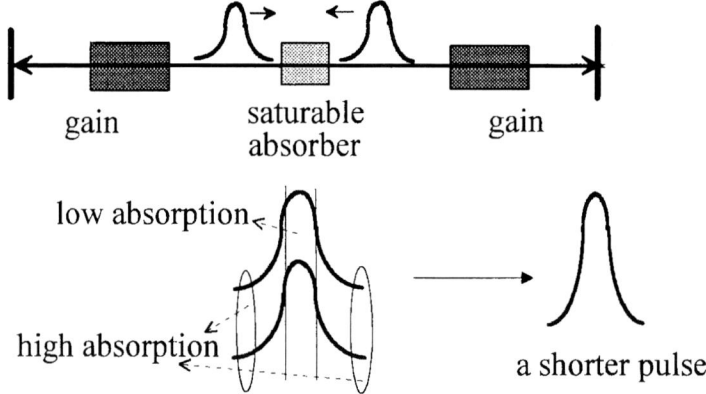

Fig. 2. Schematic diagram showing the colliding-pulse mode-locking mechanism.

### Colliding-pulse mode-locking (CPM)

The technique of colliding-pulse mode-locking also uses absorption saturation. Its operation mechanism is shown in Fig. 2. When the counter-propagating long pulses collide at the saturable absorber, the two pulses will enhance in each other the absorption saturation effect, i.e. the peaks experience lower absorption and the tails experience higher absorption, to efficiently compress the pulses. In 1980s, CPM has been widely used for mode-locking dye lasers to generate pulses in the sub-100-femtosecond range.[5] These lasers started much of the ultrafast optical research. CPM has also been used in generating ultrashort pulses from semiconductor lasers.[6,7]

### Additive-pulse mode-locking (APM)

A typical APM laser consists of a main cavity and an auxiliary cavity for the gain and nonlinear media, respectively, as shown in Fig. 3. After a long pulse splits into two at the partially reflecting mirror between the two cavities, the one in the main

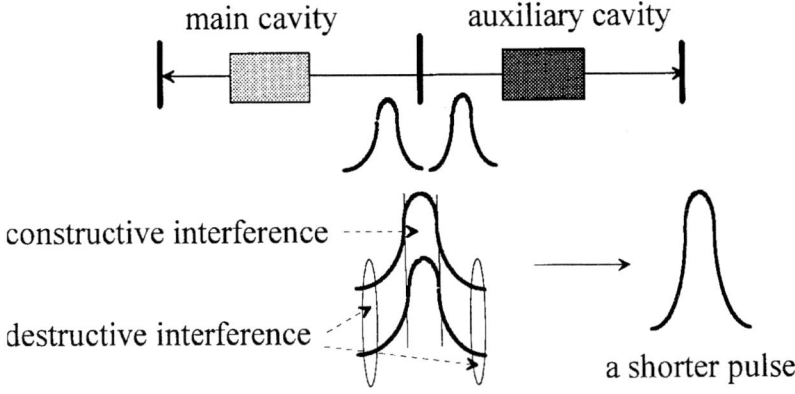

Fig. 3. Schematic diagram showing the additive-pulse mode-locking mechanism.

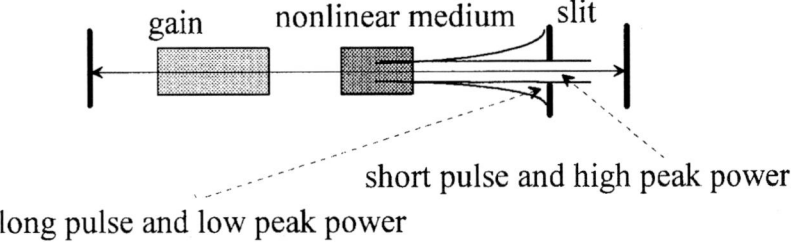

Fig. 4. Schematic diagram showing the Kerr-lens mode-locking mechanism.

cavity will receive gain after a round-trip and the one in the auxiliary cavity will experience nonlinear phase modulation, which is time dependent. The lengths of the two cavities are well matched so that the two pulses can overlap when they return to the position of the central partially reflecting mirror. If the signal power value is appropriate, the central part of the recombined pulse can be constructively interfered and the tails can be destructively interfered. In this situation, the originally long pulse can be compressed leading to passive mode-locking. APM has been widely used in mode-locking Er-doped fiber lasers,[8] Ti:sapphire lasers,[9] color-center lasers,[10] Nd:YAG lasers[11] and Nd:YLF lasers.[12] In these applications, fiber is a good material to provide the nonlinear effect.

### Kerr-lens mode-locking (KLM)

KLM uses the self-focusing effect in a Kerr medium. Its operation mechanism is shown in Fig. 4 in which a gain medium, a nonlinear medium (usually a Kerr medium) and a slit are placed inside a laser cavity. In most situations, the gain medium also has the Kerr effect and it plays both gain and Kerr-effect functions. KLM can be understood by considering the competition of a pulsed mode and the cw mode in laser oscillation. The cw mode experiences quite as much loss because a

29

great deal of the energy is stopped by the slit. However, on the other hand, because a pulse can induce self-focusing in the nonlinear medium, the narrowed beam can mostly pass through the slit and experience a lower loss. Hence, by controlling the slit width, we can force the laser to oscillate in the pulsed mode. Therefore, the basic idea of the KLM technique is to form an "environment" inside the laser cavity so that the oscillating beam with a smaller beam size at a certain position can be selected. An alternative approach to achieve this is to use the pump beam width as the effective slit. When the axes of the oscillating signal beam and the pump beam coincide, a narrower signal beam implies a larger effective gain and is more favored. Hence, without the "hard" slit KLM can work by adjusting the beam size of the pump laser. Such an approach is called the soft-aperture KLM,[13,14] in contrast to the hard-aperture KLM by using a physical slit. KLM has led to the commercialization of Ti:sapphire laser.[13–19] Around 10-femtosecond Ti:sapphire lasers have been reported based on KLM.[17–19]

### Nonlinear Polarization mode-locking (NPM)

NPM uses the nonlinear polarization rotation in a nonlinear medium. For a transient signal, the polarization evolution depends on power in a nonlinear medium when the original polarization is not along any optical axis. Hence, the time dependent polarization status allows us to discriminate the high and low power parts in a transient signal by using a polarizer. As shown in Fig. 5, we can place a nonlinear medium for power-dependent polarization rotation inside the resonance cavity of a laser. By rotating the inserted polarizer, we can allow only high power signals to oscillate. The removal of the low-power signals with the polarizer can lead to pulse narrowing and hence possibly mode-locking. This mode-locking mechanism can be interpreted as the additive-pulse action between two circularly polarized components of a signal and is also called the polarization additive-pulse mode-locking.[20] It has been widely used for passively mode-locking Er-doped fiber lasers.[21–25]

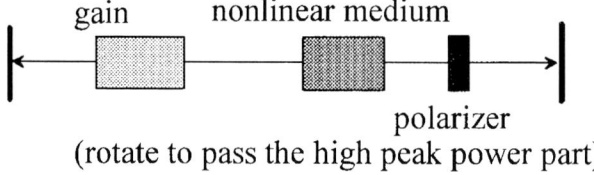

gain   nonlinear medium

polarizer
(rotate to pass the high peak power part)

Fig. 5. Schematic diagram showing the nonlinear polarization mode-locking mechanism.

### Nonlinear coupling mode-locking (NCM)

To understand the mechanism of NCM, we first explain the linear and nonlinear coupling phenomena. Two parallel waveguides close to each other can form a directional coupler and a weak signal can couple periodically back and forth between the two waveguides (linear coupling). If the two waveguides are identical, 100% energy

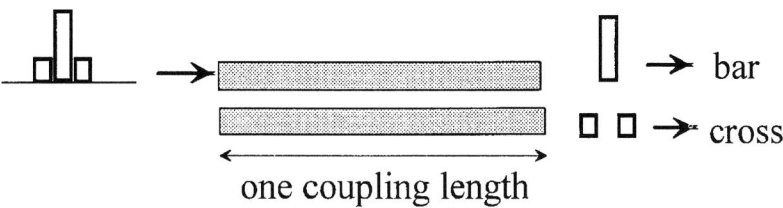

one coupling length

Fig. 6. Schematic diagram showing the mechanism of nonlinear directional coupling with the Kerr nonlinearity.

transfer from the incident waveguide (called the bar port) into the other waveguide (called the cross port) is possible and the shortest length for such a transfer is called a coupling length. Note that during the linear coupling process, the phase-matching condition, i.e. during which the propagation constants of the two waveguides are the same, is maintained. Now, if the material used for forming the waveguides is nonlinear, a strong signal may change the refractive-index of the incident waveguide and hence break the phase-matching condition for linear coupling. In this situation, the strong incident signal will emerge from the bar port, instead of the cross port in the linear coupling case. Hence, if the optical nonlinearity is Kerr-like, the tail parts of an incident Gaussian-like pulse will emerge from the cross port (low power and hence linear coupling) and the central part will emerge from the bar port (high power and hence nonlinear coupling), as demonstrated in Fig. 6.[26-28] Such a process can lead to pulse compression and possibly passive mode-locking. Therefore, if we place such a directional coupler inside a laser cavity so that the bar-port waveguide aligns with the oscillation axis, the nonlinear coupling mechanism should lead to mode-locking effect.[29] NCM has been used for passively mode-locking an Er-doped fiber laser in which a dual-core fiber was used as the directional coupler.[30]

### 3. Studies on Nonlinear Polarization Mode-Locking

In this section, we review some results of ours on NPM. This review includes the experimental observation of power-dependent polarization rotation in a single quantum well optical amplifier and the simulation of NPM based on the experimental results. This research is stimulated by the attempt of implementing pulsed semiconductor lasers based on NPM. Before the discussions on semiconductor amplifiers, we first review the experimental results of soliton fiber laser based on NPM with highly-doped fiber.

As mentioned earlier, NPM has been widely used for mode-locking Er-doped fiber lasers. Because any fiber has a certain amount of birefringence, the Kerr effect in fiber leads to power-dependent polarization evolution. Most fiber lasers based on NPM have ring configurations. The ring can be a fiber closed loop[20-22] or an open loop with a part of optical path in air.[23-25] Meanwhile, with appropriate arrangements of group-velocity dispersion, NPM fiber lasers can provide either soliton[20,21]

31

or non-soliton[22–25] outputs. The advantages of soliton lasers include the transform-limited output pulses. Their disadvantages include the limited pulse energy because a higher pulse energy leads to the formation of higher-order solitons which may become unstable under perturbations. For increasing output pulse energy, non-soliton fiber lasers are preferred.

We have also implemented a fiber soliton laser in the configuration of a closed fiber loop cavity, however, with highly doped fiber. The ring cavity of our laser, as shown in Fig. 7, included a polarization-sensitive isolator, an output coupler (20% output), a WDM coupler and two polarization controllers. The total length of the ring cavity was 8 m including the 1-m erbium-doped fiber. The highly doped fiber had $Er^{3+}$ dopant concentration 2700 ppm-wt, absorption coefficient 6.7 dB/m at 980 nm, numerical aperture 0.22, $LP_{11}$ cutoff wavelength 900 nm and core diameter 3.8 $\mu$m. The laser was pumped by a home-made Ti:sapphire laser at 980 nm. The pumping threshold of the fiber laser was about 15 mW leading to cw oscillation. With the pump power higher than 65 mW, mode-locking self-started and a stable pulse train with repetition rate 24.72 MHz emerged when the two polarization controllers were appropriately adjusted. Mode-locking could be achieved in a wide range of polarization setting. As long as the pump power was lower than 115 mW, stable mode-locking could be observed. At this pumping level, the average output power was about 3.8 mW, corresponding to an energy conversion efficiency 3.3% and a pulse energy 0.15 nJ. At this operation point, the output spectral linewidth was about 6.5 nm centered at 1560 nm. The corresponding collinear autocorrelation of the output pulse is shown in Fig. 8 showing that the FWHM pulse width is 400 fsec if a $sech^2$ pulse shape is assumed. This also implies a 374 W peak power in the output. Also, the time-bandwidth product was close to 0.31, indicating that the output pulse was nearly transform-limited. Actually, it was expected that the output pulses should be solitons. When the pump power was higher than 115 mW, higher harmonic pulses appeared. It is attributed to the generation of higher-order

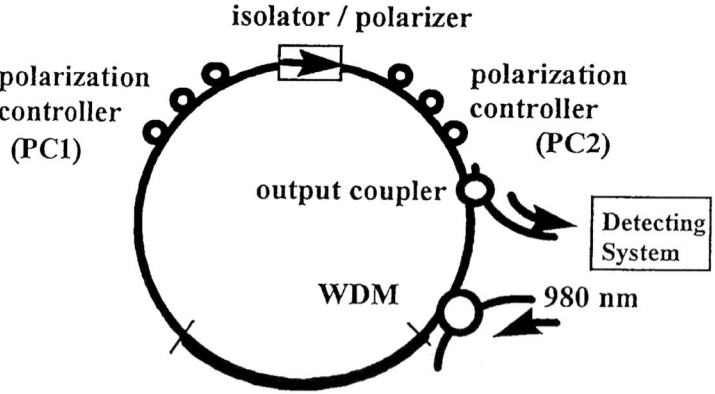

Fig. 7. Setup for the closed-loop ring-cavity fiber laser based on NPM.

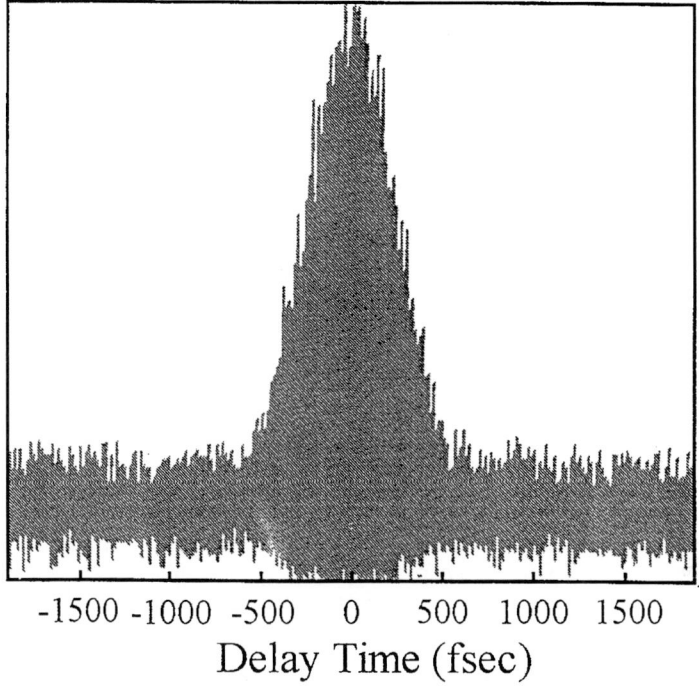

-1500 -1000 -500   0   500  1000  1500
Delay Time (fsec)

Fig. 8. Collinear autocorrelation trace from the closed-loop ring-cavity fiber laser. The trace shows that the FWHM pulse width is about 400 fsec.

solitons as the intra-cavity pulses have sufficiently large energy. The higher-order solitons would split into multiple fundamental solitons when any perturbations exist. We have made the comparisons of several laser parameters between our results and two similar works.[20,21] We found that our energy conversion efficiency was higher, the pulse width was shorter and the peak power was much higher compared with the other femtosecond result.

In the attempt to implement pulsed semiconductor lasers based on NPM, we first need to observe power-dependent polarization evolution in a semiconductor optical amplifier. Such phenomena are expected to be more prominent in quantum well amplifiers because of the anisotropy of gain/absorption saturation between the TE and TM polarizations in such a device.[31] This anisotropy comes from the differences in the selection rules of electron transitions between the two polarization modes. We have observed power-dependent polarization evolution in an InGaAs/GaAs single quantum well amplifier.[32] The electro-luminescence of the sample peaks at 974 and 940 nm in the TE and TM modes, respectively. It indicates the energy difference between the heavy-hole and light-hole subbands. The optical signals in the amplifier were laterally confined in a broad area with a 50-$\mu$m ridge. We used a psec Ti:Sapphire laser (also provides cw laser) as our light source. Figure 9 shows a comparison of output polarization ellipse between a cw and a psec input signals

33

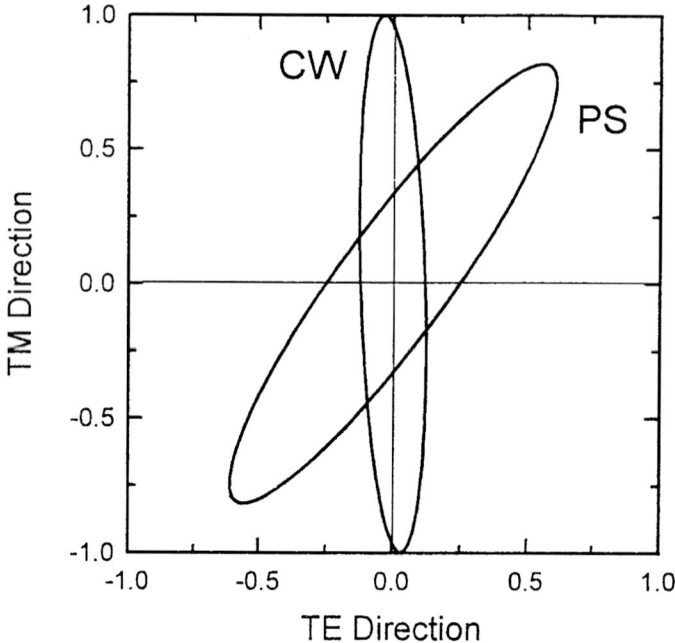

Fig. 9. Comparison between the output polarization ellipses of (a) the cw and (b) the picosecond signals at 940 nm with zero injection current and 70 mW average power. The linear input polarization angle is 15° from the TE direction.

with the same average power. To obtain the results, a cw signal and a pulse of 3 psec in width at 940 nm, both with average power 70 mW and input polarization 15 degrees from the TE direction, were used. The injection current was zero, implying that the involved optical nonlinearity was absorption saturation in both polarization modes. Although the two kinds of signal had the same average power, the peak power of the psec signal was much higher than the cw power. In this situation, psec and cw signals experienced different absorption saturation and ended up with different output polarization ellipses. Although the power-dependent polarization shown in Fig. 9 was due to absorption saturation, we have also observed the similar phenomena based on gain saturation.

To implement a NPM semiconductor laser, an external cavity in air for inserting an polarizer is required. In this situation, efforts need to be made to prevent multiple reflection at the air-semiconductor interfaces for mode-locking stabilization. To this end, two possible approaches can be tried: high-quality anti-reflection coating and slant waveguides for semiconductor amplifiers. Before the implementation of such a mode-locked laser, we first conducted simulations to see the possibility of NPM in semiconductor lasers. Here, we briefly review the results.[33] We considered a ring cavity shown in Fig. 10, in which a traveling-wave optical amplifier with a quantum well structure was followed by a polarizer. An isolator was inserted to guarantee

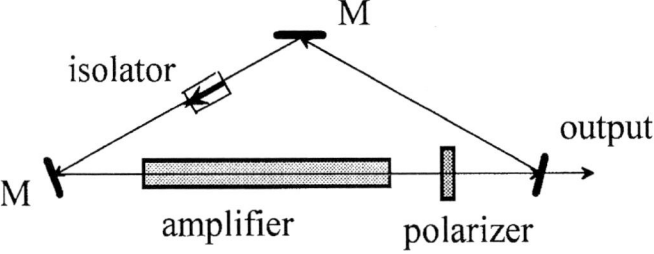

Fig. 10. Ring cavity for passive mode-locking based on nonlinear polarization rotation in a travelling-wave optical amplifier. The end facets of the semiconductor amplifier are assumed to be perfectly anti-reflection coated.

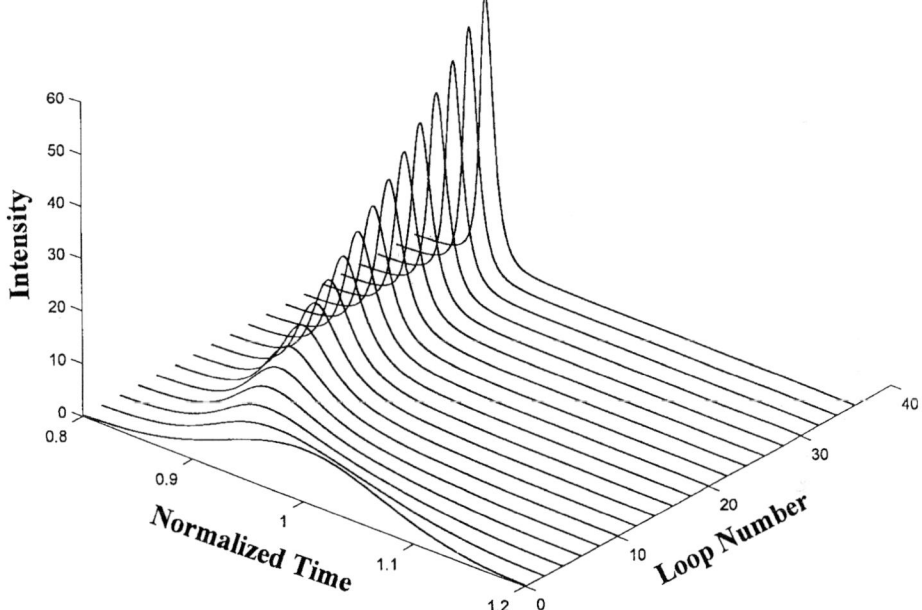

Fig. 11. Pulse evolution in the ring cavity with loop circulation. Pulse compression can be clearly observed.

one-way oscillation. A set of appropriate equations[31] were numerically solved for each loop circulation with a careful arrangement for the time window of computations to account for the finite ring cavity length. Figure 11 shows pulse evolution along circulation in the cavity when the cavity cycle time is two times carrier lifetime and the initial pulse width is 0.1 times carrier lifetime. The amplifier is one beat length long, the initial peak intensity is 10 times the saturation intensity and the output coupler has a reflectivity of 0.5. In Fig. 11, we can see that the originally long pulse is rapidly shortened and the temporal position of the pulse is stabilized in a few tens of loops. From other data, we also observed that although the pulse peak position and pulse energy were stabilized after 80 loops circulation, the pulse width kept narrowing. It is believed that the narrowing process will be stopped by some mechanisms not considered in our theoretical model, such as group-velocity dispersion and ultrafast phenomena in semiconductors. Detailed numerical simulations showed that there existed a quite large parameter space, in which mode-locking could occur, for the variations of the gain constants in the two polarization modes. It implied that the implementation of such a mode-locked laser should be feasible.

## 4. Studies on Nonlinear Coupling Mode-Locking

In this section, we review our results of numerical simulations on NCM for pulsed semiconductor lasers.[34] The design of the passively mode-locked semiconductor laser is schematically shown in Fig. 12. The three mirrors form a ring cavity with its optical path following one of the amplifier (bar amplifier). All the three mirrors (M) have 100% reflectivity. We use the other amplifier (cross amplifier) as the laser output coupler. The bar and cross amplifiers can be independently pumped with injection currents. An isolator is used to guarantee one-way oscillation of the laser. Also we assume that both end facets of the directional coupler are perfectly anti-reflection coated.

The equations used to describe wave evolution inside the active directional coupler can be found in Refs. 34 and 35. Again, we start the simulation with a long Gaussian pulse to see whether the pulse can be compressed. We assume that the coupler length is equal to one coupling length and the gain constants of the two amplifiers are the same. Also, we use the parameter values as follows: linewidth enhancement factor = 6, carrier lifetime = 0.25 nsec, saturation energy = 5 pJ, gain factor = 50, initial pulse energy = 0.4 times saturation energy and initial pulse width = 1 nsec.

Figure 13 shows the pulse evolution emerging from the bar and cross amplifiers for the cycle period of the ring cavity equal to 1 nsec. We can see that the pulse is tremendously compressed after a few loops in ring oscillation. Also, the temporal position of the pulse is stabilized rapidly. Meanwhile, the output from the cross amplifier is a pulse with the pulse width shorter and the peak power higher than that emerging from the bar amplifier. This means that if we use the cross amplifier as the output coupler, the output pulse energy is higher than the intra-cavity pulse energy. The observed phenomenon can be explained as follows. When the leading tail of the pulse enters the bar amplifier, linear coupling transfers the weak power into the cross amplifier, causing the steepening of the bar pulse. When the central part (high power) of the pulse enters the coupler, gain saturation causes this part of the pulse to stay in the bar amplifier. However, because of the gain saturation, the trailing tail of the bar pulse is effectively depressed leading to effective pulse compression. The long tail with low power in the resulting pulse is actually the residual of the initial pulse. Since only a short leading tail of the bar pulse is coupled into the cross amplifier, after efficient amplification the cross pulse is quite

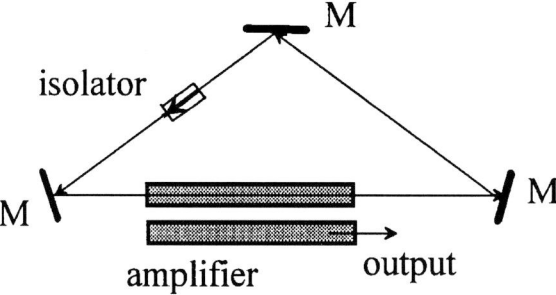

Fig. 12. Ring cavity for passive mode-locking based on nonlinear directional coupling. The three mirrors (M) have 100% reflectivity. The end facets of the directional coupler are assumed to be perfectly anti-reflection coated.

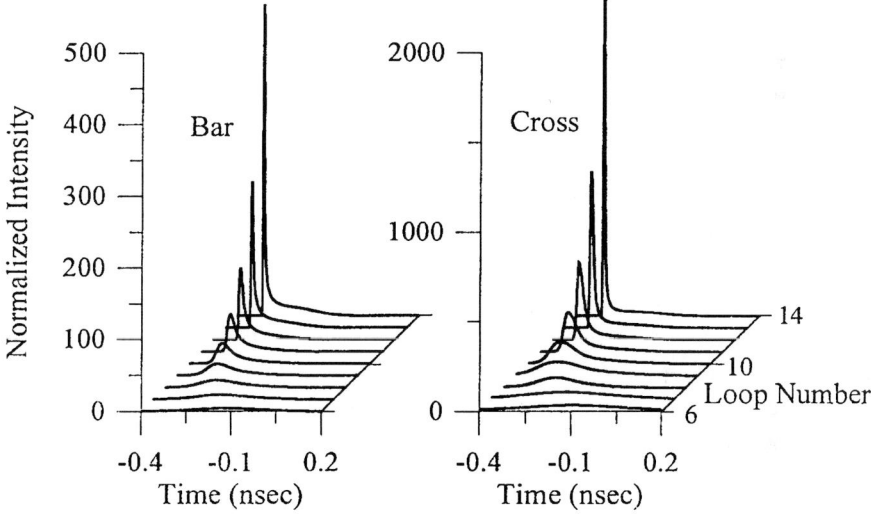

Fig. 13. Pulse shapes emerging from the bar and cross amplifiers. The intensity is normalized to the peak intensity of the initial pulse.

narrow with a relatively higher power. The slight lead of the cross pulse in temporal position is a proof that the cross pulse originates from the short leading tail coupled into the cross amplifier. Because the leading tail of the bar pulse becomes steeper and steeper along circulation, the coupled leading tail and hence the cross pulse, i.e. output pulse, becomes shorter and shorter.

We also observed that the peak position and pulse energy were stabilized after 22 loops; however, the pulse width kept narrowing. Like the case in the last section, it is expected that group-velocity dispersion and certain femtosecond mechanisms in semiconductors will stop the narrowing process after the pulse reaches a certain narrow width. With a sequence of simulations, we found that when cycle period

37

was longer than 1.3 nsec (about five times carrier lifetime), more than one pulse could be observed in the cavity due to the recovery from gain saturation. Hence, there is an upper bound of the ring cavity length for the mode-locking mechanism to work.

## 5. Studies on Additive-Pulse Mode-Locking

In this section, we review our results of APM Er-doped fiber lasers with fiber gratings to form coupled cavities. The APM technique has been widely used for mode-locking various laser systems. It is well-known that in implementing the APM technique, careful adjustment for matching the optical lengths of the two coupled cavities is quite critical for achieving the interferometric APM action. Typically, the mismatch of the cavity length must be controlled within the wavelength order. Recently, however, APM fiber lasers with coupled cavities formed with three fiber Bragg gratings were implemented without careful cavity length control.[36,37] We have also implemented a similar mode-locked fiber laser. Actually, it is almost impossible to control the length of fiber cavity down to the wavelength order. This accomplishment can naturally reduce the difficulty in the APM technique. In the following, we review our theoretical and simulation results which can well explain the phenomena in the APM fiber lasers with gratings.

The basic idea is that a Bragg grating serves as a wavelength-dependent delay line. For a given cavity length mismatch within a certain range, the laser system can find a suitable wavelength at which the difference of the delay between the used gratings can compensate for the cavity length mismatch. To understand the phenomenon quantitatively, we start with the reflection coefficient $r(\omega)$ and transmission coefficient $t(\omega)$ of a Bragg grating as in Ref. 38

$$r(\omega) = \frac{-j\kappa \sinh(L\sqrt{\kappa^2 - \delta^2})}{\sqrt{\kappa^2 - \delta^2} \cosh(L\sqrt{\kappa^2 - \delta^2}) + j\delta \sinh(L\sqrt{\kappa^2 - \delta^2})} \tag{4}$$

$$t(\omega) = \frac{\sqrt{\kappa^2 - \delta^2}}{\sqrt{\kappa^2 - \delta^2} \cosh(L\sqrt{\kappa^2 - \delta^2}) + j\delta \sinh(L\sqrt{\kappa^2 - \delta^2})} . \tag{5}$$

Here, $L$ is the length of the grating, $\kappa$ is the coupling coefficient and $\delta$ is defined as $\delta(\omega) = \beta(\omega) - \pi/\Lambda$, where $\beta$ is the propagation constant in the fiber and $\Lambda$ is the period of the Bragg grating. We consider a coupled-cavity fiber laser as shown in Fig. 14. Three fiber gratings with the same coupling coefficient 810.787 rad/m and the same Bragg wavelength at 1550 nm, but different lengths with $L_1 = 8$ mm, $L_2 = 3$ mm and $L_3 = 2$ mm. The calculated reflectivities, $r(\omega)$, as functions of wavelength of gratings 1 (solid line), 2 (dashed line) and 3 (dash-dotted line) are shown in Fig. 15. The corresponding phase shifts, $\phi_r(\omega) = \arg(r(\omega))$, after reflection are plotted in Fig. 16. Note that a linear phase shift in the frequency domain corresponds to a time delay in the time domain. Different slopes of phase shift at different wavelengths in this figure implies different time delays when reflected from or transmitted

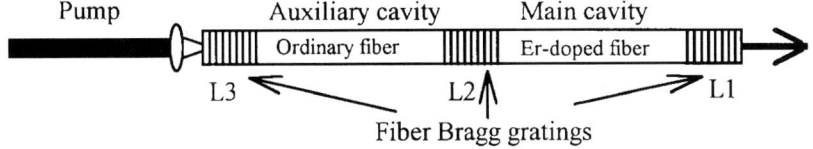

Fig. 14. Configuration of an in-line coupled-cavity APM fiber laser with fiber gratings to form the coupled cavities.

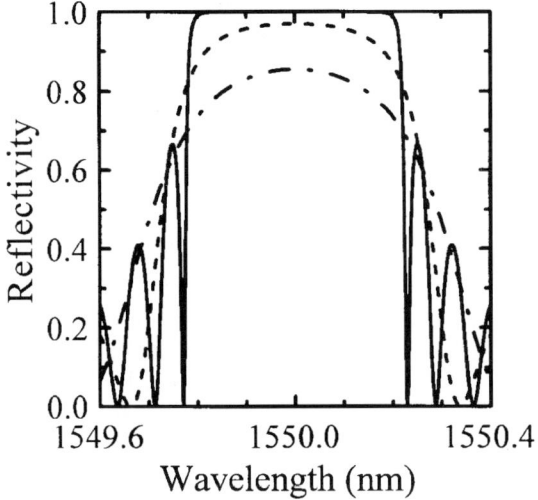

Fig. 15. Reflectivity curves for the three fiber Bragg gratings with lengths $L_1 = 8$ mm (solid line), $L_2 = 3$ mm (dashed line) and $L_3 = 2$ mm (dash-dotted line), respectively.

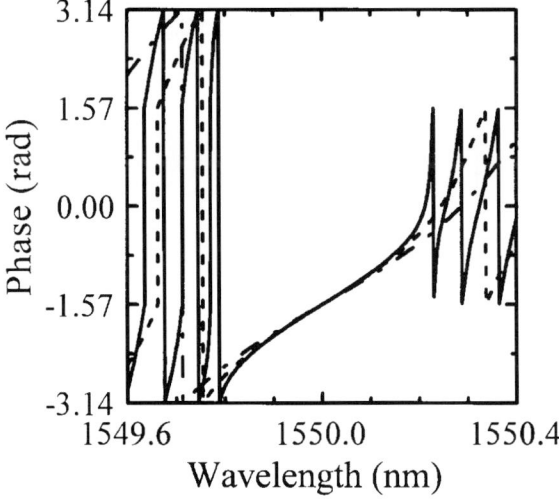

Fig. 16. Phase curves of the reflection coefficients of the three fiber Bragg gratings.

through a grating. This time delay is the same for reflected and transmitted signals since the phase difference between them is a constant $\pi/2$. The delay time $T_d(\omega)$ is the derivative of the phase shift as

$$T_d(\omega) = -\frac{d}{d\omega}\phi_r(\omega) = \frac{\kappa^2 \cosh(L\sqrt{\kappa^2 - \delta^2})\sinh(L\sqrt{\kappa^2 - \delta^2}) - L\delta^2\sqrt{\kappa^2 - \delta^2}}{\sqrt{\kappa^2 - \delta^2}[\kappa^2 \cosh^2(L\sqrt{\kappa^2 - \delta^2}) - \delta^2]}\frac{1}{v_g},$$

(6)

where $v_g$ is the group velocity. We define an effective penetration length into a grating corresponding to the delay distance of the grating as $\Delta L_{\text{eff}}(\omega) = v_g T_d(\omega)/2$. The factor 2 in the denominator accounts for the round-trip of signal into the grating in considering the reflected signal. The effective penetration lengths of the three gratings as functions of wavelength are plotted in Fig. 17. We can see that different grating lengths lead to quite different effective penetration lengths. It is the difference that results in the compensation for the cavity length mismatch. Note that because the central grating (grating 2) causes equal delay time for the two cavities, it actually makes no contribution to the aforementioned compensation. Figure 18 shows the difference of the effective penetration length between gratings 1 and 3, i.e. $\Delta L_{\text{eff1}} - \Delta L_{\text{eff3}}$. The inset shows the details near 1550 nm. We can see that between 1549.8 and 1550.2 nm, the penetration length difference ranges from 0.06 to 1.2 mm. The possibly largest value is actually the tolerance range of the cavity length mismatch. For a given mismatch within the tolerance range, the laser system can find a wavelength for oscillation so that the difference of effective penetration

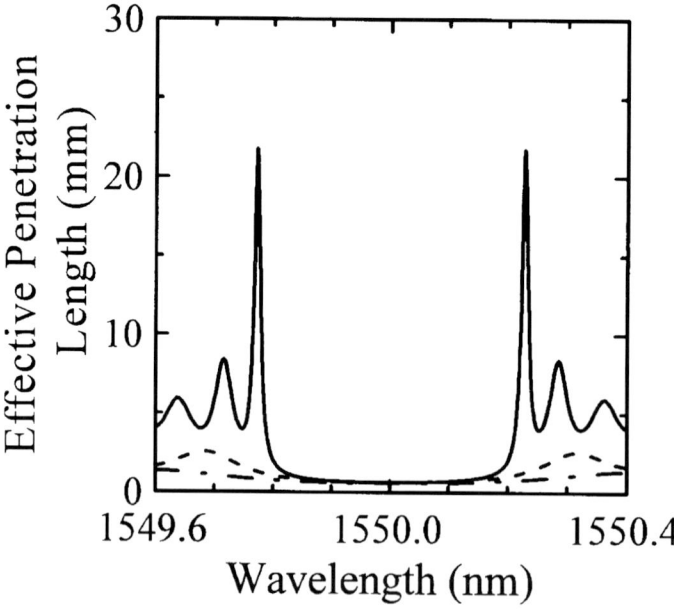

Fig. 17. Effective penetration lengths of the three Bragg gratings.

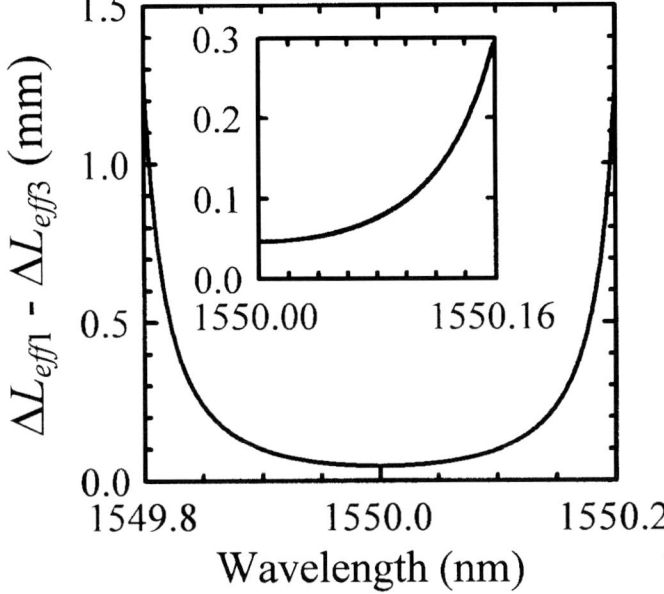

Fig. 18. Difference of the effective penetration lengths between gratings 1 and 3. The inset shows the details near the center.

length can compensate for the mismatch. For instance, if the mismatch is 0.2 mm, it can be compensated simply by choosing the wavelength at 1550.1423 nm. To show this effect, we conducted simulations of pulse evolution in such a laser system. For propagation in the fiber, we solved the modified nonlinear Schrodinger equation.[20] The lengths of the main and auxiliary cavities were assumed to be 200 cm and 200.02 cm, respectively (0.2 mm mismatch). The group-velocity dispersion was $-0.04$ psec$^2$/m and the nonlinear refractive index $n_2$ was $3.2 \times 10^{-16}$ cm$^2$/W. The gain constant in the main cavity was set at $3 \times 10^{-4}$ cm$^{-1}$. The peak power and pulse width of the initially Gaussian pulse were set at 6 mW and 100 psec, respectively. Figure 19 shows the evolution of output pulse at 1550 nm. We can see that the initial pulse diminishes after several hundred round-trips, implying that with this cavity mismatch mode-locking is not feasible at this wavelength. Actually, under the conditions that the Bragg wavelengths of the three gratings are the same and that gratings 1 and 3 have different lengths, mode-locking is difficult if the cavity lengths are exactly matched. In Fig. 20, we shifted the oscillation center wavelength to 1550.1423 nm and found that the pulse was stably compressed, implying that mode-locking could be achieved. It is noted that the compensation function for the cavity mismatch relies on the difference of the effective penetration length between the two end gratings. Therefore, these two end gratings must be different, either in length or index. Also, it can be seen that the tolerance range of cavity mismatch depends on the slope of the phase in Fig. 16. To increase the tolerance range, we

41

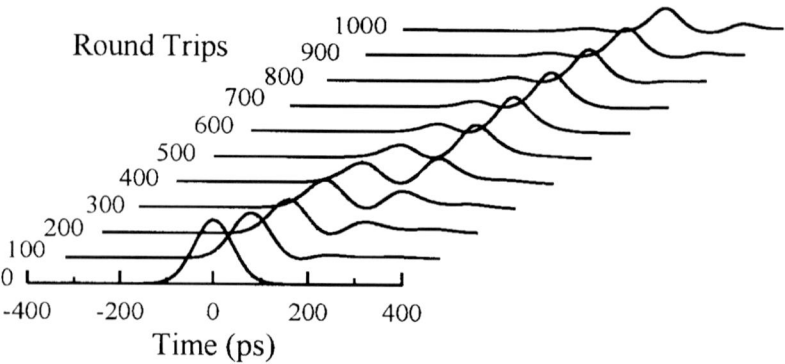

Fig. 19. Output pulse evolution when the oscillation wavelength is centered at 1550 nm. The cavity mismatch is 0.2 mm.

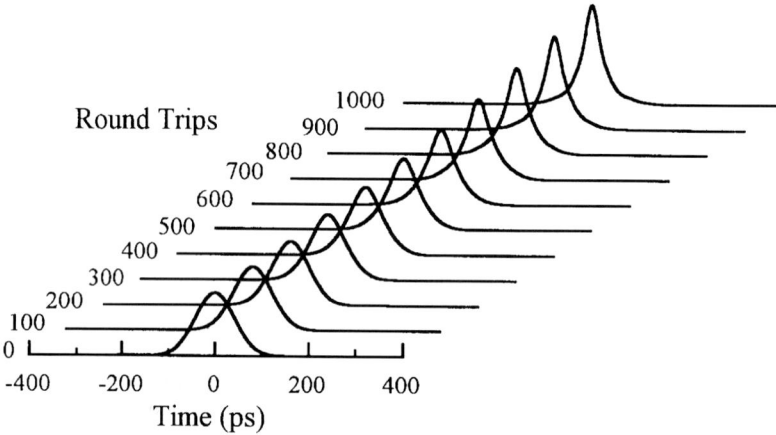

Fig. 20. Output pulse evolution when the oscillation wavelength is centered at 1550.1423 nm. The cavity mismatch is 0.2 mm.

can use a grating with its phase response more sensitive to wavelength for one of the cavity ends. This can be implemented by well designing a chirped grating. Use of chirped gratings can also lead to a broader reflectivity window, implying that the output spectrum can be broader and the output pulse can be shorter. Meanwhile, chirped gratings have the function of dispersion compensation leading to more efficient pulse compression.

## 6. Conclusions

We have reviewed several passive mode-locking techniques. We first gave general descriptions about these mode-locking mechanisms and then discussed briefly some of our related research results. The mode-locking techniques we reviewed included saturable absorption mode-locking, colliding-pulse mode-locking, additive-pulse mode-locking, Kerr-lens mode-locking, nonlinear polarization mode-locking and nonlinear coupling mode-locking. Most of these mode-locking techniques have been applied to various laser systems. Since mode-locking techniques are so important in generating short pulses, more efforts are needed for further investigations. The new directions include the applications of those techniques, which were widely used in solid-state lasers, to semiconductor lasers for compact pulsed laser sources. They also include new passive mode-locking mechanisms based on newly developed nonlinear optical phenomena.

## Acknowledgment

We wish to acknowledge the support from National Science Council, The Republic of China, under the grants NSC 84-2215-E-002-011, NSC 84-2215-E-002-012, NSC 85-2215-E-002-003, NSC 85-2215-E-002-004, NSC 85-2215-E-002-010, NSC 86-2215-E-002-010 and NSC 86-2215-E-002-011.

## References

1. U. Keller, T. H. Chiu, and J. F. Ferguson, "Self-starting and self-Q-switching dynamics of passively mode-locked Nd:YLF and Nd:YAG lasers", *Opt. Lett.* **18** (1993) 217–219.

2. U. Keller, T. H. Chiu, and J. F. Ferguson, "Self-starting femtosecond mode-locked Nd:glass laser that uses intracavity saturable absorber", *Opt. Lett.* **18** (1993) 1077–1079.

3. P. J. Delfyett, L. Florez, N. Stoffel, T. Gmitter, N. Andreadakis, G. Alphonse, and W. Geislik, "200-fsec optical pulse generation and intracavity pulse evolution in a hybrid mode-locked semiconductor diode-laser/amplifier system", *Opt. Lett.* **17** (1992) 670–672.

4. R. A. Salvatore, T. Schrans, and A. Yariv, "Wavelength tunable source of subpicosecond pulses from cw passively mode-locked two-section multiple-quantum-well laser", *IEEE Photon. Tech. Lett.* **5** (1993) 756–758.

5. J. A. Valdmanis and R. L. Fork, "Design considerations for a femtosecond pulse laser balancing self phase modulation, group velocity dispersion, saturable absorption, and saturable gain", *IEEE J. Quantum Electron.* **QE-22** (1986) 112–118.

6. Y. K. Chen, M. C. Wu, T. Tanbun-Ek, R. A. Logan, and M. A. Chin, "Subpicosecond monolithic colliding-pulse mode-locked multiple quantum well lasers", *Appl. Phys. Lett.* **58** (1991) 1253–1255.

7. C. F. Lin and C. L. Tang, "Colliding pulse mode locking of a semiconductor laser in an external ring cavity", *Appl. Phys. Lett.* **62** (1993) 1053–1055.

8. I. N. Duling III, "All-fiber ring soliton laser mode locked with a nonlinear mirror", *Opt. Lett.* **16** (1991) 539–541.

9. J. Goodberlet, J. Wang, J. G. Fujimoto, and P. A. Schulz, "Starting dynamics of additive-pulse mode-locking in the Ti:Al$_2$O$_3$ laser", *Opt. Lett.* **15** (1990) 1300–1302.

10. G. Sucha, S. R. Bolton, and D. S. Chemla, "Generation of high-power femtosecond pulses near 1.5 $\mu$m using a color-center laser system", *IEEE J. Quantum Electron.* **28** (1992) 2163–2175.

11. L. Y. Liu, J. M. Huxley, E. P. Ippen, and H. A. Haus, "Self-starting additive-pulse mode-locking of a Nd:YAG laser", *Opt. Lett.* **15** (1990) 553–555.

12. J. M. Liu and J. K. Chee, "Passive mode-locking of a cw Nd:YLF laser with a nonlinear external coupled cavity", *Opt. Lett.* **15** (1990) 685–687.

13. D. E. Spence, P. N. Kean, and W. Sibbett, "60-fsec pulse generation from a self-mode-locked Ti:sapphire laser", *Opt. Lett.* **16** (1991) 42–44.

14. M. Piche and F. Salin, "Self-mode-locking of solid-state lasers without apertures", *Opt. Lett.* **18** (1993) 1041–1043.

15. J. M. Jacobson, K. Naganuma, H. A. Haus, J. G. Fujimoto, and A. G. Jacobson, "Femtosecond pulse generation in a Ti:Al$_2$O$_3$ laser by using second- and third-order intracavity dispersion", *Opt. Lett.* **17** (1992) 1608–1610.

16. D. R. Dykaar, S. B. Darack, and W. H. Knox, "Cross-locking dynamics in a two-color mode-locked Ti:sapphire laser", *Opt. Lett.* **19** (1994) 1058–1060.

17. A. Stingl, Ch. Spielmann, F. Krausz, and R. Szipocs, "Generation of 11-fs pulses from a Ti:sapphire laser without the use of prisms", *Opt. Lett.* **19** (1994) 204–206.

18. J. Zhou, G. Taft, C. P. Huang, M. M. Murnane, H. C. Kapteyn, and I. P. Christov, "Pulse evolution in a broad-bandwidth Ti:sapphire laser", *Opt. Lett.* **19** (1994) 1149–1151.

19. A. Stingl, M. Lenzner, Ch. Spielmann, F. Krausz, and R. Szipocs, "Sub-10-fs mirror-dispersion-controlled Ti:sapphire laser", *Opt. Lett.* **20** (1995) 602–604.

20. H. A. Haus, E. P. Ippen, and K. Tamura, "Additive-pulse modelocking in fiber lasers", *IEEE J. Quantum Electron.* **30** (1994) 200–208.

21. V. J. Matsas, T. P. Newson, D. J. Richardson, and D. N. Payne, "Selfstarting passively mode-locked fiber ring soliton laser exploiting nonlinear polarization rotation", *Electron. Lett.* **28** (1992) 1391–1393.

22. K. Tamura, L. E. Nelson, H. A. Haus, and E. P. Ippen, "Soliton versus nonsoliton operation of fiber ring lasers", *Appl. Phys. Lett.* **64** (1994) 149–151.

23. K. Tamura, C. R. Doerr, L. E. Nelson, H. A. Haus, and E. P. Ippen, "Technique for obtaining high-energy ultrashort pulses from an additive-pulse mode-locked erbium-doped fiber ring laser", *Opt. Lett.* **19** (1994) 46–48.

24. K. Tamura, C. R. Doerr, H. A. Haus, and E. P. Ippen, "Soliton fiber laser stabilization and tuning with a broad intracavity filter", *IEEE Photon. Tech. Lett.* **6** (1994) 697–699.

25. H. A. Haus, K. Tamura, L. E. Nelson, and E. P. Ippen, "Stretched-pulse additive pulse mode-locking in fiber ring lasers: Theory and experiment", *IEEE J. Quantum Electron.* **31** (1995) 591–598.

26. S. R. Friberg, A. M. Weiner, Y. Silberberg, B. G. Sfez, and P. S. Smith, "Femtosecond switching in a dual-core-fiber nonlinear coupler", *Opt. Lett.* **13** (1988) 904–906.

27. A. Villeneuve, C. C. Yang, P. G. J. Wigley, G. I. Stegeman, J. S. Aitchison, and C. N. Ironside, "Ultrafast all-optical switching in semiconductor nonlinear-directional couplers at half the band gap", *Appl. Phys. Lett.* **61** (1992) 147–149.

28. R. Jin, J. P. Sokoloff, P. A. Harten, C. L. Chuang, S. G. Lee, M. Warren, H. M. Gibbs, J. N. Polky, and G. A. Pubanz, "Ultrafast modulation with subpicosecond recovery time in GaAs/AlGaAs nonlinear directional coupler", *Appl. Phys. Lett.* **56** (1990) 993–995.

29. H. G. Winful and D. T. Walton, "Passive mode-locking through nonlinear coupling in a dual-core fiber laser", *Opt. Lett.* **17** (1992) 1688–1690.

30. S. B. Reinhardt, R. J. Flynn, R. K. Erdmann, J. W. Haus, and R. L. Fork, "Experimental study of harmonically modelocked fiber lasers including dual core fiber", Paper WUU9, OSA Annual Meeting, Portland, Oregon, Sep. 1995, p. 120.

31. C. C. Yang, "Intensity dependent polarization in a semiconductor multiple quantum well amplifiers", *IEEE J. Quantum Electron.* **29** (1993) 1091–1097.

32. M. S. Lin, D. W. Huang, C. C. Yang, M. H. Hong, and Y. K. Chen, "Nonlinear polarization switching in a semiconductor single quantum well optical amplifier", *Appl. Phys. Lett.* **67** (1995) 2114–2116.
33. C. C. Yang, C. W. Lay, M. S. Lin, and D. W. Huang, "All-optical switching and passive mode-locking based on nonlinear polarization rotation in a semiconductor quantum well amplifier", *Opt. Quantum Electron.* **28** (1996) 1217–1227.
34. C. W. Hsu and C. C. Yang, "Passive mode-locking of semiconductor lasers based on nonlinear directional coupling", *Opt. Lett.* **21** (1996) 878–880.
35. S. Trillo, S. Wabnitz, J. M. Soto-Crespo, and E. M. Wright, "Ultrashort pulse self-switching in coupled-semiconductor traveling-wave amplifiers", *IEEE J. Quantum Electron.* **27** (1991) 410–415.
36. P. K. Cheo, V. G. Mutalik, and G. A. Ball, "Mode-locking of in-line coupled-cavity fiber lasers using intra-core Bragg gratings", *IEEE Photon. Tech. Lett.* **7** (1995) 980–982.
37. P. K. Cheo, L. Wang, and M. Ding, "Low-threshold, self-tuned and passively mode-locked coupled-cavity all-fiber lasers", *IEEE Photon. Tech. Lett.* **8** (1996) 66–68.
38. T. Tamir, *Integrated Optics*, 2nd Ed. (Springer-Verlag, New York, 1979) p. 72.

International Journal of High Speed Electronics and Systems, Vol. 8, No. 4 (1997) 621–642

# NICKEL-INDIFFUSION WAVEGUIDE FOR TE-TM MODE SPLITTER IN LITHIUM NIOBATE

WAY-SEEN WANG,* YU-PIN LIAO, and CHIH-HUA YANG

*Department of Electrical Engineering, National Taiwan University,
Taipei 106, Taiwan, R.O.C.*

Optical waveguides fabricated by nickel indiffusion on lithium niobate are reviewed. In particular, the fabrication process, index change versus concentration, wavelength dispersion, process-dependent polarization, propagation loss, and electro-optic modulation of the nickel indiffusion waveguide are discussed. To improve the confinement of single-ordinary polarization waveguide fabricated by nickel indiffusion, a novel waveguide made by zinc and nickel indiffusion is presented for the first time. Though the measured propagation loss of the waveguide is larger, the measured output power contours are found more symmetric. Moreover, several TE-TM mode splitters using one or more nickel indiffusion waveguides for the complete mode sorting effect are discussed.

## 1. Introduction

Integrated lithium niobate (LiNbO$_3$) optical waveguide devices have performed a wide range of operation on optical waves for signal processing. For some applications such as polarization splitters, which are key components for polarization control in optical communication system and fiber sensors, TE and TM modes of the propagating light are particularly emphasized. To date, many TE-TM mode splitters have been demonstrated for this purpose.[1-8] The reported polarization (or mode) splitters were divided into two classes.[6] One is based on the interference of optical modes.[1-3] The TE and TM modes of a directional coupler can be split by the difference in phase velocities of a fundamental and a first-order mode. The second one is based on the sorting effect of optical modes.[4-8] With an asymmetrical Y-junction structure,[4-5] the incident TE and TM waveguide modes can be split and directed to the output arms according to their preferences of polarizations. In practical application, those which use the Y-junction structure have a larger fabrication tolerance.[4] To improve the performance of TE and TM mode splitting, Goto and Yip[4] first used an asymmetric Y-junction with its waveguide branches made of different fabrication techniques, namely, the proton exchange (PE) and the titanium indiffusion (TI). As the fabricated device is based on the adiabatic mode conversion of the extraordinary polarization modes, i.e. the partial mode sorting

---

*Corresponding author: Prof. Way-Seen Wang; Fax: +886-2-2362-1950
E-mail: wswang@cc.ee.ntu.edu.tw

effect, a careful design of the waveguide pattern for a specific index distribution is then required to obtain maximum extinction ratios. Recently, a mode splitter based on the complete mode sorting effect was realized by an asymmetric Y-junction with branching waveguides supporting only TE and TM polarizations.[7] The asymmetric Y-junction may be formed by a titanium indiffusion waveguide, a nickel indiffusion waveguide (NI), and a magnesium-oxide-induced lithium outdiffusion[9] (MILO) or a proton exchange waveguide[8] as shown in Fig. 1(a). The TE and TM modes originally guided by a TI waveguide supporting random polarization can be successfully directed to the MILO waveguide supporting only TE modes[9] and the NI waveguide supporting only TM modes. The measured extinction ratios are greater than 20 dB for fundamental or higher-order TE and TM modes due to the inherent single polarization of the waveguides. Thus, mode sorting with single polarization waveguides are essential in the fabrication of high-extinction-ratio TE-TM mode splitters.

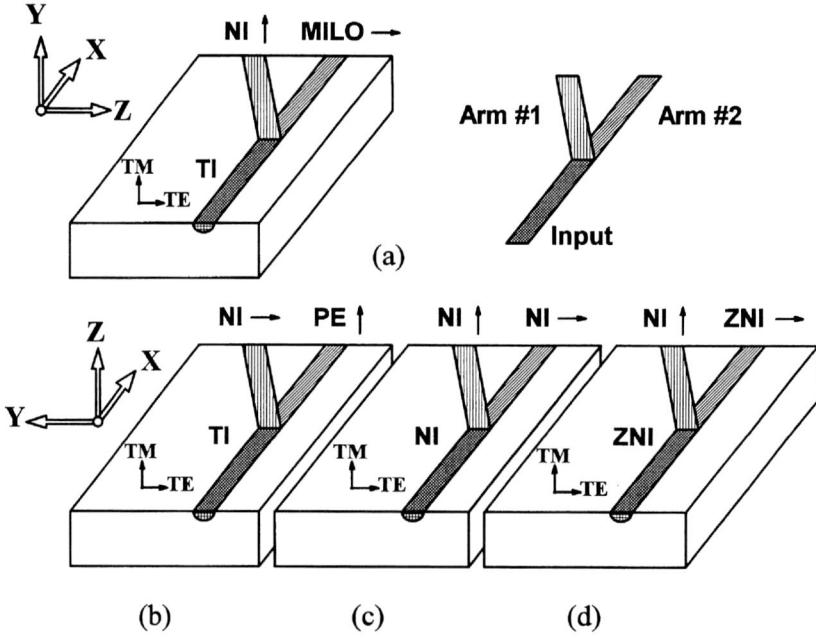

Fig. 1. Schematic diagrams of $1 \times 2$ Y-junction TE-TM mode splitters on Y-cut and Z-cut LiNbO$_3$ substrates. (a) TI, NI, and MILO waveguides, (b) TI, NI and PE waveguides, (c) NI waveguides only, and (d) NI and ZNI waveguides.

The common methods for the fabrication of optical waveguides on LiNbO$_3$ are titanium indiffusion[10] and proton exchange.[11] Titanium indiffusion is a high-temperature ($\approx 1000°C$) process that increases of both ordinary and extraordinary indices, $n_0$ and $n_e$, and therefore, provides waveguides for both the ordinary and extraordinary polarization modes. Proton exchange is a low-temperature ($\approx 250°C$)

process that produces waveguides supporting only the extraordinary polarization modes. Recently, several optical waveguides fabricated by the indiffusion of divalent metallic atoms such as nickel and magnesium have been studied.[7–10,12–14] The results show that replacements of the TI, NI, and MILO waveguides of the complete mode-sorted TE-TM mode splitter by other waveguides become possible. For example, the MILO waveguide of the splitter may be replaced by a PE waveguide fabricated on a Z-cut LiNbO$_3$ as shown in Fig. 1(b). Moreover, using the anisotropy in the refractive index changes ($\Delta n_0$ and $\Delta n_4$) caused by metal diffusants, single-ordinary ($\Delta n_0 > \Delta n_e \approx 0$), single-extraordinary ($\Delta n_e > \Delta n_0 \approx 0$), and random polarization ($n_0 > 0$ and $\Delta n_e > 0$) waveguides can be made by diffusing a single material at an appropriate temperature for a certain time.[13] Thus, a TE-TM mode splitter can even be made by using only one metal diffusant. For example, Fig. 1(c) shows a $1 \times 2$ TE-TM mode splitter[14] operating at 1.32 $\mu$m wavelength on a Z-cut LiNbO$_3$ using only nickel diffusion, in which each branching waveguide also supports only a single polarization wave similar to that was reported.[7,8] The measured extinction ratios for both TE and TM modes are also greater than 20 dB. However, the NI waveguide, supporting single-ordinary polarizations, can hardly be replaced, though its optical confinement is not as good as that supporting single-extraordinary polarizations.[13,14] The reason is that the single-ordinary polarization waveguide was formed at a lower nickel concentration, and therefore has a smaller $\Delta n_0$ for optical confinement.

In this paper, the basic waveguiding characteristics of NI waveguides are reviewed. Their applications as TE-TM mode splitters are also discussed. Moreover, to improve the confinement of ordinary-polarization NI waveguide, i.e. to have a larger $\Delta n_0$, the zinc and nickel indiffusion (ZNI) waveguide which also has a process-dependent polarization similar to that of the NI waveguide, is presented for the first time. A TE-TM mode splitter with a ZNI waveguide for the ordinary polarization mode and an NI waveguide for the extraordinary polarization mode as shown in Fig. 1(d) is also fabricated for comparison. The results show that even a wave consisting of high-order TM and TE modes at 1.32 $\mu$m can be splitted efficiently. The measured extinction ratios are also greater than 20 dB.

## 2. NI Waveguides

TI waveguides have the advantage of low propagation loss,[10] however, an out-diffusion layer near the LiNbO$_3$ surface[15] is often formed. Optical fields guided by TI channel waveguides will be affected by the unwanted planar waveguide. Some techniques are then needed to suppress it.[16,17] Moreover, decrease in the bulk electro-optic coefficients at diffusion temperatures above 950°C was also observed.[18] Thus, other materials for indiffusion should be considered. Schmidt found that the planar NI waveguides made at 800°C can support random polarization waves.[19] The measured propagation loss is less than 1 dB/cm, which makes nickel a good alternative diffusant for making waveguides in LiNbO$_3$. In the following sections, experimental verification of important waveguiding characteristics of NI waveguides in our laboratory are described.

### 2.1. Fabrication process

The typical fabrication process for an NI waveguide used in our laboratory is described as follows. First, nickel strips of thicknesses 100 to 400 Å, widths 4 to 12 $\mu$m, depending on the input laser wavelengths, were prepared on Z-cut LiNbO$_3$ chips of area about 12 mm × 6 mm by the lift-off technique. Then, the waveguide patterns were diffused in a furnace at 650–900°C for 0.4 to 7 hr. As nickel is a diffusant more active than the commonly used titanium, a shorter diffusion time or a lower diffusion temperature has to be employed. Outdiffusion of Li$_2$O is then less important compared with that of titanium indiffusion. From our experience, when diffusing at 1000°C for 1 hr, 950°C for 2 hr, and 900°C for 6 hr, no significant outdiffusion layer was observed at a wavelength of 632.8 nm. And if necessary, the sample was simply wrapped up with platinum foil. Moreover, as the melting point of nickel is lower than that of titanium, a preoxidation step for nickel at 400°C for about 1 hr is necessary to prevent the increase of the waveguide width. After diffusion, the end faces of the samples were polished for optical characterization. The optical measurement was performed at the wavelength of 632.8 nm with an He-Ne laser. The NI waveguides can be made on either one of the three cuts of LiNbO$_3$. For the Z-cut substrate just described, TE modes have ordinary polarizations, and TM modes, extraordinary polarizations. The crystal axes and index orientations are depicted in Fig. 2 for quick reference.

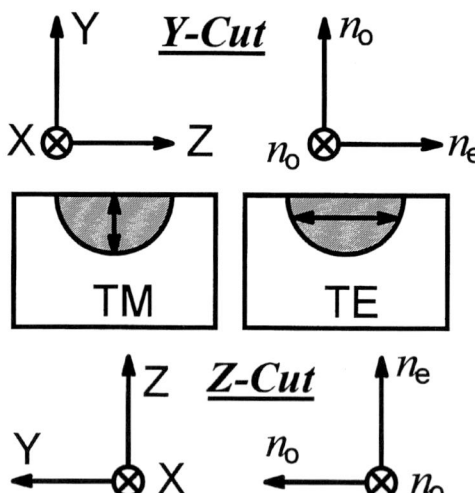

Fig. 2. The crystal axes and index orientations of Y-cut and Z-cut LiNbO$_3$ substrates.

## 2.2. *Index changes versus concentration*

To know the relative nickel concentration profiles, two planar waveguides fabricated by diffusing a 100 Å nickel film at 650°C and 750°C for 2 hr were measured by the secondary ion mass spectroscopy (SIMS) technique. The diffusion coefficients, inferred from fitting to Gaussian functions as shown in Figs. 3 and 4, are 0.022 $\mu m^2/$ hr at 650°C and 0.189 $\mu m^2/$hr at 750°C. The effective index changes of a planar waveguide made by diffusing a film of thickness 100 Å at 650°C for 5 hr were measured by a prism-coupler (Metricon 2010). The measured diffusion depth is 0.66 $\mu$m and the effective index change for the single TM mode is 0.00028. Using the normalized universal chart for a Gaussian index profile,[20] the surface refractive-index change was found to be 0.0150. However, another planar waveguide made by

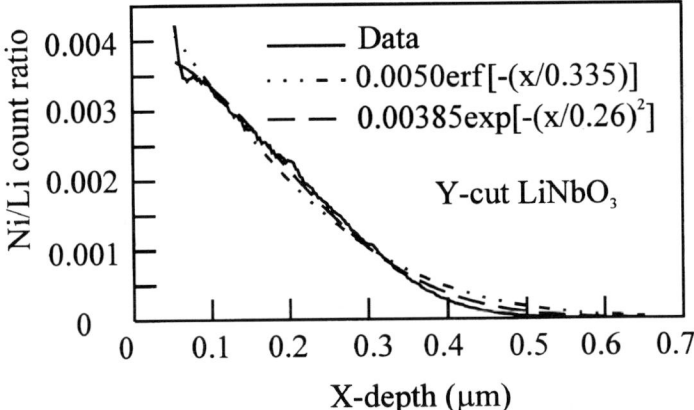

Fig. 3. SIMS data fitted by complementary error and Gaussian functions for a Y-cut substrate.

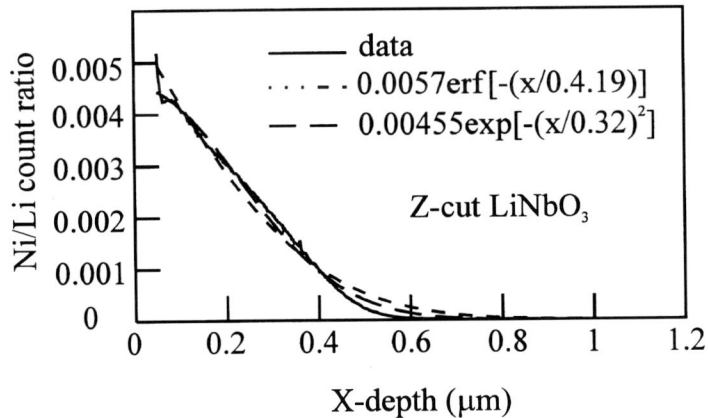

Fig. 4. SIMS data fitted by complementary error and Gaussian functions for a Z-cut substrate.

diffusing a film of thickness 300 Å at 900°C for 2 hr supports three ordinary modes and one extraordinary mode. The measured diffusion depth is 4.39 $\mu$m and the effective index changes of the TE fundamental, first order, and second order modes were 0.00483, 0.00297, and 0.00186, respectively. The surface refractive-index change found by the inverse WKB analysis[21] was 0.0067. Notice that as the diffusion for the TM mode is quite shallow, the effective index change of the fundamental TM mode is much smaller than that of the TE mode.

Figure 5 plots the refractive index changes versus nickel concentration for the ordinary and extraordinary polarizations. Evidently, $\Delta n_0$ is larger than $\Delta n_e$ at lower nickel concentration, but smaller than $\Delta n_e$ at higher nickel concentration. Moreover, as $d\Delta n_0/dC$ varies with $C$, a piecewise constant model is better used. Where $d\Delta n_e/dC$ doesn't change much, a constant model is good enough. These approximations, as shown in Table 1, are similar to those employed for Ti-indiffused waveguides.[22]

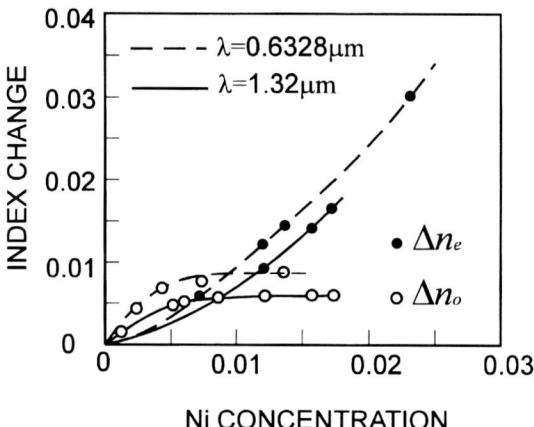

Fig. 5. The refractive index changes versus nickel concentration for the ordinary and extraordinary polarizations at 632.8 nm and 1.32 $\mu$m wavelengths.

Table 1. The variations of refractive index changes versus the nickel surface concentration at different wavelengths.

| Normalized Concentration | 632.8 nm | | 1.32 $\mu$m | |
|---|---|---|---|---|
| | $d\Delta n_e/dC$ | $d\Delta n_0/dC$ | $d\Delta n_e/dC$ | $d\Delta n_0/dC$ |
| $0 < C_{Ni} < 0.23\%$ | 1.3 | 1.96 | 0.9 | 1.27 |
| $0.23\% < C_{Ni} < 0.44\%$ | 1.3 | 1.048 | 0.9 | 1 |
| $0.44\% < C_{Ni} < 0.77\%$ | 1.3 | 0.195 | 0.9 | 0.07 |

## 2.3. *Process-dependent polarizations*

To know the waveguide polarization is dependent on the diffusion temperature and the diffusion time, planar waveguides made of nickel layers of the same thickness (100 Å) are fabricated at temperatures varying from 650°C to 900°C. The measured polarizations are shown in Table 2. The interesting behavior of polarization can be explained with the aid of Fig. 6. As the diffusion time is short, the nickel concentration is high at the surface, and the relation $\Delta n_e > \Delta n_0 > 0$ is valid from Fig. 5. In principle, both ordinary and extraordinary modes can be supported by the waveguide. However, the waveguide is not wide enough for the ordinary mode, and it becomes cut off. On the contrary, when the diffusion time is long enough, the nickel concentration becomes low near the surface, and the relation $\Delta n_0 > \Delta n_e \approx 0$

Table 2. Process-dependent polarizations of planar NI waveguides at 632.8 nm wavelength.

| Temperature (C) | Time (hr) | Polarization |
|:---:|:---:|:---:|
| 650 | 4.5 − 7 | TM |
| 800 | 1 − 6 | TE/TM |
| 900 | 0.4 − 3 | TE/TM |
| 900 | 4 − 6 | TE |

Nickel thickness 100 Å

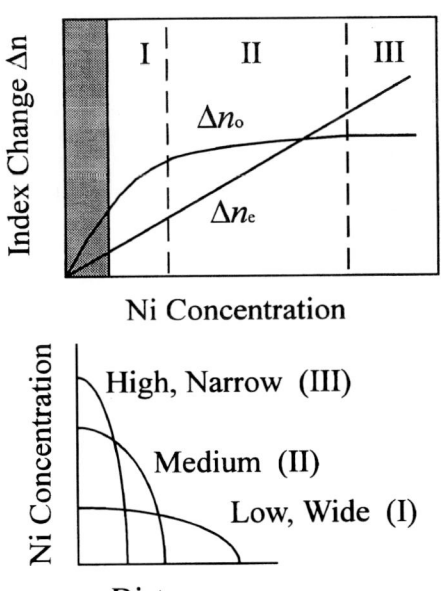

Fig. 6. The relation of the NI waveguide polarization and the nickel concentration.

becomes valid. The waveguide is now wide enough to support both modes, but $\Delta n_e$ is too small to meet the requirement of an extraordinary mode. Therefore, only the ordinary mode exits. For nickel concentration within the above two extremes, the index changes and the waveguide width are both large enough, hence both modes can be successfully supported. Thus, a fabrication process that can control the waveguide width and the nickel concentration will determine the guided wave polarization. Notice that TI waveguides also have index changes versus titanium concentration like those of the NI waveguides. However, no process-dependent polarizations of TI waveguides were reported. That is due to the fact that the difference between $\Delta n_0$ and $\Delta n_e$ of a TI waveguide is not large enough to support single polarization modes.[23]

### 2.4. Wavelength dispersion

The process-dependent polarizations of NI waveguides can also be found at a laser wavelength other than 632.8 nm. For example, a waveguide fabricated by diffusing a nickel layer of thickness 300 Å at 900°C for 1 hr supports only the extraordinary mode at the 1.32 $\mu$m laser wavelength. However, for a longer diffusion time, 3 to 4 hr, it is able to support only the ordinary mode. Some results are shown in Table 3 for comparison. The optical measurement setup performed at 1.32 $\mu$m wavelength with an Nd-YAG laser is shown in Fig. 7. As the 1.32 $\mu$m laser is invisible,

Table 3. Process-dependent polarizations of channel NI waveguides at 1.32 $\mu$m wavelength.

| Temp.<br>Time | 900°C | 950°C | 1000°C |
|---|---|---|---|
| 40 min | × | TE/TM | TE/TM |
| 1 hr | TM | TE/TM | TE/TM |
| 3 hr | TE | TE | TE |
| 4 hr | TE | × | × |
| 6 hr | × | × | × |

Nickel thickness 300 Å, mask width 7 $\mu$m

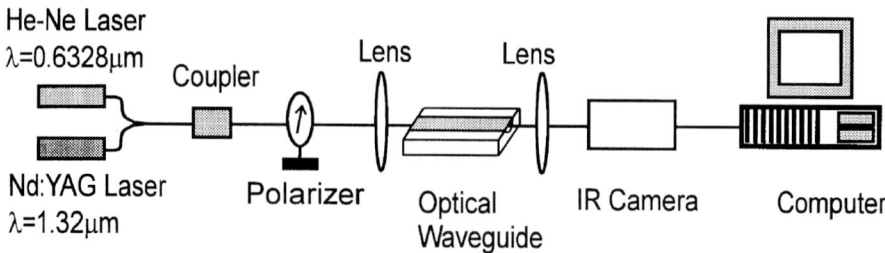

Fig. 7. The optical measurement setup at 1.32 $\mu$m wavelength with an Nd-YAG laser.

the 632.8 nm laser was used for an easier optical alignment. The incident light is focused directly to the waveguide end facet by a ×40 lens to excite both TE and TM modes. The output power distribution is enlarged by a ×40 lens and passed through a polarizer to investigate their polarization states. Finally, the output light intensity is recorded by a CCD camera connected to a personal computer.

The refractive index changes for ordinary and extraordinary polarizations versus nickel surface concentration are wavelength dependent, like that of titanium,[22] as shown in Fig. 5. The corresponding variations in refractive index changes with respective to the nickel surface concentration for the ordinary and extraordinary modes, $d\Delta n_0/dC$ and $d\Delta n_e/dC$, at the wavelengths, 632.8 nm and 1.32 $\mu$m are shown in Table 1. As shown in the table, both $d\Delta n_0/dC$ and $d\Delta n_e/dC$ at 1.32 $\mu$m are smaller than those at 632.8 nm. That is because a longer wavelength tends to be less sensitive to the local crystal defects produced by nickel indiffusion, and therefore, causes a smaller index changes. The established relations of index changes versus concentration were used for the design and fabrication of NI waveguide devices in our laboratory.

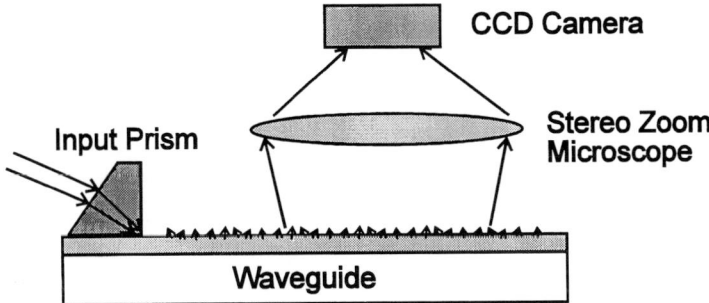

Fig. 8. The measurement setup for detecting the light scattered perpendicularly from a planar waveguide surface.

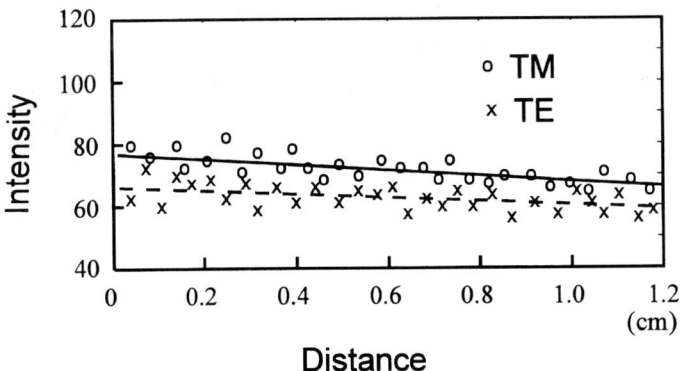

Fig. 9. The measured scattering power distribution.

Table 4. The measured losses of ordinary polarization waveguides.

| Diffusant | Loss(dB/cm) |
|-----------|-------------|
| Ni        | 0.7         |
| Zn        | 2.28        |
| Zn-Ni     | 1.5         |

## 2.5. Propagation loss

The wave propagation loss is determined by detecting the light scattered perpendicularly from a planar waveguide surface as depicted in Fig. 8. A typical measured power distribution is shown in Fig. 9. From the data, the calculated propagation losses are 0.7 dB/cm for the ordinary mode (Table 4) and 1.4 dB/cm for the extraordinary mode. These values are slightly larger than those of titanium-indiffused waveguides.[22] However, the waveguide lengths are usually on the order of about 1 cm, the little increase in loss of an NI waveguide doesn't seem to significantly affect the power transmission in real application.

## 2.6. Electro-optic modulation

Electrooptic modulation in ordinary polarization NI waveguides was demonstrated by a Mach–Zehnder interferometer operating at 632.8 nm laser wavelength in a Y-cut $LiNbO_3$, which has a branch angle of 1° and a waveguide width of 4 $\mu$m. The electrode length, defined on a 2000 Å thick aluminum layer, is 6 mm and the electrode gap is 10 $\mu$m. The measured half-wave voltage is about 6 V and the extinction ratio of electro-optic modulation is greater than 25 dB. The calculated half-wave voltage is 5.6 V, which is in good agreement with that measured experimentally. Thus, only a little decrease in electro-optic coefficients was found. Similar electro-optic modulation in extraordinary polarizations of NI waveguides were also demonstrated by a Mach–Zehnder interferometer but in a Z-cut $LiNbO_3$.[13] The device parameters are kept the same except that a passivation layer formed by depositing a 1500 Å thick silicon oxide layer was added and a wider electrode gap of 16 $\mu$m was used. The measured half-wave voltage was about 4.3 V and the electro-optic modulation extinction ratio was also greater than 25 dB. Thus, good electro-optic modulation for both ordinary and extraordinary polarizations was found.

Note that when nickel diffuses into $LiNbO_3$, no noticeable waveguide pattern remains on the substrate. However, in the case of titanium indiffusion, the remaining titanium oxide near the $LiNbO_3$ surface makes the waveguide pattern visible under the microscope. Hence, a thin zirconium oxide ($ZrO_2$) film, which has no influence on the waveguide,[9] was deposited on top of the nickel film. The $ZrO_2$ pattern remains on the $LiNbO_3$ surface, so clear waveguide patterns can be seen. Alignment of the electrodes to the waveguides is then easier when making the Mach–Zehnder interferometer.

## 3. Zn-Ni-Indiffused Waveguides

A waveguide that exhibits process-dependent polarization like that of an NI waveguide can also be made by zinc indiffusion (ZI) from a zinc strip. However, the measured propagation loss of an ordinary polarization ZI waveguide is about 2.28 dB/cm, which is larger than that of an NI waveguide, and therefore is not accepted. Note that the previously reported loss of a ZI waveguide is about 0.3 to 1.2 dB/cm,[25,26] which is smaller than that of ours. The reason may be due to the fact that their zinc diffusion was performed from the vapor phase.[27] In order to have a better ordinary polarization waveguide by our method, a combination of zinc and nickel indiffusions were then studied. As the zinc layer doesn't stick well to the LiNbO$_3$, a nickel layer of thickness about 50 Å was deposited first to improve the adhesion of zinc to LiNbO$_3$. Experimental verification, carried out in our laboratory, has shown that ZI waveguides with and without the underlying thin nickel layer are almost identical after diffusion. Thus, for the fabrication of the ZNI waveguide, a thicker (300 Å) nickel layer must be deposited first. Then, a zinc layer of thickness about 400 Å to 600 Å was deposited on top of the nickel layer. The diffusion started with a preoxidation at 350°C for 1 hr and then followed by a drive-in at about 1000°C for 30 to 120 min. After diffusion, the end faces of the sample were polished for optical characterization. The measured polarizations of ZNI waveguide varies with the zinc thickness, diffusion temperature, and diffusion time as shown in Table 5. For simplicity, the polarizations dependence on the thicknesses of the zinc and nickel strips, $\tau_1$ and $\tau_2$, at constant temperature and time are considered. From our experiments, when $\tau_1 = 500$ Å and $\tau_2 < 250$ Å or the opposite, $\tau_1 < 500$ Å and $\tau_2 = 250$ Å, a waveguide made by diffusing a nickel strip of width 8 $\mu$m at 1000°C for 1.4 hr supports only the TE modes at the 1.32 $\mu$m laser wavelength. However, when $\tau_1 = 500$ Å and $\tau_2 > 250$ Å or the opposite, $\tau > 500$ Å and $\tau_2 = 250$ Å, the waveguide starts to support random polarization modes. Table 6 lists the fabrication parameters for ordinary polarization (or TE mode) waveguides of the same width 8 $\mu$m. As can be seen from the table, the diffusion times for ZNI waveguides to support single-ordinary polarization modes are only a little longer than those for the ZI or the NI waveguides. The details of the composite diffusion mechanism are interesting and need to be further studied.

Table 5. The measured polarizations of ZNI waveguides.

| Zn | Ni | Temperature | Time | Polarization |
|------|------|-------------|-----------|--------------|
| 400 Å | 50 Å | 1000°C | < 40 min | TM |
| 500 Å | 50 Å | 1000°C | 40 − 60 min | TE/TM |
| 500 Å | 50 Å | 1000°C | > 65 min | TE |
| 560 Å | 50 Å | 1000°C | > 100 min | TE |

57

Table 6. The process parameters for single-ordinary polarization waveguides of the same width 8 $\mu$m.

| Thickness | Temperature | Time | Polarization |
|---|---|---|---|
| 300 Å (Ni) | 1000°C | > 70 min | TE |
| 500 Å (Zn) | 1000°C | > 65 min | TE |
| 500 Å (Zn), 250 Å (Ni) | 1000°C | > 80 min | TE |

Figure 10 shows output power contours of single-ordinary polarization waveguides made by ZI, NI, and ZNI. comparing the measured power contours, it is found that the ZNI waveguide has the best optical confinement and is closer to the circularly symmetric form than those of the other two waveguides. Thus, it is expected that the fiber-waveguide coupling loss can be greatly reduced.[28] A similar loss measurement was also done for the ZNI waveguide. The measured propagation loss of a ZNI waveguide at 632.8 nm is also shown in Table 4, which is slightly larger than that of the NI waveguide, but smaller than that of the ZI waveguide.

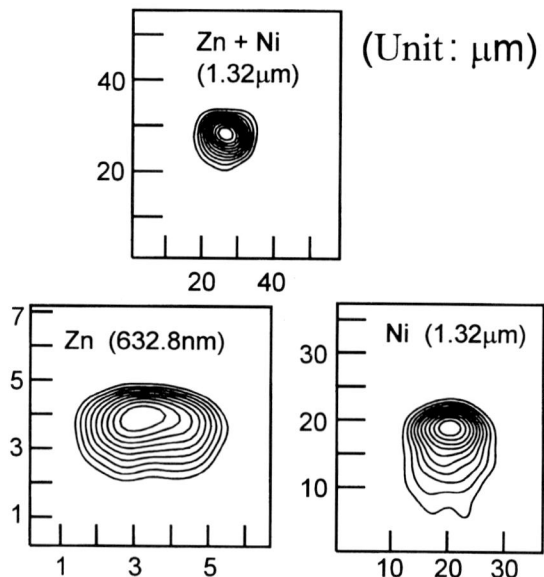

Fig. 10. Output power contours of single-ordinary polarization waveguides made by ZI, NI, and ZNI. The laser wavelengths are as indicated.

## 4. TE-TM Mode Splitters

The TE-TM mode splitters considered in this paper are essentially an asymmetric Y-junction, which consists a main and two branch waveguides as shown in Fig. 1. The main waveguide supports random polarization, and the two branch waveguides supporting single-TE and single-TM polarizations. The random polarization waveguide can be fabricated by TI, NI, ZI, a combination of NI and MILO, a combination of NI and PE, etc. For the single ordinary modes, the existing fabrication methods are NI and ZNI. However, those for the extraordinary are NI, ZI, ZNI, PE, MILO, etc. Any combination of the above waveguides can possibly be used as a TE-TM splitter. Notice that for the ordinary polarization waveguides, the use of nickel indiffusion is necessary, and therefore, is important. Due to the inherent single polarization of the waveguides, the extinction ratios are usually very high. Unfortunately, a detail comparison of all the possible splitters involves too much work and is still not available. Some results obtained by the possible combination of waveguides are discussed in the following sections.

### 4.1. *Use TI, NI, and MILO waveguides*

A TE-TM mode splitter as shown in Fig. 1(a) can be made by the diffusions of Ti, Ni, and MgO. The input waveguide is made by the TI process. Arm #1 of the Y-junction, bent from the TI waveguide with an angle $\theta$ of 0.5°, is made by the NI process, and arm #2 of the Y-junction, disconnected to TI waveguide, is made by the MILO process. Note that $\theta \leq 1°$ is chosen to reduce the bending loss. As the TI waveguide needs a longer diffusion time and higher diffusion temperature than those of the other two waveguides, the TI waveguide was made first. A titanium strip of width 4 $\mu$m, thickness 200 Å was deposited by electron gun evaporation and diffused into LiNbO$_3$ in an alumina crucible with a little lithium oxide powder to eliminate the unwanted outdiffusion guiding layer. As the diffusion conditions of the NI and MILO waveguides are similar, for simplicity, they were made at 960°C for 2.5 hr in the same alumina crucible. The TI waveguide is assumed to be hardly changed in the diffusion process. The widths of MgO and Ni are the same as that

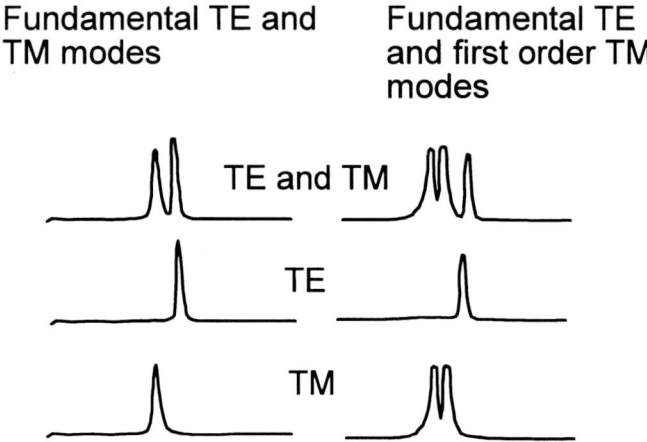

Fig. 11. Sketch of the power intensity profiles measured by a linear detector array. The device structure is shown in Fig. 1(a).

of the Ti strip. The thicknesses of MgO and Ni are 450 Å and 180 Å, respectively. Figure 11 depicts the output power distributions measured by a linear detector array.[7] The measured extinction ratios were 21 dB for the TE mode and 24 dB for the TM mode. Another TE-TM mode splitter was also made using the same diffusion conditions as those for TI, NI, and MILO waveguides, except that the strip widths of Ti, Ni, and MgO are 5 $\mu$m, 6 $\mu$m, and 4 $\mu$m, respectively. The measured output power distributions are also shown in Fig. 11. As can be seen from these figures, the NI waveguide has two modes when its strip width is 6 $\mu$m. The measured extinction ratios were 20.7 dB for the TE mode and 22 dB for the TM mode. The results are better than those reported, especially those obtained under high-order mode conditions.[29] Thus, splitters fabricated by the present method have higher extinction ratios and a large tolerance of fabrication.

### 4.2. Use TI, NI, and PE waveguides

As PE and MILO waveguides are both fabricated by increasing the extraordinary indices, an MILO waveguide in the previous TE-TM mode splitter can then be replaced by a PE waveguide. However, it should be noticed that PE is a low temperature process, and therefore cannot be fabricated with the NI waveguide in the same diffusion process. The TE-TM mode splitter on a Z-cut, X-propagating LiNbO$_3$ is shown in Fig. 1(b). As the diffusion of nickel is faster than that of titanium,[7] the TI waveguide has to be made first as before. The second step is to fabricate the ordinary polarization NI waveguide by diffusing a nickel strip of width 4 $\mu$m and thickness 300 Å at 950°C for 5 hr. The last step is the fabrication of the PE waveguide. A tantalum film of thickness 400 Å was deposited on the LiNbO$_3$ by electron gun evaporation as the mask for proton exchange. After opening a waveguide pattern of width 4 $\mu$m on the mask, the substrate was immersed into the benzoic acid at 235°C for 6 hr. To reduce the propagation loss, the PE waveguide was then annealed at 300°C for 6 hr. Measurement of the TE-TM mode splitter was also done by a He-Ne laser of wavelength 632.8 nm. The output power distributions are almost the same as those shown in Fig. 11. The measured extinction ratios were 24 dB for the TE mode and 23 dB for the TM mode. For comparison, another TE-TM mode splitter operating under high-order mode conditions was also made using the same fabrication processes as those for TI, NI, and PE waveguides, exept that the strip widths of the waveguides were 5 $\mu$m, 6 $\mu$m, and 4 $\mu$m, respectively. The measured extinction ratios were 22 dB for the TE mode and 21 dB for the TM mode. Thus, the TE-TM mode splitter works just as well, though using three different fabrication processes.

### 4.3. Use NI and MILO (or NI and PE) waveguides

The last two TE-TM mode splitters were fabricated for the 632.8 nm wavelength. As the wavelength gets longer, wider and deeper waveguides are required, which makes the fabrication more difficult. Hence, the replacement of a random polarization waveguide by two single polarization waveguides is tested. For example, the TE-TM mode splitter can also be made using NI and MILO for the TI waveguide. As only one diffusion step is required in this case, the fabrication process is greatly simplified. High extinction ratios at 540 nm, 632.8 nm, and 1.32 $\mu$m wavelengths have been measured. The details of the device characteristics will be published in the near future. Moreover, the TI waveguide can also replaced by the use of NI and PE. However, it should be noticed that the depths of NI and PE waveguides are in general not the same, though the measured extinction ratios are still quite high. The difference in depths is even larger for the 1.32 $\mu$m waveguides, which makes the coupling to fiber impractical. Further improvements are then needed in the future.

However, it is also of interest to study a Y-junction waveguide for variable-ratio power dividing and TE-TM mode splitting as shown in Fig. 12. The Y-junction waveguide consists of an NI channel waveguide and an MILO channel waveguide. The NI waveguide is made to support both ordinary (or TM) and extraordinary (or TE) modes, whereas, the MILO waveguide, just as mentioned previously, supports only extraordinary polarization modes.[9] As only the TE-modes are common in both waveguides, one can then control the TE-mode power in the waveguides electrically.

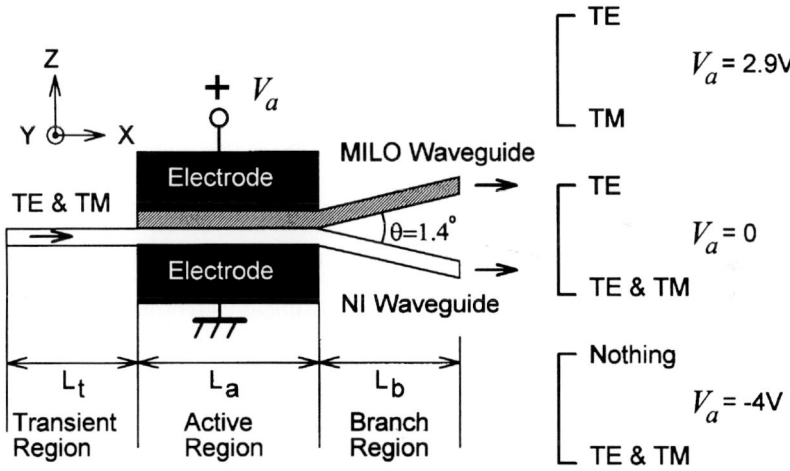

Fig. 12. Y-junction waveguide for variable-ratio power dividing and TE-TM mode splitting.

To fabricate the device, a nickel layer of thickness 250 Å is deposited and patterned to obtain the required waveguide. Similar fabrication steps are also carried out for the MILO waveguide except that the magnesium oxide thickness is 400 Å. As the gap between NI and MILO waveguides are zero, both waveguides are strongly coupled in the active region. In the branch region, both waveguides are gradually separated with an angle of 1.4°. Though MILO and NI waveguides have their own most favorable diffusion times and temperatures to be single-mode waveguides, their mode sizes are not compatible enough for efficient mode coupling. So, several test runs are required to obtain the acceptable or best combination of diffusion time and temperature. For simplicity, the sequentially deposited and patterned nickel and magnesium oxide layers are diffused simultaneously. From our experiments, diffusing both materials at 1000° for 0.6 hr gave rise to the most comparable mode sizes for coupling in the active region. Note that as the diffusion time is short enough, no significant outdiffusion waveguiding was observed. Therefore, the commonly used suppression of lithium outdiffusion[30] is not required. Finally, an aluminum layer is deposited by electron gun evaporation and etched as the contact electrodes for electro-optic modulation.

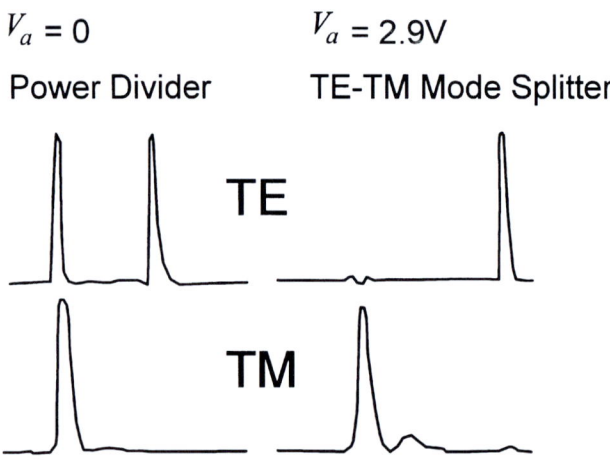

Fig. 13. Sketch of the power intensity profiles measured by a linear detector array. The device structure is shown in Fig. 12.

Figure 13 depicts the results[31] measured by a linear detector array with a laser light of wevelength 632.8 nm. When no voltage is applied, the TE-mode power in the original NI waveguide is split and directed to both NI and MILO waveguides, while the TM-mode power is mostly detected at the NI waveguide end, and negligible at the MILO waveguide end. When the applied voltage is gradually increased, the TE-mode power is continuously transferred to the MILO waveguide to become a variable-ratio power divider. Though the polarizations of the output power are different, their magnitudes can be the same by a suitable adjustment of the applied voltage. Finally, when the applied voltage is 2.9 V, all the TE-mode power goes to the MILO waveguide such that negligible TE-mode power is left in the NI waveguide. The calculated extinction ratio is about 20 dB for the TE mode. Note that the extinction ratio for the TM mode is usually greater than 20 dB due to the inherent single polarization of the MILO waveguide.[9] Thus, the total TE-TM mode splitting extinction ratios are about 20 dB. According to the coupling theory, the TE mode power will be coupled back and forth between the NI and MILO waveguides in the active region. Thus, when the applied voltages are −11, 12.3, and 38 V, complete switching of the TE-mode to become a TE-TM mode splitter is also observed, but the extinction ratios are lower. The reason is due to the excitation of higher order modes in the active region, which enhances the propagation loss. To keep the driving voltage low, only the lowest voltage is considered.

It is also of interest to know if higher-order TE waves can be successfully switched as those which appeared in Refs. 7 and 8. The results are less satisfactory because the coupling lengths in the active region for different modes are not the same. Further improvements need to be done. Moreover, when the applied voltage is −4 V all the TE and TM mode power is directed to the NI waveguide, and nothing to the MILO waveguide. That is an extreme case of power dividing. The extinction is also about 20 dB, which is quite advantageous for an optical switch. Thus, depending on the applied voltage, the device can be either a variable-ratio power divider or a TE-TM mode splitter. Detailed analysis of the device operation principle and potential applications of the device are interesting future work.

### 4.4. *Use only NI waveguides*

As different polarization waveguides can all be made by nickel indiffusion, a TE-TM mode splitter with only NI waveguides as shown in Fig. 1(c) can then be made. The input waveguide made by nickel diffusion supports ordinary (or TE) and extraordinary (or TM) modes. Arm #1 of the Y-junction bent from the input waveguide at an angle of 0.5°, supports only TM modes, whereas arm #2 of the Y-junction, supports only TE modes. From Fig. 5, single-polarization waveguides can be obtained at lower or higher nickel concentration region where the difference of ordinary and extraordinary index changes is large enough. As the polarization states change with the nickel strip thickness $\tau$ when the diffusion time and temperature remain the same, simple empirical rules were used. When $\tau < 350$ Å, a waveguide with a nickel strip of width 12 $\mu$m diffused at 1000°C for 1.5 hr supports the TE wave. However, when $\tau > 350$ Å, the waveguide starts to support the random polarization wave though under the same diffusion condition. For the single TM polarization waveguide, a thinner nickel strip (e.g. $\tau < 450$ Å) and lower diffusion temperature (e.g. 900°C for 0.9 hr) must be used.[13] The single-extraordinary polarization waveguide (arm #1) was bent from the input waveguide at an angle of 0.5° for its optical confinement is relatively better. The single-ordinary polarization waveguide (arm #2) is then directed to the input waveguide without bending. The process steps for the splitter are shown in Fig. 14. A nickel strip of width 12 $\mu$m, thickness 300 Å is deposited first. Then, an additional nickel layer of thickness 400 Å is deposited to form the input waveguide. That is two nickel strips (300 Å and 400 Å) were used for the input waveguide but only one for arm #2. For a better mask alignment, a $ZrO_2$ layer of thickness 950 Å was deposited on top of the second nickel strip. Both nickel strips were then diffused simultaneously at 1000°C for 1.5 hr, but the $ZrO_2$ strip was left on the substrate surface as an alignment mark for arm #1. Finally, a nickel strip of the same width but different thickness

(400 Å) was deposited, and then diffused at a lower temperature of 900°C for 0.9 hr to form arm #1. As the diffusion temperature and diffusion time for the second step are lower than those for the first diffusion step, the diffusion depths of the input waveguide and arm #2 are hardly changed during the second diffusion step.

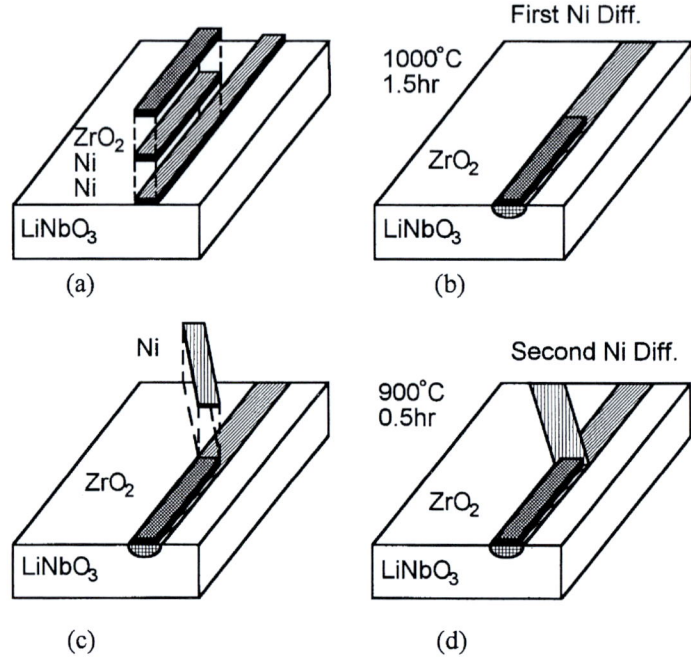

Fig. 14. Process steps for the TE-TM splitter with only NI waveguides. (a) Nickel strip deposition for arm #2. Definition of the input waveguide by depositing an extra Ni and a $ZrO_2$ film, (b) First diffusion, (c) Definition of arm #1 by depositing a nickel strip, and (d) Second diffusion.

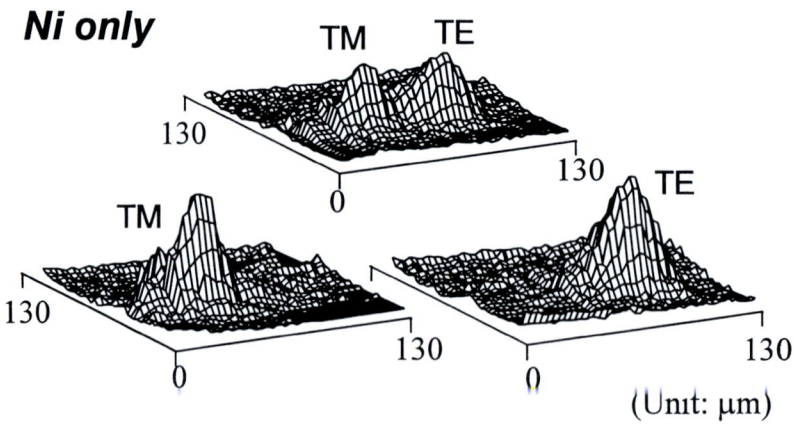

Fig. 15. Output light intensity profiles of the TE-TM mode splitter with only NI waveguides.

Characterization of the TE-TM mode splitter was carried out by an Nd-YAG laser of wavelength 1.32 $\mu$m. The output light intensity is recorded by a CCD camera. Figure 15 shows the three-dimensional output light intensity profiles at the near field. The measured extinction ratios were 21 dB for the TE mode and 23 dB for the TM mode. In contrast to the previous mode splitters, only one waveguide technology, nickel indiffusion, is required for the present splitter. This greatly enhances the prospects of integration. The concept of using only TI technology was proposed,[6] but has not been realized so far. The reason probably is due to the fact that the fabrication tolerances for the present technique are larger.

### 4.5. *Use NI and ZNI waveguides*

As mentioned previously, in an NI waveguide, the optical confinement of ordinary polarization is not as good as that of the single extraordinary polarization, therefore the ZNI waveguide is then used to replace the input and arm #2 of the splitter. The device structure is shown in Fig. 1(d). The process steps for the splitter are quite similar to those shown in Fig. 14. For simplicity, the mask for making the last splitter (with only NI waveguides) was also used for making the present splitter. A nickel strip of thickness 300 Å and a zinc strip of thickness 500 Å are deposited sequentially as shown in Fig. 16(a). Then, an additional zinc layer of thickness 500 Å is deposited to form the input waveguide. Similarly, for a better mask alignment, a ZrO$_2$ layer of thickness 950 Å was deposited on top of the second zinc strip as shown in Fig. 16(b). All the deposited strips were then diffused simultaneously at

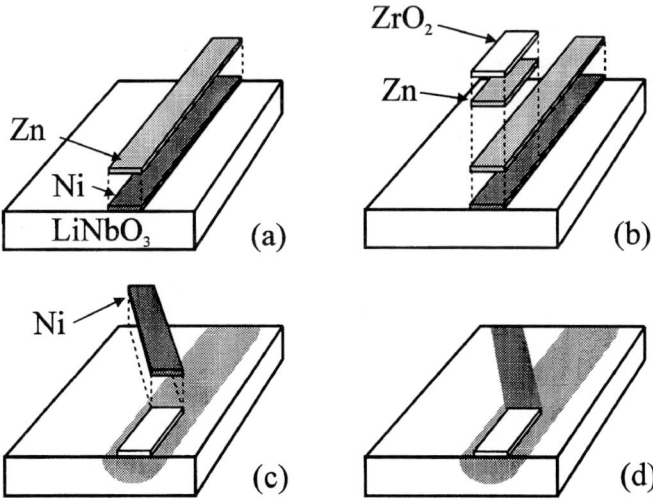

Fig. 16. Process steps for the TE-TM splitter with NI and ZNI waveguides. (a) Nickel and zinc strips deposition for arm #2, (b) Definition of the input waveguide by depositing an extra Zn and a ZrO$_2$ film, (c) First diffusion and definition of arm #1 by depositing a nickel strip, (d) Second diffusion.

1000°C for 1.5 hr. The ZrO$_2$ strip was left on the substrate surface as an alignment mark for the bent waveguide branch as shown in Fig. 16(c). Finally, a nickel strip of thickness 400 Å and the same width was deposited and then diffused at 900°C for 0.9 hr to form arm #1 of the Y-junction as shown in Fig. 16(d).

Measurement of the TE-TM mode splitter was carried out at 1.32 μm laser wavelength. Figure 17 shows the three-dimensional output light intensity profiles at the near field. Evidently, the ZNI waveguide supports high-order modes because its Δ$n_0$ is larger. The extinction ratios are 25 dB for the TE and 23 dB for the TM modes. The splitter with single mode waveguides can be easily fabricated with a suitable design and the fabrication process is still in progress. Though the present splitter is made by one more material deposition, the whole process is still simple enough to be realized and potentially useful for practical application.

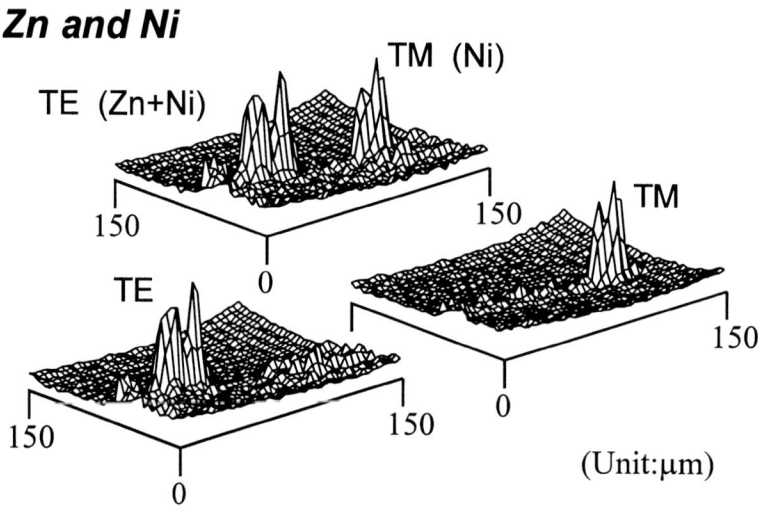

Fig. 17. Output light intensity profiles of the TE-TM mode splitter with NI and ZNI waveguides.

## 6. Conclusions

In conclusion, optical waveguides fabricated by nickel diffusion in lithium niobate are reviewed. In particular, the fabrication process for single mode waveguide is discussed, the changes of waveguide index at the 632.8 nm and 1.32 μm wavelength are compared, the process parameters for process-dependent polarizations are shown, the wave propagation losses are compared, and electro-optic modulation of NI waveguides is discussed. To improve the confinement of single-ordinary polarization waveguide fabricated by nickel indiffusion, a novel waveguide made by zinc and nickel indiffusion is presented for the first time. Though the measured propagation loss of the ZNI waveguide at 632.8 nm is larger than that of an NI waveguide (1.3–1.5 dB/cm), the measured output power contours are closer to the circularly symmetric form than that of the NI waveguide, which is believed to be better for fiber coupling. Moreover, several TE-TM mode splitters using one or more NI waveguides for TE-TM mode sorting are discussed. A detailed comparison and further improvement of TE-TM mode splitters based on the complete mode sorting effect will be of great interest in the future.

## Acknowledgment

This work was supported by the National Science Council, Taipei, Taiwan, Republic of China under Contract No. NSC86-2215-E-002-006.

## References

1. M. Kobayashi, H. Teruierui, and K. Egashira, "An optical TE-TM mode splitter", *Appl. Phys. Lett.* **32** (1979) 300–302.
2. R. C. Alferness and L. L. Buhl, "Low cross-talk waveguide polarization multiplexer/demultiplexer for $\lambda = 1.32\ \mu$m", *Opt. Lett.* **10** (1984) 6140–6142.
3. D. Yap, L. M. Johnson, and G. W. Pratt, "Passive Ti:LiNbO$_3$ channel waveguide TE-TM mode splitter", *Appl. Phys. Lett.* **44** (1984) 583–585.
4. N. Goto and G. L. Yip, "A TE-TM mode splitter in LiNbO$_3$ by proton exchange and Ti diffusion", *J. Lightwave Tech.* **LT-7** (1989) 1567–1574.
5. M. Masuda and G. L. Yip, "An optical TE-TM mode splitter using a LiNbO$_3$ branching waveguide", *Appl. Phys. Lett.* **37** (1980) 20–22.
6. J. J. van der Tol and J. H. Laarhuis, "A polarization splitter on LiNbO$_3$ using only titanium diffusion", *J. Lightwave Tech.* **9** (1991) 879–886.
7. P. K. Wei and W. S. Wang, "A TE-TM mode splitter on lithium niobate using Ti, Ni, and MgO diffusions", *Phot. Tech. Lett.* **6** (1994) 245–248.
8. P. K. Wei and W. S. Wang, "Novel TE-TM mode splitter on lithium niobate using nickel indiffusion and proton exchange techniques", *Electron. Lett.* **30** (1994) 35–37.
9. S. H. Lau, P. K. Wei, C. W. Su, and W. S. Wang, "Fabrication of magnesium-oxide-induced lithium outdiffusion waveguides", *Phot. Tech. Lett.* **4** (1992) 872–875.
10. M. N. Armenise, "Fabrication techniques of lithium niobate waveguides", *IEEE Proc. J.* **135** (1988) 85–91.
11. J. L. Jackel, C. E. Rice, and J. J. Veselka, "Proton exchange for high-index waveguides in LiNbO$_3$", *Appl. Phys. Lett.* **41** (1982) 607–608.
12. P. K. Wei and W. S. Wang, "Fabrication of lithium niobate optical channel waveguides by nickel indiffusion," *Microwave and Opt. Tech. Lett.* **7** (1994) 219–221.
13. Y. P. Liao, D. R. Chen, R. C. Lu, and W. S. Wang, "Nickel-diffused lithium niobate optical waveguide with process-dependent polarization", *Phot. Tech. Lett.* **8** (1996) 548–550.
14. Y. P. Liao, R. C. Lu, C. H. Yang, and W. S. Wang, "Passive Ni:LiNbO$_3$ polarisation splitter at 1.3 $\mu$m wavelength", *Electron. Lett.* **32** (1996) 1003–1005.
15. I. P. Kaminow and J. R. Carruthers, "Optical waveguiding layers in LiNbO$_3$ and LiTaO$_3$", *Appl. Phys. Lett.* **22** (1973) 326–328.
16. J. L. Jackel, "Suppression of outdiffusion in titanium diffused LiNbO$_3$", *J. Opt. Comm.* **3** (1977) 570–571.
17. B. U. Chen and A. C. Paster, "Elimination of Li$_2$O out-diffusion waveguide in LiNbO$_3$ and LiTaO$_3$", *Appl. Phys. Lett.* **30** (1977) 570–571.

18. J. Noda, N. Uchida, S. Saito, T. Saku, and M. Minakata, "Electro-optic amplitude modulation using three-dimensional waveguide LiNbO$_3$ fabricated by TiO$_2$ diffusion", *Appl. Phys. Lett.* **27** (1979) 19–21.
19. R. V. Schmidt and I. P. Kaminow, "Metal-diffused optical waveguides in LiNbO$_3$", *Appl. Phys. Lett.* **25** (1974) 458–460.
20. G. B. Hocker and W. K. Burns, "Modes in diffused optical waveguides of arbitrary index profile", *J. Quantum Electron.* **11** (1975) 270–275.
21. J. M. White and P. F. Heidrich, "Optical waveguide refractive index profiles determined from measurement of mode indices: a simple analysis", *Appl. Opt.* **15** (1976) 151–155.
22. M. Minakata, S. Saito, M. Shibata, and S. Miyazawa, "Precise determination of refractive-index changes in Ti-diffused LiNbO$_3$ optical waveguides", *J. Appl. Phys.* **49** (1978) 4677–4682.
23. S. Fouchet, A. Carenco, C. Daguet, R. Guglielmi, and L. Riviere, "Wavelength dispersion of Ti-induced refractive index change in LiNbO$_3$ as a function of diffusion parameters", *J. Lightwave Tech.* **5** (1987) 700–708.
24. M. Fukuma and J. Noda, "Optical properties and titanium-diffused LiNbO$_3$ strip waveguides and their coupling-to-a fiber characteristics", *Appl. Opt.* **19** (1980) 591–597.
25. W. M. Young, R. S. Feigelson, M. M. Fejer, M. J. F. Digonnet, and H. J. Shaw, "Photorefractive-damage-resistant Zn-diffused waveguides in MgO:LiNbO$_3$", *Opt. Lett.* **16** (1991) 995–997.
26. W. M. Young, M. M. Fejer, M. J. F. Digonnet, A. F. Marshall, and R. S. Feigelson, "Fabrication, characterization and index profile modeling of high-damage resistance Zn-diffused waveguides in congruent and MgO:lithium niobate", *J. Lightwave Tech.* **10** (1992) 1238–1246.
27. B. Herreros and G. Lifante, "LiNbO$_3$ optical waveguides by Zn diffusion from vapor phase", *Appl. Phys. Lett.* **66** (1995) 1449–1451.
28. K. Komatsu, M. Konodo, and Y. Ohta, "Titanium/magnesium diffusion method for efficient fiber-LiNbO$_3$ waveguide coupling", *Electron. Lett.* **22** (1986) 881–882.
29. M. Masuda and G. L. Yip, "An optical TE-TM mode splitter using a LiNbO$_3$ branching waveguide", *Appl. Phys. Lett.* **37** (1980) 20–22.
30. A. Rasch, M. Rottschalk, and W. Karthe, "Suppression of out-diffusion in Ti:LiNbO$_3$", *J. Opt. Comm.* **6** (1985) 14–17.
31. C. H. Chang and W. S. Wang, "A novel Y-branch waveguide for power dividing and mode splitting", *Opt. and Quan. Electron.* **28** (1996) 1371–1377.

International Journal of High Speed Electronics and Systems, Vol. 8, No. 4 (1997) 643–663

# DUAL ANTIRESONANT REFLECTING OPTICAL WAVEGUIDE DEVICES

YANG-TUNG HUANG, JAU-JAN DENG, YEONG-HER CHEN, and
CHIOU-HUNG JANG

*National Chiao Tung University,*
*1001 Ta-Hsueh Road, Hsinchu 300, Taiwan, R.O.C.*
*E-mail: huangyt@cc.nctu.edu.tw*


CHIH-LIN WANG

*Department of Electrical Engineering,*
*Ming Hsin Institute of Technology and Commerce*

Basic theories to analyze and design dual antiresonant reflecting optical waveguide (ARROW) devices are discussed. These theories include modal analysis for all ARROW devices, coupling efficiency analysis between dual ARROW waveguides, and eigenmode expansion analysis with step discontinuities in the devices. Various dual ARROW devices of power dividers, hybrid couplers, wavelength filters, polarization beamsplitters, and pressure sensors are introduced.

## 1. Introduction

Dual optical waveguides involving mode coupling to construct directional couplers, switches, modulators, and filters are very important components in many applications such as optical communications, optical integrated circuits, and sensing systems.[1-6] For conventional optical waveguides, the guiding mechanism is based on total internal reflections and the coupling strength between dual waveguides decreasing as an exponential function of the waveguide separation. The new type of waveguides, i.e. antiresonant reflecting optical waveguides (ARROW), have been proposed and demonstrated.[7-19] In comparison with conventional structures, ARROW waveguides utilize antiresonant reflection as the guiding mechanism instead of total internal reflection. With this structure, ARROW devices can guide waves in low-index cores with a large core size such that their core index and size can be compatible with single-mode fiber index and diameter, which provide efficient connections to fibers. A dual-ARROW stacked structure with the decoupled phenomena between two ARROW waveguides has been presented and experimentally demonstrated for optical interconnect applications.[8] A directional coupler consisting of two identical ARROW's was also proposed for power coupling.[10] The additional advantage of this ARROW-based directional coupler over a conventional waveguide coupler is that its coupling-length is not increasing but varies as a periodic function with increasing waveguide separation. Therefore, a remote ARROW directional coupler can be realized, which significantly enhances the flexibility of design and implementation of the device, and various dual ARROW waveguide devices have been proposed to be investigated by many researchers.[10–18]

In this paper, we discuss basic theories to analyze design dual ARROW devices and introduce some typical dual ARROW configurations for various applications. In Sec. 2, the basic structure of a dual ARROW device is introduced, which is constructed by transverse resonance for guiding layers and antiresonance for cladding layers. In addition, model analysis of dual ARROW coupler is briefly discussed. Dual ARROW waveguides with leaky modes belong to strongly coupled structures. Many coupling analytical methods based on weakly coupled approximation are difficult to apply to strongly coupled waveguides. In Sec. 3, we discuss the theory to analyze the coupling efficiency between dual ARROW waveguides for strongly coupled structures. Since in many ARROW devices there exist step discontinuities in the structures and there might be many modes with low propagation loss, the coupling between modes in two discontinuous regions must be investigated in detail and suitably designed for the required device characteristics. In Sec. 4, we use eigenmode expansion analysis to analyze the coupling between two discontinuous regions and optimize these ARROW devices with step discontinuities. In Sec. 5, we introduce some typical dual ARROW configurations for various applications. For all devices, we also use BPM (beam propagation method) simulations to verify the theories and device characteristics. In conclusion, we summarize our discussions and address some important issues which should be further investigated for ARROW devices.

## 2. Modal Analysis of Dual ARROW Devices

The configuration of a dual-ARROW device structure $(n_a/n_{l_1}/n_{h_1}/n_{g_1}/n_{h_1}/n_{sep}/n_{h_2}/n_{g_2}/n_{h_2}/n_{l_2}/n_s)$ is depicted in Fig. 1(a), which consists of two ARROW waveguides and a separation cladding layer. The core layers of two ARROW waveguides have low refractive indices of $n_{g_1}$ and $n_{g_2}$, and thicknesses of $d_{g_1}$ and $d_{g_2}$, respectively. The upper waveguide is sandwiched between two high index $(n_{h_1})$ cladding layers of thicknesses $d'_{h_1}$ and $d_{h_1}$ respectively, and a low index $(n_{l_1})$ upper cladding layer of thickness $d_{l_1}$ is grown atop them. The lower waveguide is sandwiched between two high index $(n_{h_2})$ cladding layers of thickness $d_{h_2}$ with a low index $(n_{l_2})$ lower cladding layer of thickness $d_{l_2}$. Between two ARROW waveguides there is a separation cladding layer with an index of $n_{sep}$ and thickness of $d_{sep}$. In order to achieve low loss, the core layer of the lower ARROW waveguide must satisfy the transverse resonance condition. The thickness $d_{g_2}$ is given as[7]

$$d_{g_2} = \frac{\lambda}{2n_{g_2}} \left[ 1 - \left( \frac{n_{g_1}}{n_{g_2}} \right)^2 + \left( \frac{\lambda}{2n_{g_2}d_{g_1}} \right)^2 \right]^{-1/2}. \tag{1}$$

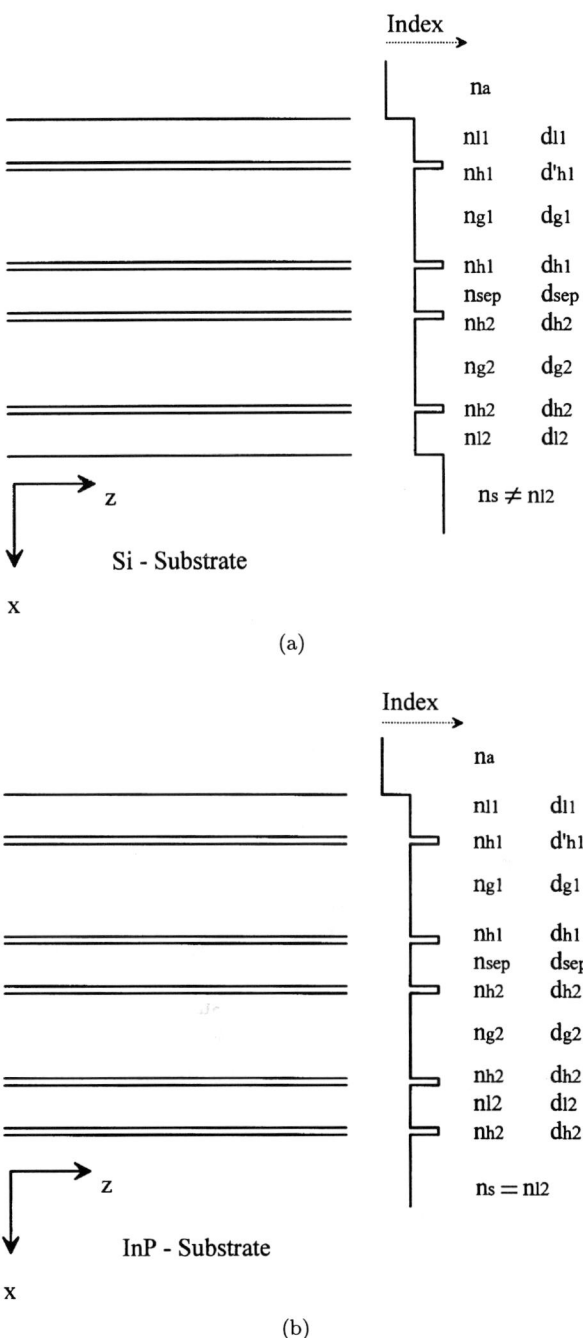

Fig. 1. (a) Basic coupling structure of the proposed based on dual-ARROW waveguides with Si substrate, (b) Basic coupling structure of the proposed based on dual-ARROW waveguides with InP substrate.

Except for the upper cladding layers of $d_{l_1}$ and $d'_{h_1}$, all cladding layers satisfy the antiresonance condition as

$$d_j = \frac{\lambda}{4n_j} \left[ 1 - \left( \frac{n_{g_1}}{n_j} \right)^2 + \left( \frac{\lambda}{2n_j d_{g_1}} \right)^2 \right]^{-1/2} (2P_j + 1) , \quad P_j = 0, 1, 2, 3, \ldots , \quad (2)$$

where $j = h_1$ (and $h_2$), $sep$, and $l_1$ (and $l_2$), representing corresponding high-index, separation, and low-index cladding layers, respectively. Since the coupling strength between dual ARROW waveguides strongly depends on the degree of their symmetry, we can easily adjust the thickness of the upper cladding layer to change the degree of their symmetry and thus vary the coupling efficiency.

By the characteristic matrix method, the dispersion relation for a TE-polarized field in a multilayer slab is given as,[6,10]

$$k_{a,x}(m_{11} + k_{s,x}m_{12}) + (m_{21} + k_{s,x}m_{22}) = 0 , \quad (3)$$

where $k_{a,x}$ and $k_{s,x}$ represent the transverse propagation constant in air and the substrate is given as

$$k_{a,x} = \sqrt{k_0^2 n_a^2 - \beta^2} = k_0 \sqrt{n_a^2 - N_{eff}^2} , \quad (4)$$

$$k_{s,x} = \sqrt{k_0^2 n_s^2 - \beta^2} = k_0 \sqrt{n_s^2 - N_{eff}^2} . \quad (5)$$

$k_0$ is the wavenumber in air, $n_a$ is the index of air, and $N_{eff}$ is the effective index of the propagation wave. The characteristic matrix $\mathbf{M}$ with elements $m_{ij}$ is given as

$$\mathbf{M} = \begin{bmatrix} m_{11} & m_{12} \\ m_{21} & m_{22} \end{bmatrix} = \prod_i \mathbf{M}_i = \prod_i \begin{bmatrix} \cos k_{i,x} d_i & (j/k_{i,x}) \sin k_{i,x} d_i \\ j k_{i,x} \sin k_{i,x} d_i & \cos k_{i,x} d_i \end{bmatrix} , \quad (6)$$

where $i$ indicates each layer except for air and substrate. When $n_{l_2} = n_s$, such as in the InGaAsP material system, a destructive interference layer with index of $n_{h_2}$ and thickness of $d_{h_2}$ between this low index cladding layer ($n_{l_2}$) and substrate ($n_s$) should be added to maintain low radiation loss into the substrate. This structure $(n_a/n_{l_1}/n_{h_1}/n_{g_1}/n_{h_1}/n_{sep}/n_{h_2}/n_{g_2}/n_{h_2}/n_{l_2}/n_{h_2}/n_s)$ is shown in Fig. 1(b).

For a TM-polarized field, the discussions are still valid if $k_{a,x}$ and $k_{a,x}$ in Eqs. (3) and (6) are substituted by $-k_{a,x}/n_a^2$ and $-k_{s,x}/n_s^2$.[6]

## 3. Coupling-Efficiency Analysis

Coupling between two parallel waveguides has been widely investigated.[1-6,20-23] Most analyses employ the coupled mode formulations developed by Marcuse, Taylor and Yariv.[3,20-23] Their results are accurate only in weakly coupling situations. For dual-ARROW structures with leaky modes, the strong coupling between two waveguides must be considered. We employ the method based on interference of the even and odd lowest order modes to analyze the coupling efficiency of a dual-ARROW structure.[24] Although there might exist some other higher order modes with low propagation loss, only these two lowest order modes can be efficiently excited by the fundamental mode from a single-mode fiber (or waveguide) input-coupling in our cases. The field of a dual-ARROW guided system can thus be expressed as

$$E(x, z) = A_e E_e(x) \exp(-jk_0 N_e z) + A_o E_o(x) \exp(-jk_0 N_o z), \tag{7}$$

$$H(x, z) = A_e H_e(x) \exp(-jk_0 N_e z) + A_o H_o(x) \exp(-jk_0 N_o z), \tag{8}$$

where $A_e$ and $A_o$ are amplitudes of the normalized even and odd modes with effective indices $N_e$ and $N_o$, respectively. Both $E_e$ ($H_e$) and $E_o$ ($H_o$) are the normalized electric (magnetic) fields of even and odd modes, respectively. The even mode and odd mode are orthonormal with respect to the Poynting power. The wave is normalized as

$$P = \int_{-\infty}^{\infty} S_z(x, z)dx = P_{g_1} + P_{g_2} + P_{else} = A_e^2 + A_o^2 = 1, \tag{9}$$

where

$$P_{g_1}(z) = \int_{g_1} S_z(x, z)dx, \quad P_{g_2}(z) = \int_{g_2} S_z(x, z)dx,$$

$$\text{and} \quad P_{else}(z) = \int_{else} S_z(x, z)dx, \tag{10}$$

$P_{g_1}$ is the guided power in the upper waveguide $g_1$, $P_{g_2}$ is the guided power in the lower waveguide $g_2$, and $P_{else}$ represents the remaining power in the region outside guides $g_1$ and $g_2$.

Light is launched to the upper ARROW waveguide in Fig. 2 at the reference plane $z = 0$ such that there is a reference power $P_{g_1}$ guided in the upper waveguide $g_1$. The coupling efficiency $\eta$ can be obtained as[24,16]

$$\eta(z) = \frac{P_{g_2}(z) - P_{g_2}(0)}{P_{g_1}(0)} = \eta_o \sin^2(\beta_c z), \tag{11}$$

where

$$\beta_c = \frac{k_0(N_e - N_o)}{2}, \tag{12}$$

and $\eta_o$ is the maximum power coupling efficiency at the coupling length $z = L_c$. In the case that light is launched to the lower ARROW waveguide, the above formulas will also be satisfied if $P_{g_1}$ and $P_{g_2}$ are exchanged with each other.

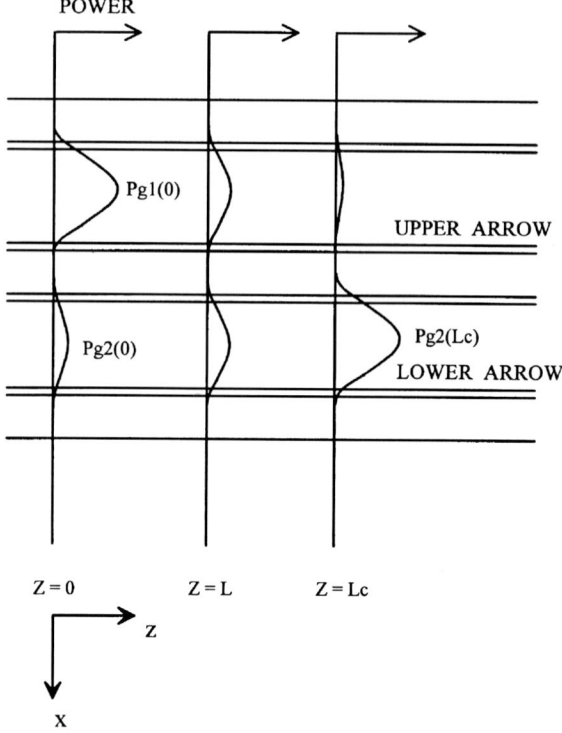

Fig. 2. Schematic diagram for optical power coupling from the upper waveguide to the lower waveguide.

## 4. Eigenmode Expansion Analysis with Step Discontinuities

In many ARROW devices, there exist step discontinuities in the structures, such as an ARROW power divider consisting of a coupling region and a decoupling region with different upper cladding thicknesses.[15,16] Since there might exist many modes with low propagation loss for an ARROW device, the coupling between modes in two discontinuous regions must be investigated in detail and suitably designed for required device characteristics. In order to analyze the coupling between two discontinuous regions and optimize these ARROW devices with step discontinuities, we use the eigenmode expansion analysis.[18]

In our eigenmode expansion analysis eigenmodes solved from Maxwell's equations and associated boundary conditions are used to form an expansion set. The eigenmodes contain discrete guided modes and continuous radiation modes. An ARROW devices with a high refractive-index substrate forms a leaky structure and thus tedious calculations of a large amount of radiation modes are involved. To conquer this problem, only the quasi-guided modes, of which the fields are approximately confined in the core region, are of concern.[25] Moreover, such quasi-guided modes form few packets of radiation modes which can be replaced by leaky modes with complex propagation constants.[26] The eigenequation for the leaky modes is the same as for the guided modes except for extending the solutions into the complex plane.[27] The unphysical problem associated with the leaky mode representation can also be relieved by the truncated method[28] with a suitable and systematic method to meet the orthogonality relation.

The eigensolutions, so called local normal modes, form a complete set which can be superposed with their individual expansion coefficients to construct any field distribution $f(x, z)$ at any position within section $k$ as

$$f^{(k)}(x, z) = \sum_g \left( a_g^{(k)} e^{-j\beta_g^{(k)} z} + b_g^{(k)} e^{j\beta_g^{(k)} z} \right) u_g^{(k)}(x)$$

$$+ \int_r \left( a_r^{(k)} e^{-j\beta_g^{(k)} z} + b_r^{(k)} e^{j\beta_g^{(k)} z} \right) u_r^{(k)}(x; \beta) d\beta, \tag{13}$$

where subscript $g$ represents the discrete guided modes, which should be summed up, and subscript $r$ represents the continuous radiation modes which should be integrated over the entire spectrum, respectively. Parameters $a, b$ indicate the expansion coefficients for the forward and backward waves, respectively. $\beta$ is the propagation constant. The normalized field distribution of a local normal mode $u(x)$ is multiplied by the phase term and its own expansion coefficient to express the wave propagation. The integration over the whole packet of radiation modes can be calculated numerically by sampling the continuous set either by equally spaced or by adding the hypothetical boundaries.[29-31] The leaky mode representation whose eigensolutions are solved in the complex plane can be employed instead of the continuous set of radiation modes to simplify the eigenmode expansion analysis.[27] Therefore, the normalization and the coupling problem of the unphysical modes can be solved by limiting the observation range in a reasonable region to get an approximate orthogonal set,[28,32] and Eq. (13) can be replaced as

$$f^{(k)}(x, z) \approx \sum_g \left( a_g^{(k)} e^{-j\beta_g^{(k)} z} + b_g^{(k)} e^{j\beta_g^{(k)} z} \right) u_g^{(k)}(x)$$

$$+ \sum_r \left( a_r^{(k)} e^{-j\beta_g^{(k)} z} + b_r^{(k)} e^{j\beta_g^{(k)} z} \right) u_r^{(k)}(x) \Delta\beta$$

$$\approx \sum_g \left( a_g^{(k)} e^{-j\beta_g^{(k)} z} + b_g^{(k)} e^{j\beta_g^{(k)} z} \right) u_g^{(k)}(x)$$

$$+ \sum_l \left( a_l^{(k)} e^{-j\beta_g^{(k)} z} + b_l^{(k)} e^{j\beta_g^{(k)} z} \right) u_l^{(k)}(x)$$

$$= \sum_m \left( a_m^{(k)} e^{-j\beta_g^{(k)} z} + b_m^{(k)} e^{j\beta_g^{(k)} z} \right) u_m^{(k)}(x), \tag{14}$$

where $\Delta\beta$ is the sampling interval of continuous spectrum of the radiation modes, $\Sigma_l$ represents the summation of discrete leaky modes, and $\Sigma_m$ represents the summation of well-guided modes and truncated leaky modes.

The boundary conditions at the step discontinuity for a TE-mode give the relations as

$$\sum_{m=1}^{s_k} \left(a_m^{(k)} + b_m^{(k)}\right) u_m^{(k)}(x) = \sum_{m=1}^{s_{k+1}} a_m^{(k+1)} u_m^{(k+1)}(x),$$

(15)

$$\sum_{m=1}^{r} \left(a_m^{(k)} - b_m^{(k)}\right) \beta_m^{(k)} u_m^{(k)}(x) = \sum_{m=1}^{s} a_m^{(k+1)} \beta_m^{(k+1)} u_m^{(k+1)}(x),$$

(16)

where $s_k$ and $s_{k+1}$ are the total numbers of selected modes at the $k$th section and $(k+1)$th section, respectively. Here, it is assumed that the reflection from the next section is negligible, i.e. the terms in which $b_m^{(k+1)}$ are neglected at the right side of Eq. (16). This assumption is especially appropriate for ARROW waveguides since the amplitude of the leaky mode is more or less decaying along a straight section.

Combining the above equations with the orthogonal relations, all expansion coefficients for mode $n$ at the $(k+1)$th section can be solved as

$$a_n^{(k+1)} = \sum_m \frac{2\beta_m^{(k)}}{\beta_m^{(k)} + \beta_n^{(k+1)}} a_m^{(k)} \int u_m^{(k)}(x) \left[u_n^{(k+1)}(x)\right]^* dx,$$

$$\equiv \sum_m \frac{2\beta_m^{(k)}}{\beta_m^{(k)} + \beta_n^{(k+1)}} a_m^{(k)} \langle u_m^{(k)}(x) | u_n^{(k+1)}(x) \rangle,$$

(17)

where the integration is performed over the entire cross section for the guided modes and the limited range for the leaky modes. Therefore, we obtain

$$\mathbf{A}^{(k+1)} = \mathbf{A}^{(k)} \cdot \mathbf{P}^{(k)} \cdot \mathbf{T}^{(k,k+1)},$$

(18)

where $\mathbf{A}^{(k)}$ is the input expansion matrix, which is composed of expansion coefficient of each mode at the beginning of the $k$th section, i.e. $\mathbf{A}^{(k)} = [a_1, a_2 \cdots a_r]^{(k)}$; $\mathbf{P}^{(k)}$ is the propagation matrix in the $k$th section given as

$$P_{ij}^{(k)} = \left[\exp\left(-j\beta_i^{(k)} d^{(k)}\right)\right] \cdot \delta_{ij},$$

(19)

$d^{(k)}$ is the length of the $k$th section; and $\mathbf{T}^{(k,k+1)}$ is the transfer matrix which describes the coupling phenomena between a step discontinuity, defined as the multiplication of the reflection matrix $\mathbf{R}$ and the coupling matrix $\mathbf{C}$ element by element, i.e.

$$T_{ij}^{(k,k+1)} = R_{ij}^{(k,k+1)} \cdot C_{ij}^{(k,k+1)},$$

(20)

and

$$R_{ij}^{(k,k+1)} = \frac{2\beta_i^{(k)}}{\beta_i^{(k)} + \beta_j^{(k+1)}},$$

(21)

$$C_{ij}^{(k,k+1)} = \langle u_i^{(k)}(x)|u_j^{(k+1)}(x)\rangle. \qquad (22)$$

For a TM mode, $\beta_m^{(k)}$ in Eqs. (15), (16) and (21) is substituted by $\beta_m^{(k)}/n_k^2$, where $n_k$ is the refractive index in the $k$th section.

## 5. Various Dual ARROW Devices

### 5.1. *Power dividers*

Based on our investigation, it is found that the maximum coupling efficiency $\eta_0$ of a dual ARROW waveguide in Eq. (11) strongly depends on its symmetry degree, and thus this maximum coupling efficiency can be controlled from 100% to zero by simply varying the outermost cladding thickness. Our ARROW power divider is shown in Figs. 3(a) and (b), which consists of two ARROW waveguides and a separation cladding layer in both coupling (symmetric) and decoupling (asymmetric) regions.[16] For the Si substrate ($n_s = 3.5$) as shown in Fig. 3(a), SiO$_2$ with refractive index 1.46 acts as the guide layers, separation layer and low-index cladding layers, i.e. $n_{g_1} = n_{g_2} = n_{sep} = n_{l_1} = n_{l_2} = 1.46$. TiO$_2$ acts as the high-index cladding layers and the refractive index is $n_{h_1} = n_{h_2} = 2.3$. The upper waveguide thickness $d_{g_1}$ is 4 $\mu$m such that this large core is compatible with the optical fiber efficiently.[7–19] Then we have $d_{g_2} = 4$ $\mu$m, $d_{l_2} = d_{sep} = 2$ $\mu$m, and $d_{h_1} = d_{h_2} = 0.089$ $\mu$m at the operating wavelength of $\lambda = 0.6328$ $\mu$m. The thickness variation of the upper cladding layers $d_{l_1}$ and $d'_{h_1}$ changes the symmetry degree of dual ARROW waveguides, and thus affects the coupling efficiency, and the maximum coupling efficiency $\eta_0$ in Eq. (11) versus the thickness of the upper cladding layer is shown in Fig. 4.[16] In the symmetric region, i.e. $d_{l_1} = d_{l_2} = 2$ $\mu$m and $d'_{h_1} = d_{h_1} = d_{h_2} = 0.089$ $\mu$m, the maximum coupling efficiency $\eta_0$ is about 100% and the coupling length is calculated as $L_c = \lambda/(2|N_e - N_o|) = 59$ mm. To maintain only two modes (one even and one odd) coupled from the coupling region to guide the waves in this decoupling region, we select $d_{l_1} = 0$ $\mu$m and $d'_{h_1} = 0.01$ $\mu$m in the decoupling region and the maximum coupling efficiency $\eta_0$ is obtained as near zero. Given a specified value $\eta = \eta(z = L_1)$, i.e. the power ratio between two guides given as $\eta/(1 - \eta)$, we have the length of the coupling region $L_1$ as

$$L_1 = \frac{2L_c}{\pi} \sin^{-1} \sqrt{\eta}. \qquad (23)$$

For a 3 dB divider, i.e. equal power distributed to two channels and $\eta = 50\%$, we obtain $L_1 = 0.5L_c = 29.5$ mm. BPM simulation results shown in Fig. 5 verify the design.[16] In our BPM simulations, we use the finite difference beam propagation method and the transparent boundary condition.[33,34]

For the InP/InGaAsP material system as shown in Fig. 3(b), in the coupling region, $n_{g_1} = n_{g_2} = n_{l_1} = n_{l_2} = n_{sep} = 3.16$, $n_{h_1} = n_{h_2} = 3.55$, $d_{g_1} = d_{g_2} = 4$ $\mu$m, $d_{l_1} = d_{l_2} = d_{sep} = 2$ $\mu$m, $d'_{h_1} = d_{h_1} = d_{h_2} = 0.237$ $\mu$m, and $\lambda = 1.55$ $\mu$m, the coupling length is $L_c = 7.34$ mm; in the decoupling region, $n_{g_1} = n_{g_2} = n_{l_1} = n_{l_2} = n_{sep} = 3.16$, $n_{h_1} = n_{h_2} = 3.55$, $d_{l_1} = 0$ $\mu$m, $d'_{h_1} = 0.162$ $\mu$m, $d_{g_1} = d_{g_2} = 4$ $\mu$m, $d_{l_2} = d_{sep} = 2$ $\mu$m, $d_{h_1} = d_{h_2} = 0.237$ $\mu$m, and $\lambda = 1.55$ $\mu$m. With a length in the coupling region of $L_1 = 0.5L_c = 3.67$ mm, a 3 dB divider is constructed.

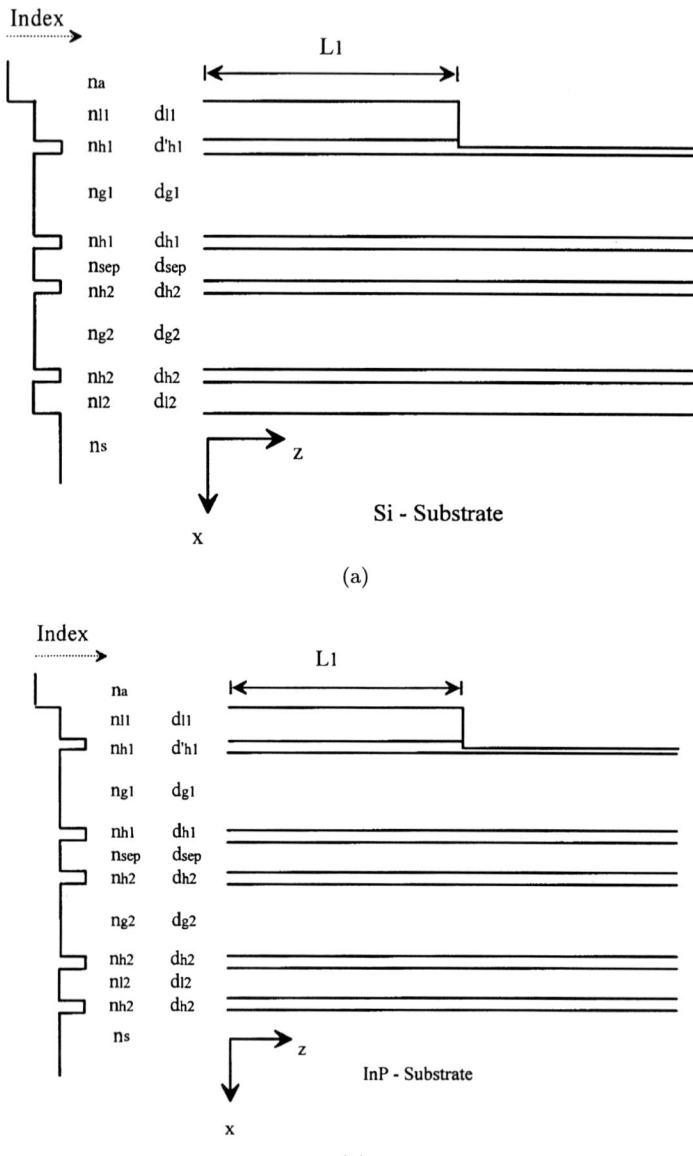

Fig. 2. The configuration of an ARROW power divider consisting of a coupling region $L_1$ and a decoupling region. (a) Si substrate, (b) InP substrate.

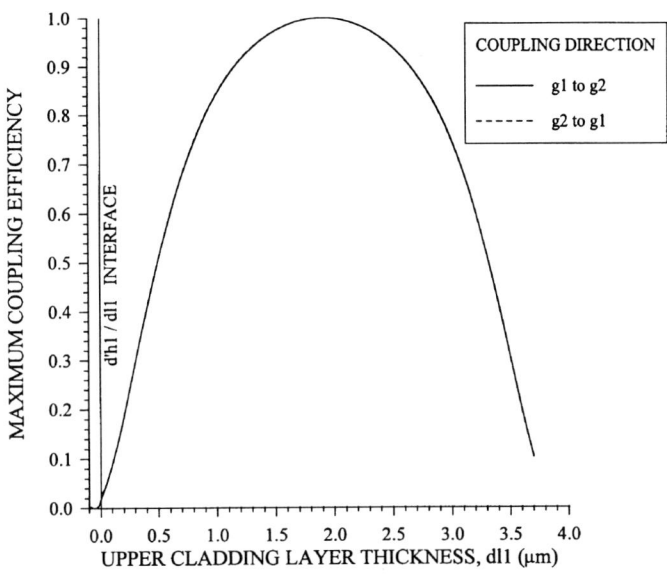

Fig. 4. The maximum coupling efficiency versus the upper cladding layer thickness $d_{l_1}$ for the configuration in Fig. 1(a). (Si substrate: $n_{l_1} = n_{l_2} = n_{g_1} = n_{g_2} = 1.46$, $n_{h_1} = n_{h_2} = 2.3$, $d_{g_1} = d_{g_2} = 4$ $\mu$m, $d_{l_2} = 2$ $\mu$m, $d_{h_1} = d_{h_2} = 0.089$ $\mu$m, and $\lambda = 0.6328$ $\mu$m.)

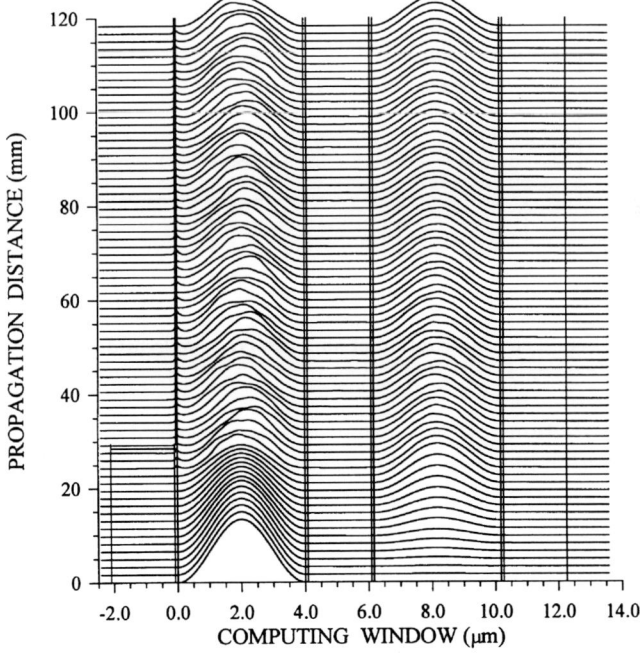

Fig. 5. BPM simulation results of a 3 dB ARROW power divider with the structure in Fig. 3(a) and the parameter values in Fig. 4. Coupling region: $d_{l_1} = 2$ $\mu$m $(= d_{l_2})$, $d'_{h_1} = 0.089$ $\mu$m $(= d_{h_2})$; decoupling region: $d_{l_1} = 0$ $\mu$m, $d'_{h_1} = 0.01$ $\mu$m.

## 5.2. *Hybrid couplers*

Optical hybrid couplers can provide the functions of beam splitting and beam combining.[35] A conventional hybrid coupler consists of a symmetric and an asymmetric Y-junctions connected directly. In each Y-junction, there are two normal modes, even and odd modes, traveling along the propagation direction. For the input symmetric Y-junction, the amplitudes of the fields for both modes in two individual waveguides are the same; in the output asymmetric Y-junction, the fields of the even and odd modes are mainly confined in the wide- and narrow-arm, respectively. The input conditions will determine the outputs of the wide and narrow-arm in the asymmetric Y-junction. The configuration of a novel ARROW hybrid couplers is shown in Fig. 6.[17] The outermost cladding layer is tapered from the exactly symmetric structure to the extremely asymmetric one. The fields in two guides can be efficiently coupled in the exactly symmetric region, and decoupled in the extremely asymmetric region as described in Sec. 5.1 — Power Dividers.

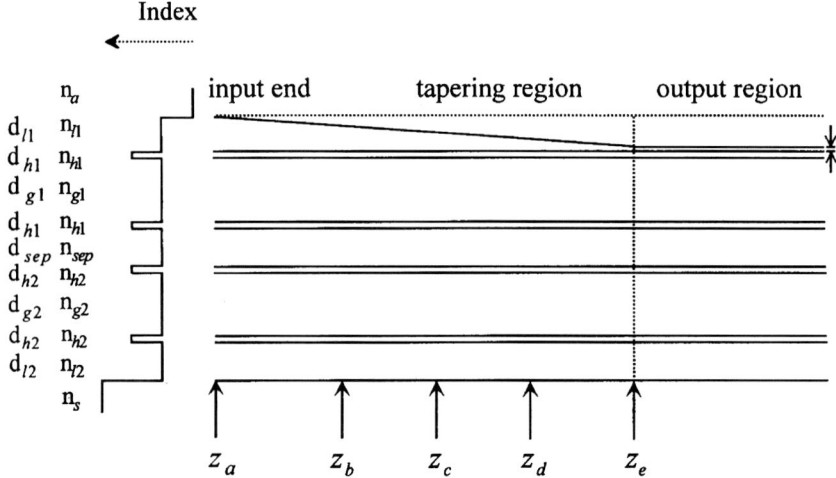

Fig. 6. The configuration of an ARROW-type hybrid coupler.

The field distributions of two normal modes at several corresponding positions along the propagation distance of this ARROW hybrid coupler are shown in Fig. 7, respectively. The peak amplitudes of the fields for both modes in two individual waveguides are the same at the input end. The tapering angle is carefully designed to meet the adiabatic invariance condition such that the power resided in the initial modes at the beginning remain in the same modes during travelling along the device.[36] The fields of the even and odd modes at the output end are mainly confined in guide 1 ($g_1$) and guide 2 ($g_2$), respectively. If two beams with the same amplitudes in phase are launched into two guides $g_1$ and $g_2$ at the input end, only the even mode can be excited and the power is confined within guide 2 ($g_2$) at the

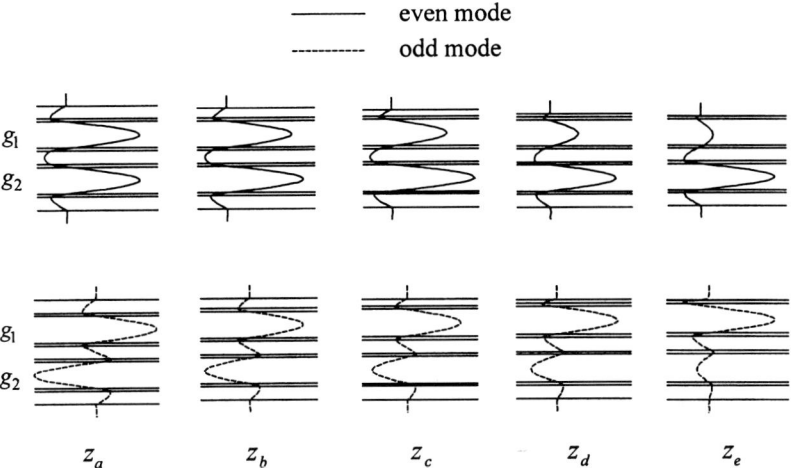

Fig. 7. The field distributions of two normal modes at several corresponding positions along the propagation distance.

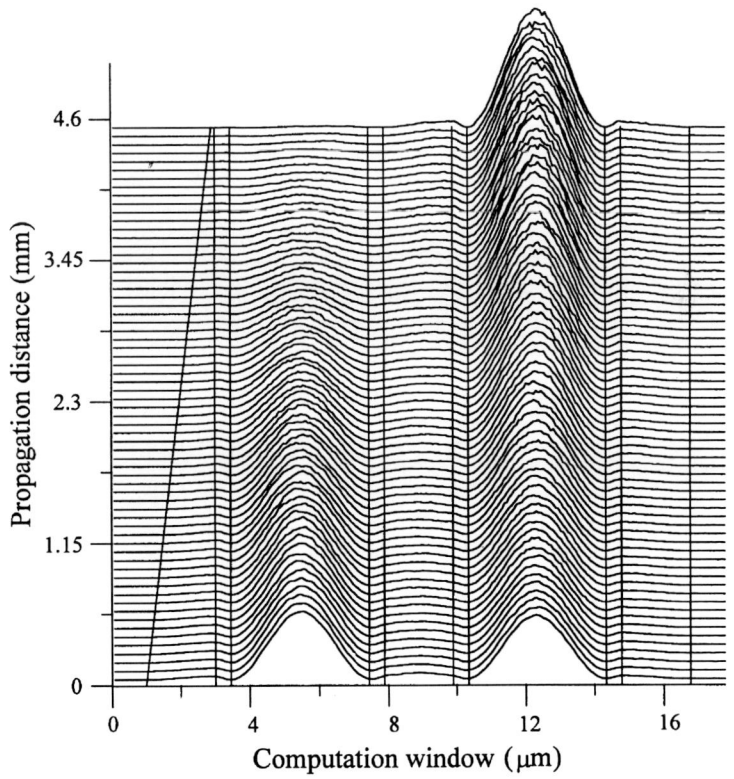

Fig. 8. The power evolution profile along the propagation distance for an ARROW hybrid coupler as shown in Fig. 6.

output end. On the other hand, when two input beams with the same amplitudes are out of phase, only the odd mode will be excited and the power confined within guide 1 ($g_1$) at the output end as shown in Fig. 7. In such a way, the power initially in two guides can be combined into one of two cores depending on the phase difference between two input beams. In another case, if only a single beam is launched, even and odd modes are equally excited and then adiabatically transferred into two guides ($g_1$ and $g_2$), respectively, and the device functions as a power divider. We have also used BPM simulations to verify our design. BPM simulation of the power evolution in the device for combining two input beams in phase to guide 2 (the even mode) is shown in Fig. 8. Device parameters are: $n_{g_1} = n_{g_2} = n_{l_1} = n_{l_2} = n_{sep} =$ 1.46 (SiO$_2$), $n_{h_1} = n_{h_2} = 1.5$ (glass mixture, BaO and SiO$_2$), $d_{g_1} = d_{g_2} = 4$ $\mu$m, $d_{l_1} = d_{l_2} = d_{sep} = 2$ $\mu$m, $d'_{h_1} = d_{h_1} = d_{h_2} = 0.237$ $\mu$m, and $\lambda = 0.6328$ $\mu$m, the optimum tapering angle is limited from 0.02° to 0.035°.

Based on the reciprocity theorem, the reversed hybrid coupler can convert the original power combiner to a power divider when only one beam is input to guide 2 ($g_2$) and BPM simulation results are shown in Fig. 9. By combining an original and a reversed hybrid couplers, an integrated-optical Michelson interferometer can also be realized.[37]

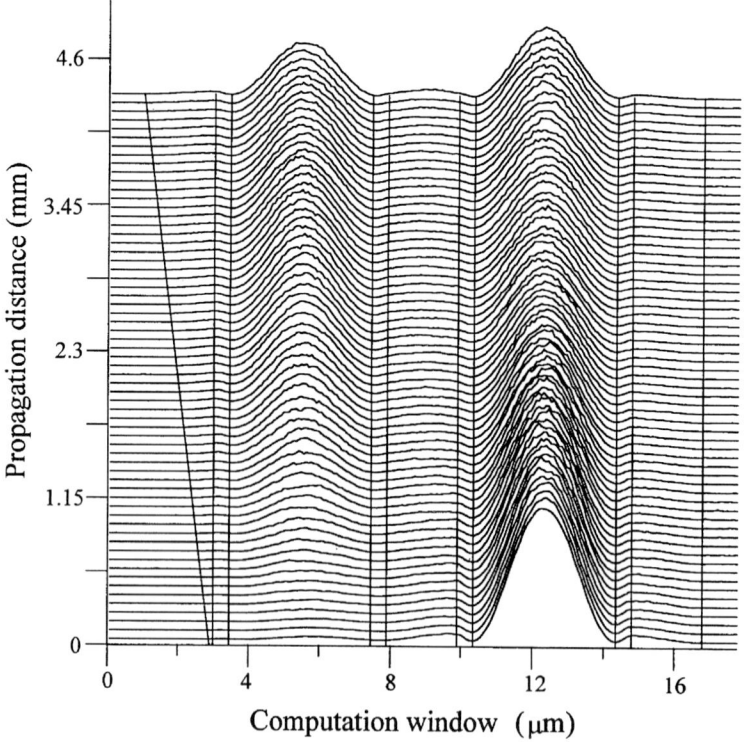

Fig. 9. The power evolution profile along the propagation distance for a reversed ARROW hybrid coupler.

## 5.3. *Wavelength filters*

Since a coupled structure of a dual ARROW waveguide can be designed as a directional coupler and this coupler is sensitive to operating wavelength, an ARROW optical wavelength filter with a narrow bandwidth has been presented.[13] This type of wavelength filters was designed based on $SiO_2/TiO_2$ and $InP/InGaAsP$ material systems. The configurations of these filters are the same as the figures in Figs. 1(a) and (b). To achieve a narrow bandwidth, two guides $g_1$ and $g_2$ are chosen to have different refractive indices, i.e. $n_{g_1} \neq n_{g_2}$. For Si substrate with $SiO_2/TiO_2$ material system as in Fig. 1(a), and parameters chosen as $n_{g_1} = n_{sep} = n_{l_1} = n_{l_2} = 1.46$, $n_{g_2} = 1.46$, $n_{h_1} = n_{h_2} = 2.3$, and $d_{g_1} = 4$ $\mu$m, $d_{g_2} = 1.15$ $\mu$m, $d_{sep} = d_{l_1} = d_{l_2} = 2$ $\mu$m, $d_{h_1} = d_{h_2} = 0.089$ $\mu$m, the center wavelength is $\lambda_0 = 0.6328$ $\mu$m; the full width at half maximum (FWHM) of the filter is 7 Å with 11 mm device length. For $InP/InGaAsP$ material system in Fig. 1(b), and parameters chosen as $n_{g_1} = n_{sep} = n_{l_1} = n_{l_2} = 3.16$, $n_{g_2} = 3.25$, $n_{h_1} = n_{h_2} = 3.553$, and $d_{g_1} = 4$ $\mu$m, $d_{g_2} = 0.9$ $\mu$m, $d_{sep} = d_{l_1} = d_{l_2} = 2$ $\mu$m, $d_{h_1} = d_{h_2} = 0.237$ $\mu$m, the center wavelength is $\lambda_0 = 1.55$ $\mu$m; the full width at half maximum (FWHM) of the filter is 4 nm with 2.6 mm device length. The detailed analysis and design can be seen in Ref. 13.

## 5.4. *Polarization beamsplitters*

An ARROW-B structure has been presented for polarization-insensitive waveguiding.[9] The difference between an ARROW-B and a conventional ARROW is that the refractive index of the first cladding layer, i.e. the index of the layer just under the core, is lower as shown in Fig. 10. If this first cladding layer is thick enough, total internal reflections occur at the interface between the core and the first cladding. However, this layer is so thin that frustrated total internal reflections occur, i.e. the evanescent field reaches the second cladding layers. For an ARROW-B, the thickness of the second cladding layer is designed to be half that

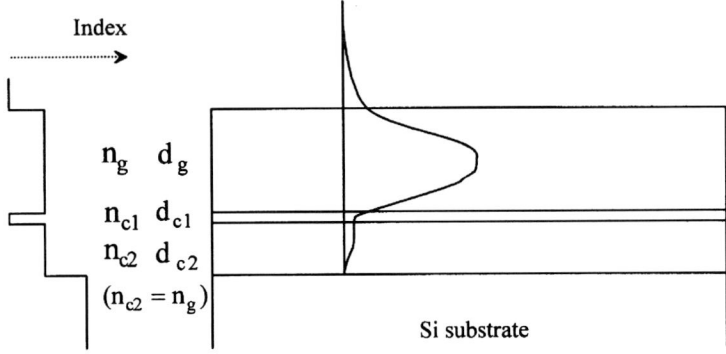

Fig. 10. The structure of an ARROW-B.

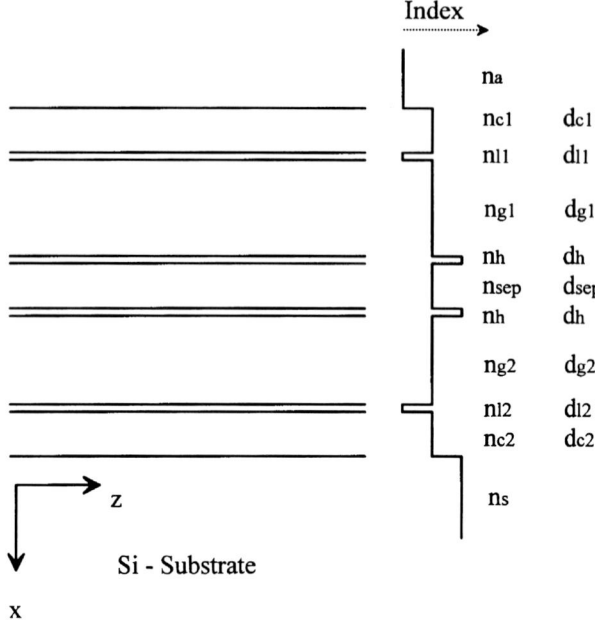

Fig. 11. The configuration of an ARROW polarization beamsplitter.

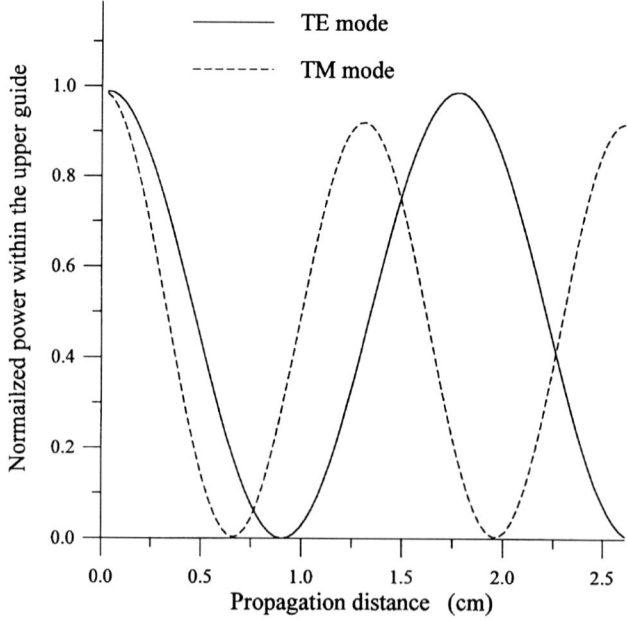

Fig. 12. Power coupling of TE and TM fields along the propagation distance of the ARROW polarization beamsplitter.

of the core as in the conventional ARROW such that the reflection is a kind of interference reflection, and higher order modes are thus filtered out due to low reflectivities. Since the total internal reflection dominates the overall reflection, the reflectivity in an ARROW-B is less dependent on the polarization than in the conventional ARROW. The device with losses smaller than 1 dB/cm for $TE_0$ and $TM_0$ modes and larger than 10 dB/cm for higher order modes was demonstrated.[9]

Based on the ARROW-B concept, we design an ARROW polarization beam-splitter as shown in Fig. 11. Guide 2 ($g_2$) near the substrate with the first cladding of a low index ($n_{l_2}$ and the second cladding layer ($n_{c_2} = n_{g_2}$) of a transversely anti-resonance thickness is an ARROW-B structure. The symmetric structure of guide 1 ($g_1$) is used to provide efficient coupling (maximum coupling efficiency $\eta_0 = 100\%$) between two guides as described in Sec. 5.1 — Power Dividers. The separation layers ($n_h/n_{sep}/n_h$), the same as that in a convention dual ARROW device, provide different coupling lengths between the TE and TM modes. When an optical beam for a TE or TM mode is input in guide 1 ($g_1$), the normalized power remaining within this same guide ($g_1$) along the propagation distance of this device is shown in Fig. 12. Device parameters are: $n_{g_1} = n_{g_2} = n_{c_1} = n_{c_2} = n_{sep} = 1.54$ (NA45 glass), $n_{l_1} = n_{l_2} = 1.46$ (SiO$_2$), $n_h = 1.65$ (Al$_2$O$_3$), $d_{g_1} = d_{g_2} = 4$ $\mu$m, $d_{l_1} = d_{l_2} = d_{sep} = 2$ $\mu$m, $d_h = 0.265$ $\mu$m, and $\lambda = 0.6328$ $\mu$m. It can be seen that the coupling length is about 8.76 mm for the TE mode and 6.52 mm for the TM

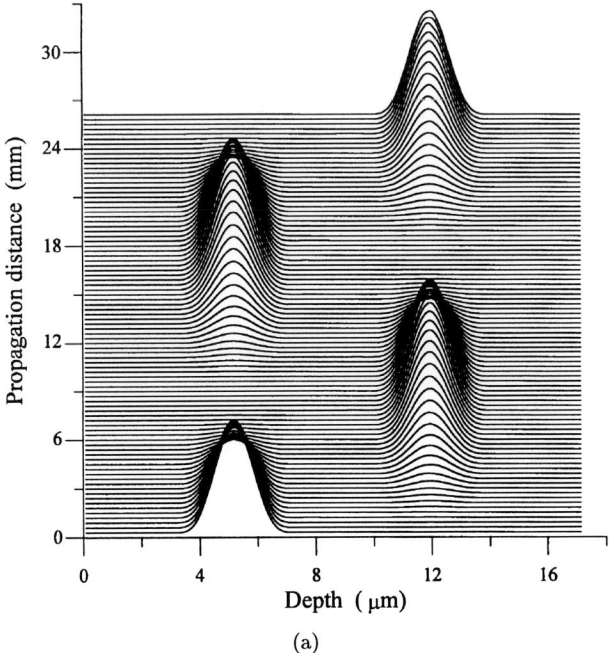

(a)

Fig. 13. BPM simulation results of power coupling along the propagation distance of the ARROW polarization beamsplitter. (a) TE mode, (b) TM mode.

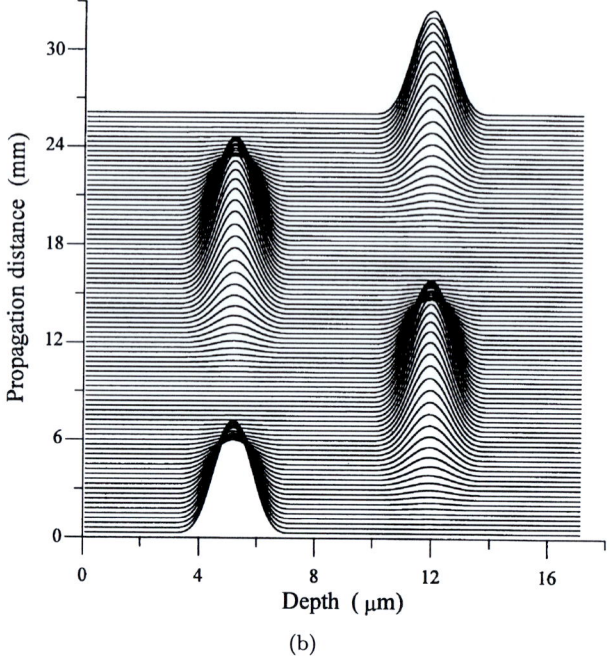

Fig. 13. (*Continued*)

mode, respectively. Choosing the device length as 26 mm, we obtain 100% and 0% coupling for the TE and TM modes, respectively, and the two modes are separated with losses lower than 1 dB. BPM simulation results shown in Figs. 13(a) and (b) verify the design.

### 5.5. *Pressure sensors*

This pressure sensor consists of an ARROW interferometer on a silicon wafer, with the sensing arm located on a fully clamped, suspended silicon diaphragm as shown in Fig. 14.[14] This ARROW stack is made of $SiO_2$ and $Si_3N_4$. The sensing arms of 2250 and 4000 $\mu$m were investigated. This interferometer, when subject to an applied pressure, results in mechanic-optic effects on the sensing arm, i.e. elongation of the optical path due to deflection and stress induced change in the refractive index in the ARROW layer. These effects lead to the phase shift of the sensing arm to the reference arm, and can be used to sense the pressure. The detailed analysis and design can be seen in Ref. 14.

Since conventional optical waveguides have been proposed for many sensing systems, such as chemical and biochemical sensing, dual ARROW devices might also be applied to those applications, and it is worth further investigation.

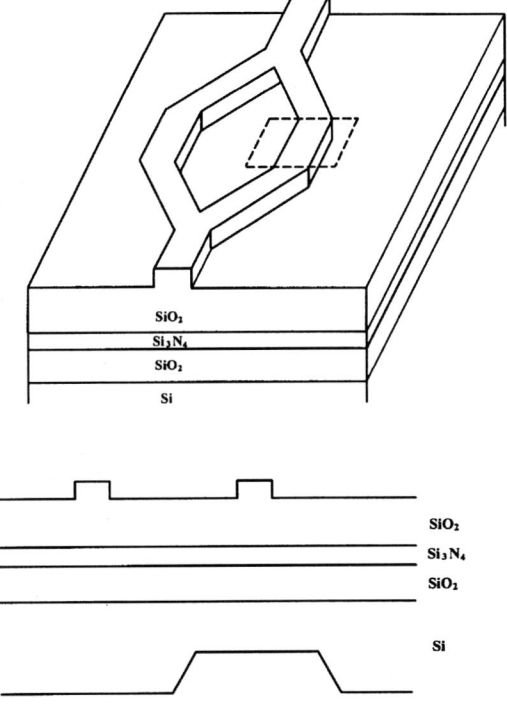

Fig. 14. The structure of an ARROW pressure sensor.

## 6. Conclusions

The basic structure of a dual ARROW device is introduced, which is constructed by transverse resonance for guiding layers and antiresonance for cladding layers. In order to design dual ARROW devices, theories of modal analysis for ARROW devices, coupling efficiency analysis between dual ARROW waveguides, and eigenmode expansion analysis for devices with step discontinuities are discussed. Based on presented theories dual ARROW structures of power dividers, hybrid couplers, wavelength filters, polarization beamsplitters, and pressure sensors are introduced. BPM simulation results also verify the theories and device characteristics. However, the control of refractive index and the thickness (or the width for strip structures) of each film layer of the devices strongly depends on the fabrication processes. The characteristic sensitivity of dual ARROW devices to index and thickness (or width) deviations have not been investigated yet, which should be done in future.

## Acknowledgment

This work was supported by the National Science Council of the Republic of China under contract NSC86-2221-E-009-040.

# References

1. E. A. J. Marcatili, "Dielectric rectangular waveguide and directional coupler for integrated optics", *Bell Syst. Tech. J.* **48** (1969) 2071–2102.
2. D. Marcuse, *Light Transmission Optics*, Van Nostrand, New York, 1972.
3. H. F. Taylor and A. Yariv, "Guided wave optics", *Proc. IEEE* **62**, 8 (1974) 1044–1060.
4. W. K. Burns and A. F. Milton, "Mode conversion in planar-dielectric separating waveguides", *IEEE J. Quantum Electron.* **QE-11**, 1 (1975) 32–39.
5. H. Nishihara, M. Haruna, and T. Suhara, *Optical Integrated Circuits*, McGraw-Hill, New York, 1989.
6. T. Tamir, (ed.), *Guided-Wave Optoelectronics*, Springer Series in Electronics and Photonics 26, Springer-Verlag, New York, 1990.
7. M. A. Duguay, Y. Kokubun, and T. L. Koch, "Antiresonant reflecting optical waveguides in $SiO_2$-Si multilayer structures", *Appl. Phys. Lett.* **49**, 1 (1986) 13–15.
8. T. Baba, Y. Kokubun, T. Sakaki, and K. Iga, "Loss reduction of an ARROW waveguide in shorter wavelength and its stack configuration", *IEEE J. Lightwave Technol.* **LT-6**, 9 (1988) 1440–1444.
9. T. Baba and Y. Kokubun, "New polarization-insensitive antiresonant reflecting optical waveguide", *IEEE Photonics Tech. Lett.* **1**, 8 (1989) 232–234.
10. M. Mann, U. Trutschel, C. Wachter, L. Leine, and F. Lederer, "Directional coupler based on an antiresonant reflecting optical waveguide", *Opt. Lett.* **16**, 11 (1991) 805–807.
11. J. M. Kubica, "Numerical analysis of InP/InGaAsP ARROW waveguides using transfer matrix approach", *IEEE J. Lightwave Technol.* **LT-10**, 6 (1992) 707–771.
12. S. Asakawa, Y. Kokubun, M. Ohyama, and T. Baba, "Three-dimensional optical interconnects by stacked ARROW waveguides", *Electron. Lett.* **29**, 16 (1993) 1485–1486.
13. Z. M. Mao and W. P. Huang, "An ARROW optical wavelength filters: Design and analysis", *IEEE/OSA J. Lightwave Technol.* **LT-11**, 7 (1993) 1183–1188.
14. A. Vadekar, A. Nathan, and W. P. Huang, "Analysis and design of an integrated silicon ARROW Mach-Zehnder micromechanical interferometer", *IEEE/OSA J. Lightwave Technol.* **12**, 1 (1994) 157–162.
15. Y.-T. Huang and Y.-H. Chen, "A novel power divider based on dual antiresonant reflecting optical waveguides", *IEEE CLEOS/Pacific Rim '95*, Chiba, Japan, July 1995.
16. Y.-H. Chen and Y.-T. Huang, "Coupling efficiency analysis and control of dual antiresonant reflecting optical waveguides", *IEEE/OSA J. Lightwave Technol.* **IT-14**, 6 (1996) 1507–1513.
17. J.-J. Deng and Y.-T. Huang, "A novel hybrid coupler based on antiresonant reflecting optical waveguides", *IEEE CLEO/Europe-EQEC '96*, Hamburg, Germany, Sept. 1996.
18. J.-J. Deng and Y.-T. Huang, "Eigenmide expansion analysis and design of antiresonant reflecting optical waveguide devices with step discontinuities", *Photonics/Taiwan '96*, Hsinchu, Taiwan, R.O.C., Dec. 1996.
19. J.-J. Deng and Y.-T. Huang, "Loss reduction of abrupt waveguide-bends using Fabry-Perot cavity", *SPIE Photonics West '97*, San Jose, CA, USA, Feb. 1997.
20. D. Marcuse, "The coupling of degenerate modes in two parallel dielectric waveguides", *Bell Syst. Tech. J.* **50** (1971) 1791–1816.
21. H. Kogelnik and R. V. Schmidt, "Switched directional couplers with alternating $\Delta\beta$", *IEEE J. Quantum Electron.* **QE-12**, 7 (1976) 396–401.
22. A. Yariv, "Coupled mode theory for guided-wave optics", *IEEE J. Quantum Electron.* **QE-9**, 9 (1973) 919–933.

23. A. Hardy and W. Streifer, "Coupled mode theory of parallel waveguides", *IEEE J. Lightwave Technol.* **LT-3**, 5 (1985) 1135–1146.
24. Y. Suematsu and K. Kishino, "Coupling coefficient in strongly coupled dielectric waveguides", *Radio Science* **12**, 4 (1977) 587–592.
25. Y. Suematsu and K. Furuya, "Quasi-guided modes and related rediation losses in optical dielectric waveguides with external higher index surroundings", *IEEE Trans. on Microwave Theory and Tech.* **MTT-23**, 1 (1975) 170–175.
26. A. K. Ghatak, K. Thyagarajan, and H. R. Shenoy, "Numerical analysis of planar optical waveguides using matrix approach", *J. Lightwave Technol.* **5**, 5 (1987) 660–667.
27. A. W. Snyder and J. D. Love, "Optical Waveguide Theory" (Chapman and Hall, London, 1983) chap. 24.
28. R. Sammut and A. W. Snyder, "Leaky modes on a dielectric waveguide: orthogonality and excitation", *Appl. Opt.* **15**, 14 (1976) 1040–1044.
29. D. Yap and L. M. Johnson, "Coupling between successive Ti:LiNbO$_3$ waveguide bends and branches", *Appl. Opt.* **23** (1984) 2991–2999.
30. G. H. Brook and M. M. Z. Kharadly, "Step discontinuities on dielectric waveguides", *Electron. Lett.* **12**, 9 (1976) 473–475.
31. K. Tsutaumi, Y. Imada, H. Hirai, and Y. Yuba, "Analysis of single-mode optical Y-junction by the bounded step and bend approximation", *J. Lightwave Tech.* **6**, 4 (1988) 590–600.
32. S. L. Lee, Y. Chung, L. A. Coldren, and N. Dagli, "On Leaky mode approximations for modal expansion in multilayer open waveguides", *IEEE J. Quantum Electron.* **31**, 10 (1995) 1790–1802.
33. H. J. W. H. Hoekstra, G. J. M. Krijnen, and P. V. Lambeck, "Efficient interface conditions for the finite difference beam propagation method", *J. Lightwave Technol.* **10**, 10 (1992) 1352–1355.
34. G. R. Hadley, "Transparent boundary condition for beam propagation," *Opt. Lett.* **16**, 9 (1991) 624–626.
35. M. Izutsu, A. Enokihara, and T. Sueta, "Optical hybrid coupler", *Opt. Lett.* **7**, 11 (1982) 549–551.
36. Y. Shani, C. H. Henry, R. C. Kistler, R. F. Kazarinov, and K. J. Orlowsky, "Integrated optic adiabatic devices on silicon", *IEEE J. Quantum Electron.* **27**, 3 (1991) 556–566.
37. M. Izutsu, A. Enokihara, and T. Sueta, "Optical-waveguide micro-displacement sensor", *Electron. Lett.* **18**, 20 (1982) 867–868.

International Journal of High Speed Electronics and Systems, Vol. 8, No. 4 (1997) 665–684
© World Scientific Publishing Company

# NUMERICAL ANALYSIS OF NONLINEAR DIRECTIONAL COUPLERS

CHIH-HSIEN LAI*, HUNG-CHUN CHANG†, and JIA-PANG PANG‡

*Department of Electrical Engineering and
Graduate Institute of Electro-Optical Engineering,
National Taiwan University, Taipei, Taiwan 106-17, R.O.C.
E-mail: hcchang@cc.ee.ntu.edu.tw*

The original coupled-mode theory for the nonlinear directional coupler (NLDC) and two later improved theories are reviewed and compared with the analysis using the segmentation method proposed in this work. The segmentation method is more accurate in analyzing the NLDC because it takes into account the real situation that the local nonlinear guided modes in the NLDC will vary along the propagation direction due to the accompanying variation in the local power distribution. In the coupled-mode formulations reviewed, however, either linear guided modes or nonlinear modes at a fixed power level are employed when evaluating related coupling quantities.

## 1. Introduction

The nonlinear directional coupler (NLDC), first proposed by Jensen,[1] has been one of the promising structures for an ultrafast all-optical switch and has since attracted great interest in related studies. The function of this device is based on the nonlinear interaction resulting from the optical power induced change of the refractive index of the coupler in addition to the linear interaction between the fields of the individual waveguides. Theoretically, the NLDC has most often been analyzed by using the coupled-mode theory.[2-6] Other analysis methods include the beam propagation method[7,8] and the supermode combination method.[9] The coupled-mode theory provides an analytical description of the coupling behavior of a NLDC. Jensen[2] used the coupled-mode theory to derive the characteristics of the NLDC, but he neglected the butt-coupling (i.e. overlap of individual waveguide mode fields) effect and some nonlinear coupling effect. Later, based on the improved coupled-mode formulations,[10-13] Chen[5] derived a more complete set of nonlinear coupled-mode equations by including the nonlinear coupling and the butt-coupling terms. More recently, Meng and Okamoto[6] used the generalized reciprocity relation to

---

*Now with Comtrend Corporation, Taipei, Taiwan 241, Republic of China.
†Corresponding author.
‡Now with the Department of Electronic Engineering, The University of Tokyo, 7-3-1 Hongo, Bunkyoku, Tokyo 113, Japan.

derive an improved set of nonlinear coupled equations in which all the coefficients became power dependent.

One advantage of the coupled-mode analysis lies in that analytical solution could be obtained under suitable assumptions. Such assumptions, however, set limits to the range of applicability of the solution. For a waveguide composed of nonlinear media, the mode field profiles would be power dependent. Although Chen[5] included the nonlinear coupling terms in his theory, the coefficients in his equations were evaluated based on linear waveguide modes, and were thus power independent. Meng and Okamoto's equations[6] contain power-dependent coefficients. However, those coefficients are evaluated using the nonlinear guided modes assuming that each individual waveguide carries the full input power. In the real situation the total input power is divided between the waveguides composed of the NLDC and such division varies along the interaction region. Therefore, the above coefficients should also be position dependent, making a rigorous analysis more difficult.

In this paper we propose a numerical analysis method based on an adiabatical approximation, called the segmentation method, for the study of the NLDC problem and try to examine the accuracy of the previous coupled-mode formulations. In the method a NLDC is divided into many segments. Each segment is treated as a linear structure with the refractive-index profile determined by the local optical intensity, and then the propagation of light is solved by using the linear coupled-mode theory or the normal mode theory. A NLDC with nonlinear guiding layers is used as a numerical example for comparing the predictions of the NLDC behavior by the above-mentioned three coupled-mode formulations[2,5,6] and our proposed method.

This paper is organized as follows. Sections 2 reviews the prior coupled-mode formulations for the NLDC. Section 3 describes the numerical scheme of the proposed segmentation method. Section 4 presents numerical results and comparison of different analysis methods. Section 5 summarizes the findings of this study.

## 2. The Nonlinear Coupled-Mode Equations — Review of Prior Formulations

Usual procedures of applying the coupled-mode theory to analyze the NLDC consist of writing down the nonlinear coupled-mode equations which describe the behavior of the NLDC, and then solving these equations. As was mentioned in the introduction, the development of nonlinear coupled-mode equations for the NLDC thus far could be divided into three stages: first, the equations are derived by the use of the coupled-mode theory with perturbation method[2]; second, the nonlinear coupling effect and the butt-coupling effect are considered[5]; third, a set of improved nonlinear coupled-mode equations, which is based on the generalized reciprocity relation, is proposed,[6] leading to a more reasonable result such that all the coefficients in the coupled equations, including the coupling coefficient, become power dependent. These formulations are reviewed in this section.

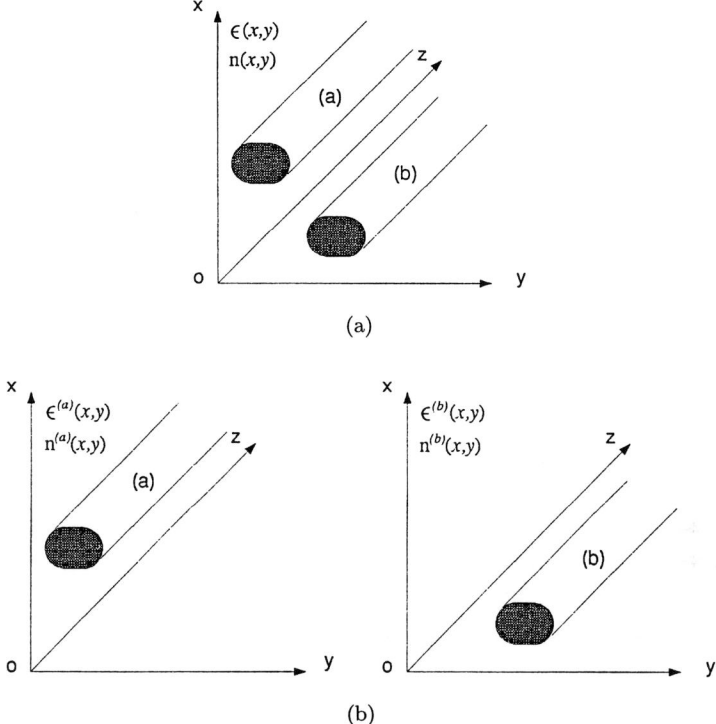

(a)

(b)

Fig. 1. Schematic diagrams for various media under consideration: (a) $\epsilon(x,y)$ and $n(x,y)$ for the system with both waveguides "a" and "b", (b) $\epsilon^{(a)}(x,y)$ and $n^{(a)}(x,y)$ for waveguide "a" only and $\epsilon^{(b)}(x,y)$ and $n^{(b)}(x,y)$ for waveguide "b" only.

Figure 1(a) shows a schematic of the NLDC device. This device is composed of two waveguides labeled "$a$" and "$b$" which are placed in close proximity so that they will couple with each other. The permittivity and the refractive index of the composite waveguide system are denoted as $\epsilon(x,y)$ and $n(x,y)$, respectively. For the isolated waveguides "$a$" and "$b$" as shown in Fig. 1(b), the permittivity and the refractive index distributions are denoted as $\epsilon^{(a)}(x,y), \epsilon^{(b)}(x,y), n^{(a)}(x,y)$, and $n^{(b)}(x,y)$, respectively. The nonlinear materials are assumed to be of Kerr type, which have the relative dielectric constants of the form $\epsilon = \epsilon_L + \alpha|\bar{E}|^2$, where $\epsilon_L$ is the linear part of the permittivity, $\alpha$ is the nonlinear coefficient, and $\bar{E}$ is the electric field intensity. In nonlinear optics the nonlinear coefficient $\alpha$ is usually written in terms of the intensity-dependent refractive index $n = n_L + n_{NL}I$, where $I$ is the local optical intensity, and $n_L$ and $n_{NL}$ are the linear and nonlinear refractive indices, respectively. The relation between $\alpha$ and $n_{NL}$ is $\alpha = c\epsilon_0 n_L^2 n_{NL}$, where $c$ is the light velocity in vacuum and $\epsilon_0$ is the permittivity of vacuum. The time convention $\exp(-j\omega t)$ will be used for the time harmonic fields, so that the fields propagating along the $+z$ direction are described by $\exp(j\beta z)$. Only transverse-electric (TE) waves are examined here.

93

## 2.1. *The original nonlinear coupled-mode equations*[2]

Assuming that the coupler is composed of two identical single-mode waveguides and the transverse components of the system total electric and magnetic fields could be represented as the superposition of the transverse components of the local guided modes of the two guides as

$$\bar{E}(x, y, z) = [A(z)\bar{e}_t^{(a)}(x, y) + B(z)\bar{e}_t^{(b)}(x, y)] \exp(j\beta z) \tag{1}$$

$$\bar{H}(x, y, z) = [A(z)\bar{h}_t^{(a)}(x, y) + B(z)\bar{h}_t^{(b)}(x, y)] \exp(j\beta z), \tag{2}$$

where $\bar{e}_t^{(a)}(x, y), \bar{e}_t^{(b)}(x, y), \bar{h}_t^{(a)}(x, y)$, and $\bar{h}_t^{(b)}(x, y)$ are the transverse components of the local waveguide modes of guides "*a*" and "*b*" which are normalized such that

$$\frac{1}{2} \int_{-\infty}^{\infty} \int_{-\infty}^{\infty} \hat{z} \cdot [\bar{e}_t^{(u)} \times \bar{h}_t^{(u)}] \, dx \, dy = 1 \quad u = a, b \tag{3}$$

and $A(z)$ and $B(z)$ are the partition model amplitudes of the modes.[14]

Jensen[2] derived the nonlinear coupled-mode equations for the NLDC using the coupled-mode theory by properly identifying the contributions to the perturbing polarization. The coupled equations are

$$-j\frac{dA}{dz} = Q_1 A + Q_2 B + (k_s|A|^2 + 2k_c|B|^2)A \tag{4}$$

$$-j\frac{dB}{dz} = Q_1 B + Q_2 A + (k_s|B|^2 + 2k_c|A|^2)B, \tag{5}$$

where the coupling coefficients are defined as

$$Q_1 = \frac{\omega}{4} \int_{-\infty}^{\infty} \int_{-\infty}^{\infty} [\epsilon_L - \epsilon_L^{(a)}] |\bar{e}_t^{(a)}|^2 \, dx \, dy \tag{6}$$

$$Q_2 = \frac{\omega}{4} \int_{-\infty}^{\infty} \int_{-\infty}^{\infty} [\epsilon_L - \epsilon_L^{(a)}] |\bar{e}_t^{(a)}||\bar{e}_t^{(b)}| \, dx \, dy \tag{7}$$

$$k_s = \frac{\omega}{4} \int_{-\infty}^{\infty} \int_{-\infty}^{\infty} \alpha|\bar{e}_t^{(a)}|^4 \, dx \, dy \tag{8}$$

$$k_c = \frac{\omega}{4} \int_{-\infty}^{\infty} \int_{-\infty}^{\infty} \alpha|\bar{e}_t^{(a)}|^2|\bar{e}_t^{(b)}|^2 \, dx \, dy. \tag{9}$$

The terms involving $Q_1$ in (4) and (5) will only modify the propagation constants of the modes. The $Q_2$ terms account for linear coupling between the waveguides. The terms with $k_s$ are the nonlinear terms due to the nonlinear interaction of a mode with itself. The terms with $k_c$ correspond to the nonlinear interaction of one mode with the mode in the adjacent guide.

The nonlinear coupled equations (4) and (5) can be solved analytically, hence the power propagating in each waveguide has analytical solutions. These solutions are very complicated. However, when the power $P$ is initially launched into one waveguide, i.e. $P_a(0) = P$ and $P_b(0) = 0$, there exists a simple solution for the power remaining in waveguide "$a$" along the propagation direction $P_a(z)$:

$$P_a(Z) = P\{1 + cn(2Z|m)\}/2\,,$$

where

$$Z = Q_2 z \qquad (11)$$

$$m = P^2/P_c^2\,, \qquad (12)$$

$P_c$ is the critical power defined by

$$P_c = 4Q_2/(k_s - 2k_c)\,, \qquad (13)$$

and $cn(\phi|m)$ is a Jacobi elliptic function[15] which is periodic with a period of $4K(m)$ with $K(m)$ being a complete elliptic integral of the first kind.[15] For $m \simeq 0$ (very small input intensities), (10) becomes

$$P_a(Z) = P\{1 + \cos(2Z)\}/2 \qquad (14)$$

which says that the optical power swaps between the waveguides with a transfer length of $Z = \pi/2Q_2$. The increase in the input intensity, and thus the parameter $m$, would lead to an increase in $K(m)$, and hence the period of the elliptic function $cn(\phi|m)$.

## 2.2. Nonlinear coupled-mode equations including the Butt coupling[5]

In Jensen's analysis on nonlinear phenomena of an optical coupler, the conventional coupled-mode theory is employed and only the self-phase modulation and the cross-phase modulation terms are included as the nonlinear effects. Chen[5] derived a set of full nonlinear coupled equations by including the nonlinear coupling effect and the butt-coupling effect, as described in the following. Again, the coupler is assumed to consist of two identical single-mode waveguides and the total field of the composite structure is supposed to be the superposition of the individual waveguide modal fields as given by (1) and (2). Chen[5] used the coupled-mode approach to arrive at the following coupled-mode equations governing the amplitudes $A(z)$ and $B(z)$:

$$-j\left(\frac{dA}{dz} + C\frac{dB}{dz}\right) = Q_1 A + Q_2 B + \left(k_s|A|^2 + 2k_c|B|^2\right)A$$
$$+ \left(2k_t|A|^2 + k_t|B|^2\right)B + k_c A^* B^2 + k_t A^2 B^* \qquad (15)$$

$$-j\left(\frac{dB}{dz} + C\frac{dA}{dz}\right) = Q_1 B + Q_2 A + \left(k_s|B|^2 + 2k_c|A|^2\right)B$$
$$+ \left(2k_t|B|^2 + k_t|A|^2\right)A + k_c A^2 B^* + k_t A^* B^2\,, \qquad (16)$$

95

where $Q_1, Q_2, k_s$, and $k_c$ have been defined in Eqs. (6)–(9),

$$C = \frac{1}{2} \int_{-\infty}^{\infty} \int_{-\infty}^{\infty} \hat{z} \cdot [\bar{e}_t^{(u)} \times \bar{h}_t^{(v)}] \, dx \, dy \tag{17}$$

$$k_t = \frac{\omega}{4} \int_{-\infty}^{\infty} \int_{-\infty}^{\infty} \alpha |\bar{e}_t^{(a)}|^3 |\bar{e}_t^{(b)}| \, dx \, dy \tag{18}$$

and the asterisk denotes the complex conjugate.

In Eqs. (15) and (16) the terms in the first parentheses on the right-hand side are the self- and cross-phase modulation terms which have been included in Jensen's equations, the terms in the second parentheses appear to be the power-dependent coupling coefficients, and the last two terms on the right-hand side correspond to the nonlinear coupling. Note that the butt-coupling, or the overlap integral, $C$, is introduced here, which plays an important role in the improved coupled-mode theory.[10] By letting $C = 0$ and $k_t = 0$, and neglecting the nonlinear coupling effect, (15) and (16) reduce to Jensen's equations (4) and (5).

In the improved coupled-mode formulation the cross power $P_{ab} = 2C \operatorname{Re}\{AB^*\}$ is introduced so that the total power $P = P_a(z) + P_b(z) + P_{ab}(z)$ is conserved along the $z$ direction,[12] where $P_a = |A|^2$ and $P_b = |B|^2$. For the case in which the power is initially launched into one of the waveguides, i.e. $P_a(0) = P$ and $P_b(0) = 0$, the solution to (15) and (16) becomes

$$P_{a,b}(z) = \frac{1}{2}[P - CS(z)] \pm \frac{1}{2} Pq(z) \left\{ 1 + C\frac{P_c}{P} \right.$$
$$\left. - \left[ 1 + \left( 2\frac{k_t}{k_s} - C \right) 2\frac{P}{P_c} + \frac{k_c}{k_s} \right] \frac{P_c}{P^2} S(z) - 2\frac{k_c}{k_s} \frac{S^2(z)}{P^2} \right\}^{1/2} \tag{19}$$

$$P_{ab}(z) = CS(z) \tag{20}$$

$$S(z) = \frac{P^2}{P_c} \frac{\frac{CP_c}{P} + \left[ 1 + \left( 2\frac{k_t}{k_s} - C + \frac{k_c}{k_s}\frac{P}{P_c} \right) 2\frac{P}{P_c} \right] sn^2(\alpha z|m)}{1 + \left( 2\frac{k_t}{k_s} - C + \frac{2k_c}{k_s}\frac{P}{P_c} \right) 2\frac{P}{P_c} - 3\frac{k_c}{k_s} - 2\frac{k_c}{k_s}\frac{P^2}{P_c^2} sn^2(\alpha z|m)} \tag{21}$$

$$\alpha = 2Q_2 \left\{ 1 - \left( 3C - 4\frac{k_t}{k_s} - 2\frac{k_c}{k_s}\frac{P}{P_c} \right) 4\frac{P}{P_c} \right\}^{1/4} \tag{22}$$

$$m = \frac{P}{P_c} \left[ 1 + \frac{k_c}{k_s} \left( 1 - \frac{P^2}{P_c^2} \right) + \left( C - \frac{k_t}{k_s} \right) 2\frac{P}{P_c} \right], \tag{23}$$

where the upper sign goes together with the subscript $a$, while the lower sign goes together with the subscript $b$, with $sn(\phi|m)$ being a Jacobi elliptic function,[15] and $P_c = 4Q_2/k_s$. $q(z)$ in (19) is a sign function[5] taken to be 1 or $-1$.

Chen's equations based on the improved coupled-mode theory provide a slightly more accurate description of a NLDC's behavior than that given by Jensen's equations. More detailed comparison will be given in Sec. 4.

### 2.3. *Nonlinear coupled-mode equations derived from the generalized reciprocity relation*[6]

In Jensen's and Chen's formulations the individual waveguide mode fields are assumed to be those of the linear waveguide ones so that the coupling coefficient becomes a constant independent of the input power. This is only an approximation since the field distribution in the nonlinear waveguide should depend on the optical power. Taking this power-dependent field distribution into account, all of the coefficients in the coupled-mode equations should be power dependent. Meng and Okamoto[6] derived improved nonlinear coupled-mode equations with power-dependent coefficients for the NLDC based on the generalized reciprocity relation. The equations thus derived are given in the following:

$$-j\left(\frac{dA}{dz} + C\frac{dB}{dz}\right) = (Q_1 - k_s)A + (Q_2 - k_t)B + \left(k_s|A|^2 + 2k_c|B|^2\right)A$$
$$+ \left(2k_t|A|^2 + k_t|B|^2\right)B + k_t A^2 B^* + k_c A^* B^2 \qquad (24)$$

$$-j\left(\frac{dB}{dz} + C\frac{dA}{dz}\right) = (Q_1 - k_s)B + (Q_2 - k_t)A + \left(k_s|B|^2 + 2k_c|A|^2\right)B$$
$$+ \left(2k_t|B|^2 + k_t|A|^2\right)A + k_t B^2 A^* + k_c B^* A^2. \qquad (25)$$

In (24) and (25)

$$P = \frac{1}{2}\int_{-\infty}^{\infty}\int_{-\infty}^{\infty} \hat{z}\cdot\left[\bar{e}_t^{(u)} \times \bar{h}_t^{(u)}\right] dx\,dy \quad u = a,b \qquad (26)$$

$$C = \frac{1}{2P}\int_{-\infty}^{\infty}\int_{-\infty}^{\infty} \hat{z}\cdot\left[\bar{e}_t^{(a)} \times \bar{h}_t^{(b)}\right] dx\,dy \qquad (27)$$

$$Q_1 = \frac{\omega}{4P}\int_{-\infty}^{\infty}\int_{-\infty}^{\infty} (\Delta\epsilon_L + \Delta\epsilon_{NL})\left|\bar{e}_t^{(a)}\right|^2 dx\,dy \qquad (28)$$

$$Q_2 = \frac{\omega}{4P}\int_{-\infty}^{\infty}\int_{-\infty}^{\infty} (\Delta\epsilon_L + \Delta\epsilon_{NL})\left|\bar{e}_t^{(a)}\right|\left|\bar{e}_t^{(b)}\right| dx\,dy \qquad (29)$$

$$k_s = \frac{\omega\epsilon_0}{4P}\int_{-\infty}^{\infty}\int_{-\infty}^{\infty} \alpha\left|\bar{e}_t^{(a)}\right|^4 dx\,dy \qquad (30)$$

$$k_c = \frac{\omega\epsilon_0}{4P}\int_{-\infty}^{\infty}\int_{-\infty}^{\infty} \alpha\left|\bar{e}_t^{(a)}\right|^2\left|\bar{e}_t^{(b)}\right|^2 dx\,dy \qquad (31)$$

97

$$K_t = \frac{\omega \epsilon_0}{4P} \int_{-\infty}^{\infty} \int_{-\infty}^{\infty} \alpha \left| \bar{e}_t^{(a)} \right|^3 \left| \bar{e}_t^{(b)} \right| dx\, dy \,, \tag{32}$$

where $\Delta\epsilon_L = \epsilon_L - \epsilon_L^{(a)}$, $\Delta\epsilon_{NL} = \epsilon_0(\alpha - \alpha^{(a)})\left|\bar{e}_t^{(a)}\right|^2$, and $P$ denotes the power in the isolated guide "$a$" or "$b$". The model amplitudes $A(z)$ and $B(z)$ in (24) and (25) are those in (1) and (2) except that when the fields in the NLDC are approximated as a linear combination of the fields in isolated nonlinear guides "$a$" and "$b$" as in (1) and (2), $\bar{e}_t^{(u)}$ and $\bar{h}_t^{(u)}$, $u = a, b$, now represent nonlinear guided mode fields which depend on the power flux in the guide. Note that the coupled-mode equations (24) and (25) are a little different from those presented by Meng and Okamoto[6] who have used a power conservation relation $|A(z)|^2 + |B(z)|^2 = 1$. If we add this relation into (24) and (25), similar equations will be obtained.

If the two guides are not very closely coupled, $C$ can be neglected. Also if the input is launched into only guide "$a$" of the NLDC, then the power guided in waveguide "$a$", $P_a(z) = |A(z)|^2 P$, can be obtained as:

$$P_a = \begin{cases} P\left\{1 + cn\left[2Q_2(4\zeta\eta + 1)^{1/4}z|m\right]\right\}/2 & m \leq 1 \\ P\left\{1 + dn\left[2Q_2(\zeta(\zeta - \eta)^{1/2}z|m^{-1}\right]\right\}/2 & m > 1 \,, \end{cases} \tag{33}$$

where

$$\zeta = (k_s - k_c)/(4Q_2) \tag{34}$$

$$\eta = k_c/(2Q_2) \tag{35}$$

$$m = \zeta(\zeta - \eta) \tag{36}$$

and $dn(\phi|m)$ is a Jacobi elliptic function.[15]

The major difference between the nonlinear coupled-mode equations based on the reciprocity relation here and those based on the perturbation method as obtained in Jensen's and Chen's formulations lies in that all the coefficients of the nonlinear coupled equations are calculated using nonlinear guided modes in the former, but linear guided modes in the latter. Thus the Jensen's and Chen's theories are valid only for low power levels at which the field distribution is almost not affected by the optically induced refractive index change. Comparison of results predicted by these different theories will be discussed in Sec. 4.

## 3. The Segmentation Method

In reality the total input power $P$ will distribute to waveguide "$a$" and waveguide "$b$" in the coupling region. The guided powers of these two guides, $P_a(z)$ and $P_b(z)$, must satisfy $0 \leq P_a(z) \leq P$ and $0 \leq P_b(z) \leq P$. In Chen's Analysis[5] the coefficients in the nonlinear coupled mode equations are calculated by using linear guided modes which are evaluated at $P_a(z) = 0$ and $P_b(z) = 0$, leading to underestimation of the nonlinear effect. Although nonlinear guided modes are considered in Meng and

Okamoto's analysis,[6] their modes are evaluated at $P_a(z) = P$ and $P_b(z) = P$, leading to a possible overestimation of the nonlinear effect. To take into account the more realistic nonlinear effect relevant to the division of the total power into the respective waveguides, we propose an adiabatic approach, in which the whole nonlinear system structure is divided into a series of segments, and each segment is treated as a linear structure. This method, called the "segmentation method", is simple and easy to implement, and will be more suitable for analyzing nonlinear coupled waveguide systems with complicated structures. The analysis procedure is described as follows.

Consider a nonlinear coupled system, as shown in Fig. 2(a). The refractive index is again assumed to be $n = n_L + n_{NL}I$. To analyze the behavior of the nonlinear system, the waveguides are divided into a series of segments along the propagation

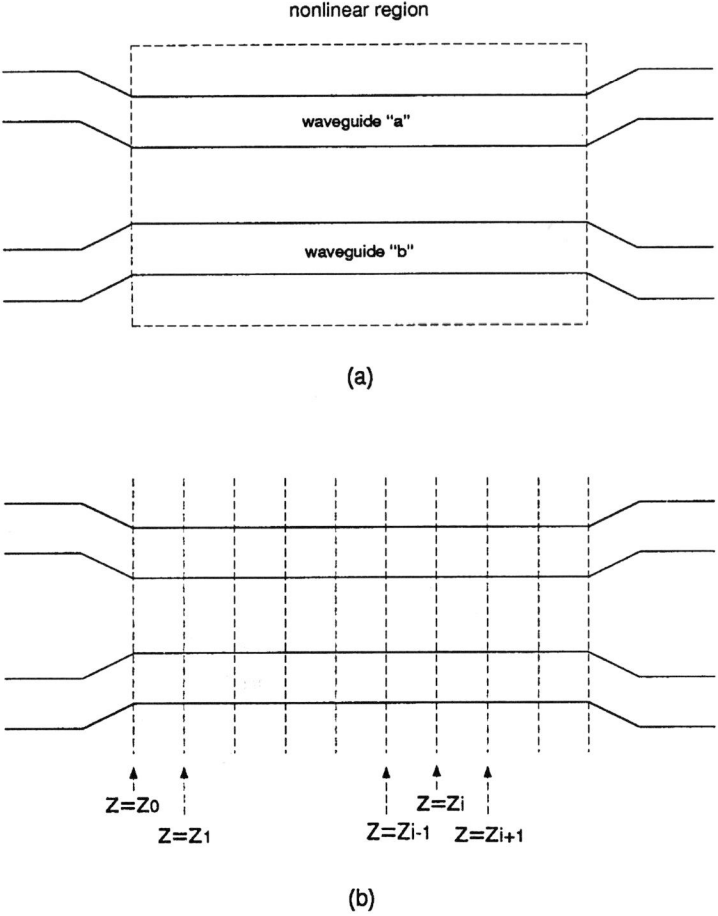

Fig. 2. (a) Schematic of an integrated optic nonlinear directional coupler. (b) Diagram showing that the nonlinear coupler in (a) is modeled as a series of short sections with boundary at $z = z_i$, $i$ being an integer.

direction as shown in Fig. 2(b). According to the nonlinear property, as the field propagates, the refractive index profile of the whole system will vary from place to place, owing to the variation of the local optical intensity distribution. This makes the composite structure a complicated one.

Consider one of the segments, say, the $i$th segment. When the field is launched into the $i$th segment, the refractive index profile at the input end of this segment could be obtained from the local optical intensity at the same end from the nonlinear property of the material $n = n_L + n_{NL}I$ in the present case. Essentially, due to the propagation variation of the field, the refractive-index profile at any cross section along the propagation direction of this segment will not be the same as that at the input end of the segment. But, they can be assumed to be the same, if the segmentation number is large enough, or the length of each segment is small enough.

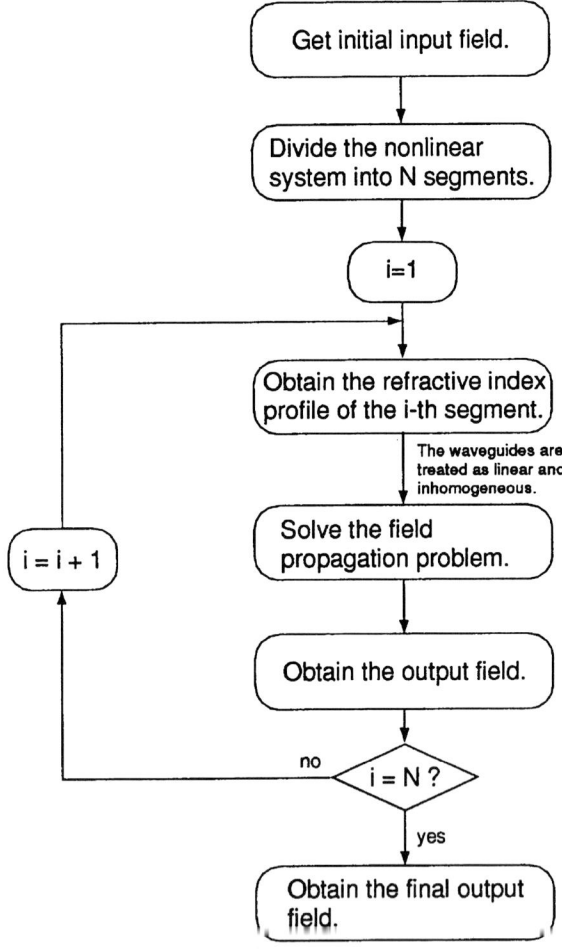

Fig. 3. Flow chart for the segmentation method.

Under this assumption, as long as the refractive index profile at the input end of the $i$th segment is obtained, this segment can be treated as power independent, i.e. the waveguides of the $i$th segment become linear but inhomogeneous in the transverse plane. So, the propagation of field through that segment could be solved by any linear theory, for example, the coupled-mode theory or the normal mode theory. When the output field of the $i$th segment is obtained, it is passed into the $(i+1)$th segment as its input field and the refractive-index profile of the $(i+1)$th segment is calculated. Then the field propagation is solved, and the output of the $(i+1)$th segment is passed into the $(i+2)$th segment, and so on. The procedure is repeated segment by segment, until the output end of the entire system is reached. To summarize this algorithm, a flow chart which explains the method is shown in Fig. 3.

According to the idea described above, some method is needed to solve the wave propagation problem in the linear segment. Two theories are used here, the coupled-mode theory and the normal mode theory.

### 3.1. *Segmentation method with the coupled-mode analysis*

The single-mode waveguide coupler is considered here. If the coupled-mode theory is chosen to solve the linear part of the problem, then the procedure to solve the propagation problem of a NLDC is as follows. The transverse components of the systems total electric and magnetic fields are expressed as linear combinations of the transverse modal amplitudes of the guided modes on guides "$a$" and "$b$" as

$$\bar{E}_t(x, y, z) = A(z)\bar{e}_t^{(a)}(x, y) + B(z)\bar{e}_t^{(b)}(x, y) \tag{37}$$

$$\bar{H}_t(x, y, z) = A(z)\bar{h}_t^{(a)}(x, y) + B(z)\bar{h}_t^{(b)}(x, y), \tag{38}$$

where $A(z)$ and $B(z)$ are the partition modal amplitudes[14] of guides "$a$" and "$b$", respectively. The coupling between these two dielectric waveguides can be described by the following coupled-mode equations[10,12]

$$\frac{dA(z)}{dz} = j\gamma_a A(z) + j\kappa_{ab}B(z) \tag{39}$$

$$\frac{dB(z)}{dz} = j\kappa_{ba}A(z) + j\gamma_b B(z), \tag{40}$$

where

$$\gamma_a = \beta_a + \frac{\tilde{K}_{aa} - \tilde{K}_{ab}\bar{C}}{1 - \bar{C}^2} \tag{41}$$

$$\gamma_b = \beta_b + \frac{\tilde{K}_{bb} - \tilde{K}_{ba}\bar{C}}{1 - \bar{C}^2} \tag{42}$$

are the modified propagation constants with $\beta_a$ and $\beta_b$ being the propagation constants of the waveguide modes of guides "$a$" and "$b$", respectively, and

$$\kappa_{ab} = \frac{\tilde{K}_{ba} - \tilde{K}_{bb}\bar{C}}{1 - \bar{C}^2} \tag{43}$$

$$\kappa_{ba} = \frac{\tilde{K}_{ab} - \tilde{K}_{aa}\bar{C}}{1 - \bar{C}^2} \tag{44}$$

are the modified coupling coefficients. The butt-coupling coefficient $\bar{C}$ is defined by $\bar{C} = \frac{1}{2}(C_{ab} + C_{ba})$ where

$$C_{uv} = \frac{1}{2} \int_{-\infty}^{\infty} \int_{-\infty}^{\infty} \hat{z} \cdot \left[ \bar{e}_t^{(u)} \times \bar{h}_t^{(v)} \right] dx\, dy \quad u, v = a, b \tag{45}$$

with the fields being normalized such that $C_{aa} = C_{bb} = 1$. Furthermore, $\tilde{K}_{uv}$ is defined by

$$\tilde{K}_{uv} = \frac{\omega}{4} \int_{-\infty}^{\infty} \int_{-\infty}^{\infty} \left( \epsilon - \epsilon^{(u)} \right) \left[ \bar{e}_t^{(u)} \cdot \bar{e}_t^{(v)} - \frac{\epsilon^{(v)}}{\epsilon} \bar{e}_z^{(u)} \cdot \bar{e}_z^{(v)} \right] dx\, dy \quad u, v = a, b. \tag{46}$$

The transverse component of the electric field at the input end of the system $z = z_0$ can be represented as the superposition of the linear guided modes of waveguides "$a$" and "$b$" as

$$\bar{E}_t(x, y, z_0) = A(z_0) \bar{e}_{t, n_{NL}=0}^{(a)}(x, y, z_0) + B(z_0) \bar{e}_{t, n_{NL}=0}^{(b)}(x, y, z_0),$$

where $\bar{e}_{t, n_{NL}=0}^{(a)}(x, y, z_0)$ and $\bar{e}_{t, n_{NL}=0}^{(b)}(x, y, z_0)$ are the linear local waveguide modes of waveguides "$a$" and "$b$" with nonlinearity $n_{NL}$ set to zero. First, the nonlinear coupler is divided into $N$ segments, where $N$ is the segmentation number. If the input field is given as in (47), then the refractive index profile of the first segment $n(x, y, z_0)$ can be obtained through the nonlinearity relation such as that for the Kerr media: $n = n_L + n_{NL} I$. Having obtained the refractive-index profile, the local waveguide modes of the first segment, $\bar{e}_t^{(a)}(x, y, z_0)$ and $\bar{e}_t^{(b)}(x, y, z_0)$, are found. The coefficients of the coupled-mode equations which describe the propagation in the first segment can be obtained by Eqs. (41)–(46). By solving the linear coupled-mode equations (39) and (40), the modal amplitudes at the end of the first segment, $A(z_1)$ and $B(z_1)$, can be obtained. Thus we can construct the field at the beginning of the second segment as $\bar{E}_t(x, y, z_1) = A(z_1) \bar{e}_t^{(a)}(x, y, z_0) + B(z_1) \bar{e}_t^{(b)}(x, y, z_0)$. Then the refractive-index profile of the second segment $n(x, y, z_1)$ can be obtained by the field at the beginning of this segment $\bar{E}_t(x, y, z_1)$. The local waveguide modes are found, and the coefficients of the coupled mode equations are calculated. Then these equations are solved and the modal amplitudes at the end of the second segment can be obtained. Following this procedure, the process iterates until the modal amplitudes of the last segment, i.e. the $N$th segment, $A(z_N)$ and $B(z_N)$ are obtained. Then the output field of the NLDC can be constructed as $\bar{E}(x, y, z_N) = A(z_N)\bar{e}_t^{(a)}(x, y, z_{N-1}) + B(z_N)\bar{e}_t^{(b)}(x, y, z_{N-1})$.

### 3.2. *Segmentation method with the normal mode analysis*

If the theory chosen to describe the wave propagation in the linear segment is the normal mode theory, the procedure to deal with an NLDC is simpler. We assume the coupler is composed of single-mode waveguides again, so the transverse component of the system total electric field could be represented as

$$\bar{E}_t(x, y, z) = A_s(z)\bar{e}_{st}(x, y, z)\exp\left(j\beta_s z\right) + A_a(z)\bar{e}_{at}(x, y, z)\exp\left(j\beta_a z\right), \quad (48)$$

where $\bar{e}_{st}(x, y, z)$ and $\bar{e}_{at}(x, y, z)$ are the symmetric (or symmetric-like) and anti-symmetric (or anti-symmetric-like) normal modes of the system, $\beta_s$ and $\beta_a$ are the corresponding propagation constants, and $A(z)$ and $B(z)$ are the corresponding modal amplitudes. Note that in (48) only the guided modes are considered. As with the coupled-mode analysis, we divide the NLDC into $N$ segments. The field launched at the beginning of the NLDC $z = z_0$ is given by $\bar{E}_t(x, y, z_0) = A_s(z_0)\bar{e}_{st,n_{NL}=0}(x, y, z_0) + A_a(z_0)\bar{e}_{at,n_{NL}=0}(x, y, z_0)$, where $\bar{e}_{st,n_{NL}=0}(x, y, z_0)$ and $\bar{e}_{at,n_{NL}=0}(x, y, z_0)$ are the linear normal modes with $n_{NL} = 0$. The index profile of the first segment $n(x, y, z_0)$ is obtained through the nonlinearity relation. Then the normal modes of the first segment, $\bar{e}_{st}(x, y, z_0)$ and $\bar{e}_{at}(x, y, z_0)$, and the corresponding propagation constants, $\beta_s(z_0)$ and $\beta_a(z_0)$, are calculated. Thus the field propagating in the first segment can be described as

$$\bar{E}_t(x, y, z) = A_s(z_i)\bar{e}_{st}(x, y, z_i)\exp\left[j\beta_s(z_i)z\right]$$
$$+ A_a(z_i)\bar{e}_{at}(x, y, z_i)\exp\left[j\beta_a(z_i)z\right] \quad z_i \le z \le z_{i+1} \quad (49)$$

with $i = 0$. The total electric field at the end of the first segment $z = z_1$ is

$$\bar{E}_t(x, y, z_i) = A_s(z_i)\bar{e}_{st}(x, y, z_{i-1}) + A_a(z_i)\bar{e}_{at}(x, y, z_{i-1}), \quad (50)$$

where

$$A_s(z_i) = A_s(z_{i-1})\exp\left[j\beta_s(z_{i-1})\Delta z_i\right] \quad (51)$$

$$A_a(z_i) = A_a(z_{i-1})\exp\left[j\beta_a(z_{i-1})\Delta z_i\right] \quad (52)$$

and

$$\Delta z_i = z_i - z_{i-1} \quad (53)$$

with $i = 1$. When $\bar{E}_t(x, y, z_1)$ is calculated, the refractive index profile of the second segment, $n(x, y, z_1)$, can also be obtained. Then the system normal modes and the corresponding propagation constants are thus solved, and the field travelling in the second segment is expressed as (49) with $i = 1$, where $\bar{e}_{st}(x, y, z_1), \bar{e}_{at}(x, y, z_1)$ and $\beta_s(z_1), \beta_a(z_1)$ are the normal modes and the corresponding propagation constants solved with the refractive-index profile $n(x, y, z_1)$, respectively. The field at the end of the second segment is similar to (50), with $i$ set to 2. The process iterates until the end of the last segment is reached.

## 4. Numerical Examples and Discussions: Comparison of Different Analysis Methods

In this section the behavior of the NLDC is investigated numerically. The NLDC to be analyzed is composed of two slab waveguides. The nonlinear material will be introduced in the films (i.e. the guiding layers). Results obtained from various nonlinear coupled-mode equations and from the segmentation methods are compared. We examine TE-wave propagation only.

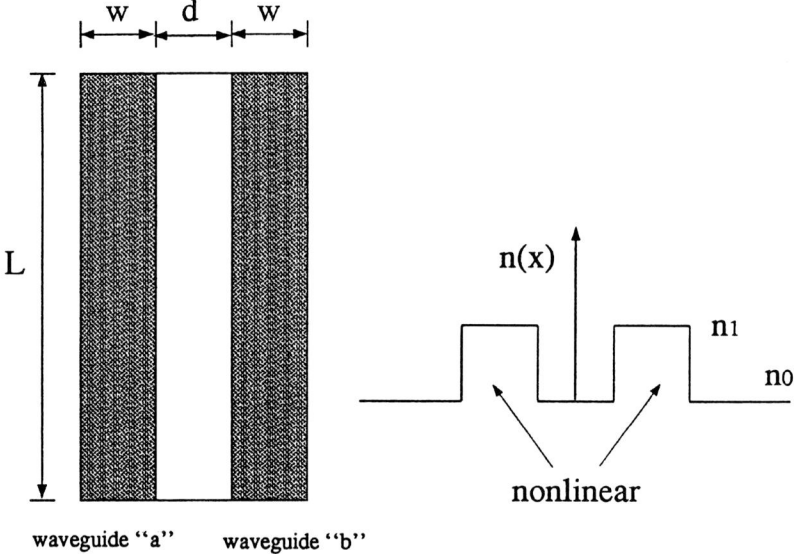

Fig. 4. Sketch of a directional coupler with the guiding layers being nonlinear.

The geometry of the NLDC adopted here is shown in Fig. 4. This coupler is composed of two identical nonlinear films bounded by linear media. The waveguides are 3 $\mu$m in thickness, and are 3 $\mu$m apart. The linear refractive index of the films and the cladding are $n_1 = 1.525$ and $n_0 = 1.52$, respectively. The nonlinearity is assumed to be of the Kerr type with the nonlinear coefficient $n_{1NL} = 10^{-9} \text{m}^2/\text{W}$. The wavelength of light signal is assumed to be 1.0 $\mu$m. The optical power is launched from waveguide "$a$". The length of the coupling region is taken to be 4 mm.

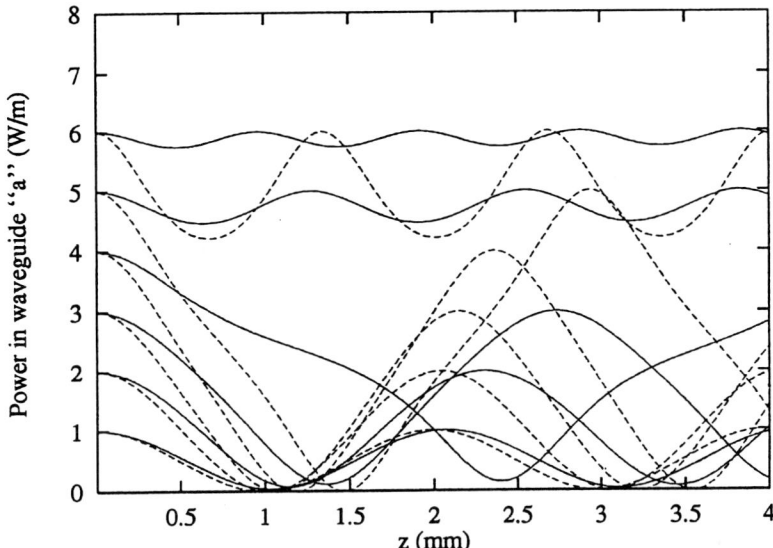

Fig. 5. The amount of power remaining in guide "*a*" as a function of the distance along the nonlinear coupler of Fig. 4. Solid curves: Chen's analysis;[5] dashed curves: Jensen's analysis.[2]

Figure 5 shows the numerical results obtained from Jensen's equations, (4) and (5), and Chen's equations, (15) and (16). The amount of power remaining in guide "*a*" is plotted as a function of the length along the nonlinear coupler shown in Fig. 4. The solid curves and the dashed curves correspond to Chen's and Jensen's analyses, respectively. The same differences between the two sets of results as pointed out by Chen[5] are seen in this figure. These differences, from the viewpoint of Chen's analysis, include three features: first, the critical power (defined as the input power level at which the coupling length becomes infinity and over which the complete power transfer between two guides becomes impossible) is lower; second, the period of power transfer is larger in the low power region; third, at high power (larger than the critical power), both the period of power exchange and the amount of maximum power transfer are smaller. These three features will be used to characterize the differences between different analyses.

Results obtained from Meng and Okamoto's improved equations, (24) and (25), (solid curves) are plotted with those from Chen's equations (dashed curves) in Fig. 6 for comparison. At low power, the results they predict are closely matched, with the coupling length in Meng and Okamoto's analysis a little smaller. As the power gets larger, the difference becomes more obvious. The critical power predicted by Meng and Okamoto's equations is lower than that predicted by Chen's equations, and in the high power region the period of power exchange in Meng and Okamoto's analysis is smaller. Note that in Meng and Okamoto's analysis all the coefficients in the nonlinear coupled equations are calculated using the nonlinear waveguide

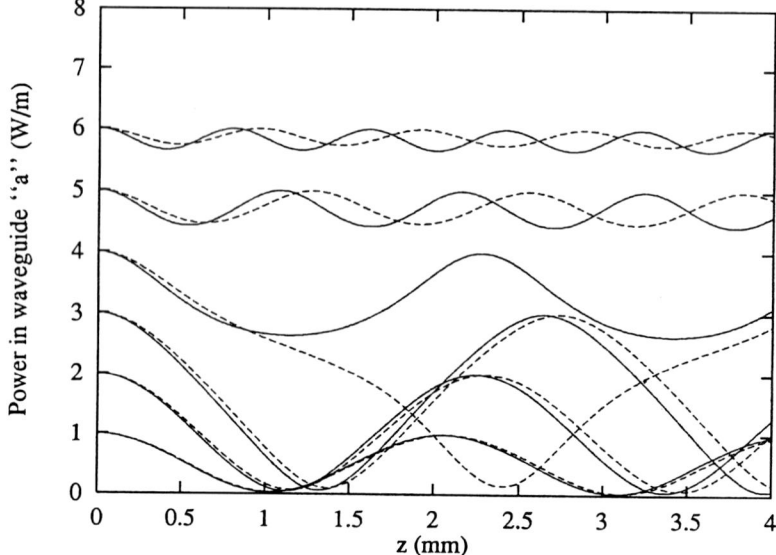

Fig. 6. The amount of power remaining in guide "a" as a function of the distance along the nonlinear coupler of Fig. 4. Solid curves: Meng and Okamoto's analysis;[6] dashed curves: Chen's analysis.[5]

modes, while in Chen's analysis only linear waveguide modes are used. Therefore, Meng and Okamoto's equations would emphasize the nonlinearity more in the high power region.

The results obtained by our segmentation method are given in Fig. 7. Both the coupled-mode analysis and the normal mode analysis are shown. The behaviors predicted by the two versions of the segmentation method agree very well with each other. To corroborate the validity of our numerical scheme, numerical results are compared with those of Chen's and Meng and Okamoto's equations. Only the segmentation method with the coupled-mode analysis is used for comparison since the results obtained by the coupled-mode and the normal mode analyses are almost indistinguishable as has been seen in Fig. 7. Figure 8 compares the results of the segmentation method (solid curves) and Chen's equations (dashed curves). The critical power predicted by the segmentation method is lower than that by Chen's analysis. In the low power region the results are quite close. In the high power region the power transfer periods of the segmentation method are smaller than those of Chen's analysis. These features suggest that the segmentation method emphasizes the nonlinearity more than Chen's analysis does. This is expected because, as we stated earlier, linear waveguide modes are used in Chen's analysis, but modes in the segmentation method are obtained from segment to segment, which could properly reflect the (nonlinear) variation of the refractive indices due to the propagation of light.

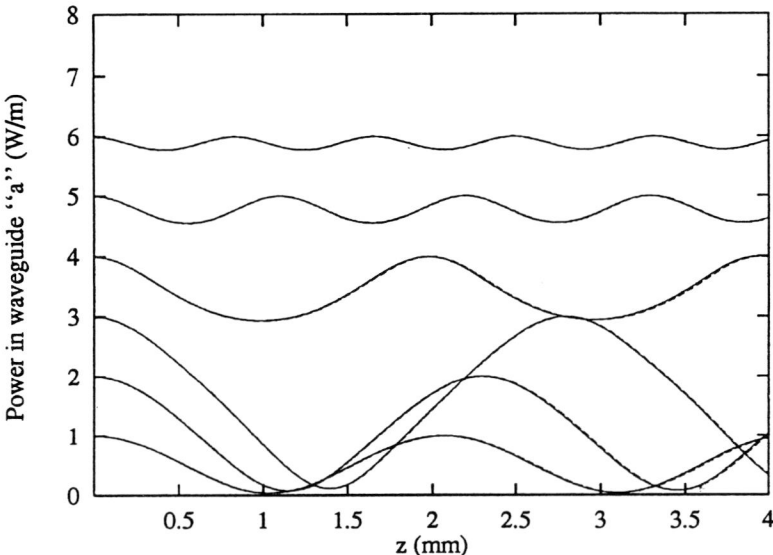

Fig. 7. The amount of power remaining in guide "*a*" calculated using the segmentation method as a function of the distance along the nonlinear coupler of Fig. 4. Solid curves: the coupled-mode analysis; dashed curves: the normal mode analysis.

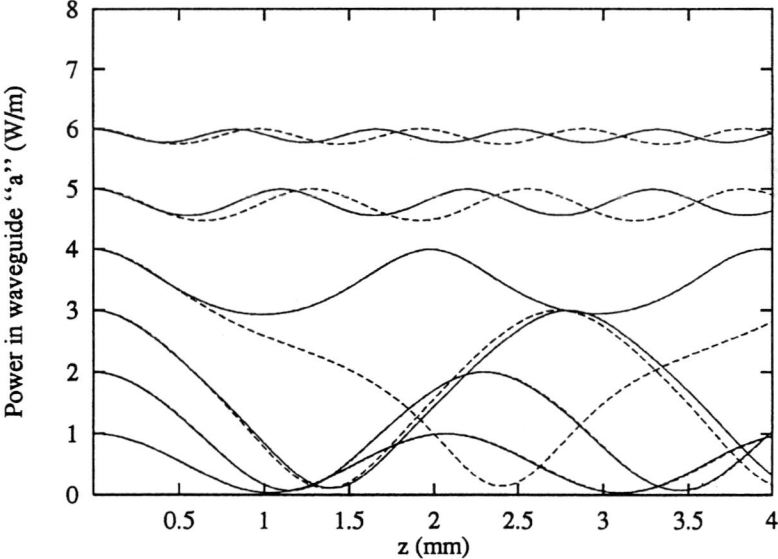

Fig. 8. The amount of power remaining in guide "*a*" as a function of the distance along the nonlinear coupler of Fig. 4. Solid curves: the segmentation method using the coupled-mode analysis; dashed curves: Chen's analysis.[5]

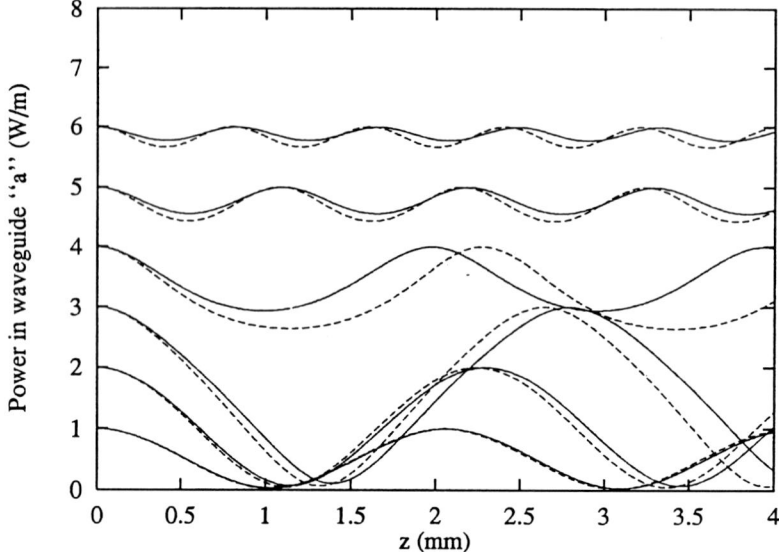

Fig. 9.  The amount of power remaining in guide "*a*" as a function of the distance along the nonlinear coupler of Fig. 4.  Solid curves: the segmentation method using the coupled-mode analysis; dashed curves: Meng and Okamoto's analysis.[6]

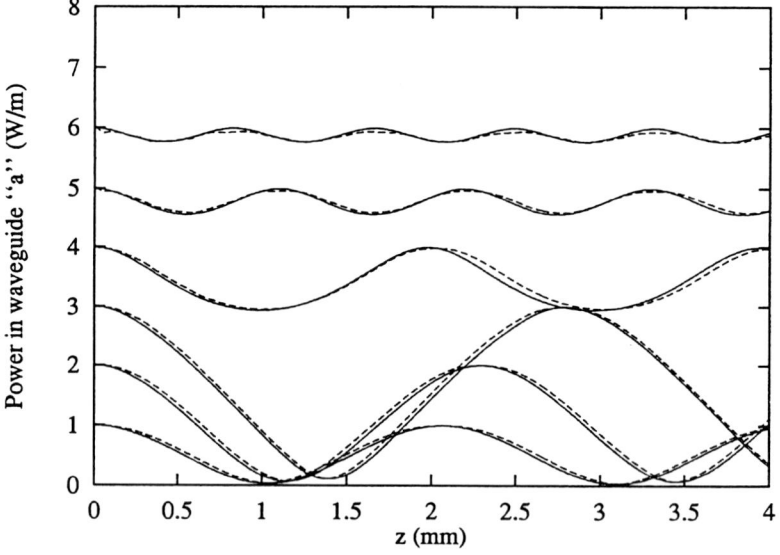

Fig. 10.  The amount of power remaining in guide "*a*" as a function of the distance along the nonlinear coupler of Fig. 4.  Solid curves: the segmentation method using the coupled-mode analysis; dashed curves: the beam propagation method.

Results obtained by the segmentation method (solid curves) and Meng and Okamoto's analysis (dashed curves) are compared in Fig. 9. In the low power region the coupling lengths of the segmentation method are larger. In the high power region the two results are much closer. Moreover, the critical power does not seem to differ much between the two analyses. These features show that Meng and Okamoto's analysis is much closer to that using the segmentation method as compared to the other two coupler-mode formulations.

To have a further check of our segmentation method, results obtained by the segmentation method are compared with those obtained using the (finite-difference) beam propagation method[16] in Fig. 10. As can be seen from this figure, not only the periods of the power transfer in the low power region but also those in the high power region are quite close. This further establishes the corroboration of our segmentation method.

As stated at the beginning of Sec. 3, a total input power $P$ will distribute to guides "$a$" and "$b$" with the guided powers of these two guides, $P_a(z)$ and $P_b(z)$, satisfying $0 \leq P_a(z) \leq P$ and $0 \leq P_b(z) \leq P$. In Chen's analysis the coefficients in the nonlinear coupled-mode equations are calculated using linear guided modes which are evaluated at $P_a(z) = 0$ and $P_b(z) = 0$, being only an approximation of the real situation. Although nonlinear guided modes are considered in Meng and Okamoto's analysis, their modes are evaluated at $P_a(z) = P$ and $P_b(z) = P$, being also an approximation. Our segmentation method is based on the adiabatic approximation and the guided modes are evaluated at the beginning of each segment, where the refractive index profile is adjusted according to the power distribution variation along the propagation direction. Thus, the results obtained by the segmentation method should be more accurate than those of Chen's and Meng and Okamoto's analyses.

## 5. Conclusions

We have reviewed the formulations of three prior coupled-mode theories for the NLDC and proposed the segmentation method as a more accurate analysis method. A NLDC composed of two Kerr-type nonlinear guiding slabs has been used as a numerical example for comparing the predictions of the NLDC behavior by the different coupled-mode formulations and the segmentation method. The original Jensen's formulation[2] is the most simplified and the least accurate. The improved set of nonlinear coupled-mode equations derived by Chen[5] include the nonlinear coupling terms and the butt-coupling terms but are with coefficients evaluated using linear guided mode fields. On the other hand, although nonlinear guided mode fields are considered in Meng and Okamoto's improved analysis,[6] the modes are evaluated using the fixed total input power. In a real situation, the local nonlinear guided modes will vary along the propagation direction due to the accompanying variation in the local power distribution. Our segmentation method takes such real situations into account under an adiabatic approximation and thus should be more accurate than the other three coupled-mode theories. Meng and Okamoto's analysis is seen to provide results closest to our analysis.

## Acknowledgment

This work was supported in part by the National Science Council of the Republic of China under grant NSC81-0417-E002-03.

## References

1. S. M. Jensen, "The nonlinear coherent coupler a new optical logical device", presented at *Conf. Integrated and Guided-Wave Opt.*, Incline Village, CA, 1980.
2. S. M. Jensen, "The nonlinear coherent coupler", *IEEE J. Quantum Electron.* **QE-18** (1982) 1580–1583.
3. B. Daino, G. Gregori, and S. Wabnitz, "Stability analysis of nonlinear coherent coupling", *J. Appl. Phys.* **58** (1985) 4512–4514.
4. S. Trillo and S. Wabnitz, "Nonlinear nonreciprocity in a coherent mismatched directional coupler", *Appl. Phys. Lett.* **49** (1986) 752–754.
5. Y. Chen, "Solution to full coupled wave equations of nonlinear coupled systems", *IEEE J. Quantum Electron.* **25** (1989) 2149–2153.
6. X. J. Meng and N. Okamoto, "Improved coupled-mode theory for nonlinear directional couplers", *IEEE J. Quantum Electron.* **27** (1991) 1175–1181.
7. L. Thylen, E. M. Wright, G. I. Stegemen, C. T. Seaton, and J. V. Moloney, "Beam propagation method analysis of a nonlinear directional coupler", *Opt. Lett.* **11** (1986) 739–741.
8. S. Wabnitz, E. M. Wright, C. T. Seaton, and G. I. Stegemen, "Instabilities and all-optical phase-controlled switching in a nonlinear directional coherent coupler", *Appl. Phys. Lett.* **49** (1986) 838–840.
9. M. Cada and J. D. Begin, "An analysis of a planar directional coupler with a lossless Kerr-like coupling medium", *IEEE J. Quantum Electron.* **26** (1990) 361–371.
10. A. Hardy and W. Streifer, "Coupled mode theory of parallel waveguides", *J. Lightwave Technol.* **LT-3** (1985) 1135–1146.
11. E. Marcatili, "Improved coupled-mode equations for dielectric guides", *IEEE J. Quantum Electron.* **QE-22** (1986) 988–993.
12. S. L. Chuang, "A coupled-mode formulation by reciprocity and a variational principle", *J. Lightwave Technol.* **LT-5** (1987) 5–15.
13. H. A. Haus, W. P. Huang, S. Kawakami, and N. A. Whitaker, "Coupled-mode theory of optical waveguides", *J. Lightwave Technol.* **LT-5** (1987) 16–23.
14. H. C. Chang, "Coupled-mode equations for dielectric waveguides based on projection and partition modal amplitudes", *IEEE J. Quantum Electron.* **QE-23** (1987) 1929–1937.
15. M. Abramowitz and I. A. Stegun, *Handbook of Mathematical Functions*, U.S. Government Printing Office, Washington, D. C., 1964.
16. Y. Chung and N. Dagli, "An assessment of finite difference beam propagation method", *IEEE J. Quantum Electron.* **26** (1990) 1335–1339.

International Journal of High Speed Electronics and Systems, Vol. 8, No. 4 (1997) 685–701
© World Scientific Publishing Company

# QUANTUM-MECHANICAL CALCULATIONS OF RESONANT SEMICONDUCTOR DEVICES: A QMWI APPROACH

HSIN-HAN TUNG

*Department of Electrical Engineering,*
*National Lien Ho Junior College of Technology and Commerce,*
*Miao-Li, Taiwan, R.O.C.*

CHIEN-PING LEE

*Department of Electronics Engineering,*
*National Chiao Tung University,*
*Hsin Chu, Taiwan, R.O.C.*

In this paper we describe two novel resonant semiconductor superlattice structures to serve as quantum-mechanical energy band-pass filters. Such structures allow the incident electrons to be nearly totally transmitted when the impinging electron energy is in the passband. On the other hand, a complete reflection occurs when the impinging energy is in the stopband. This special characteristic can be explained using the concept of quantum-mechanical wave impedance (QMWI) matching method. We also study the scattering effects on the transmission spectrum of a resonant tunneling diode (RTD). The resonant time $\tau_{well}$ calculated from QMWI method is compared with the scattering time $\tau_s$ to determine whether the tunneling mechanism is coherent or sequential tunneling.

## 1. Introduction

Semiconductor devices based on the resonant phenomena have been found in many different applications. These include: resonant tunneling diode (RTD),[1] resonant tunneling transistor (RTT),[1] vertical cavity surface-emitting semiconductor laser (VCSEL),[2] resonant-cavity enhanced (RCE) photodetector,[3] modulator,[4] quantum-mechanical energy filter,[5] optical filter,[6] etc. While some of the devices are based on resonances of optical waves, others rely on resonances of electron waves. Basically, the resonant phenomena can be explained in terms of a Fabry-Pèrot mechanism.[7] Physically, what happens is that the amplitude of the resonant modes builds up in the cavity which can be formed by two (effective) parallel plates, to the extent that the waves leaking out in both directions cancel the reflected waves and enhance the transmitted ones, resulting in a high level of transmittivity.

Heterostructure superlattices and their transport properties were first investigated by Esaki and Tsu in 1970.[8] In a superlattice, when the thickness of each individual layer becomes comparable to the carrier de Broglie wavelength, the wavefunctions of the individual wells tend to overlap due to tunneling and an energy miniband is formed. The miniband width is proportional to the tunneling probability through the barriers and can be calculated rigorously by solving the Schrödinger equation.[9] The semiconductor superlattice is an ideal system for studying the band structure and the carrier transport phenomenon. To a large extent, the early research on expitaxial crystal growth were motivated by the concept of band structure engineering; the ability tailor the shapes of the quantum wells and barriers to generate arbitrary bandstructures. Dingle[10] has demonstrated optically that the energy states of coupled wells with a finite number are discrete, but, as the number of coupled wells is increased they become quasi continuous and distributed throughout an energy band.

Recent developments in expitaxial growth technology have made it possible to control the structure, composition, and doping profile to nearly arbitrary precision. Thus one can design structures with energy band gap characteristics and more generally structures exhibiting the desired transport properties for specific applications. Multiple quantum barriers (MQBs) that enhance carrier blocking[11] and resonant tunneling structures that enhance carrier transmission[12] are good examples which demonstrated the current manipulating capability of these structures. S. Y. Yen *et al.*[13] have demonstrated that a superlattice with multiple stacks of quantum barriers can have a very high effective potential barrier. Because of the superposition of the reflectivity spectra of the MQBs, a very wide energy range for electron reflection is obtained. This can provide a good carrier confinement for double heterostructure AlGaInP/GaInP lasers to overcome the problem of carrier leakage and severe sensitivity to temperature.

The MQBs can also be used as an energy filter to allowed the electron to be transmitted when the electron energy lies within the transmission band. However, because of the finite thickness (or number of layers) of the conventional MQBs, the minibands for carrier transmission are not really "flat bands". 100% transmission cannot be achieved for all the energies within the bands. Therefore, transport of carriers with energies in the bands can never be complete. A wavepacket with a finite width or energy impinging upon such a structure will be partially reflected and partially transmitted even if its energy lies within a miniband. Recently we have proposed a new superlattice structure, which has the transmission characteristics and reflection characteristics like a perfect "energy" band-pass filter (EBPF). 100% transmission characteristic and 100% reflection can be obtained when the electron energy lies within the respective bands. The superlattice has a gaussian-function like effective potential envelope and can be realized by two different ways. In this paper we will review the design and the characteristics of these two structures.

Usually, the transmission probability is calculated using the transfer-matrix method, which is derived from the plane wave type solution[14] with assumed boundary conditions. On the other hand, an alternative method for accurately calculating the transmission probability across arbitrary potential barrier was presented by Khondker *et al.*[15] It is based on the concept of wave impedance analogous to the well-developed transmission line theory. The technique can be used for analyzing the resonant tunneling devices[16] and tunneling time calculations.[17,18] The quantum-mechanical wave impedance (QMWI) method will be briefly described and then used to explain the occurrence of total transmission of our proposed structures.

The scattering effects on the transmission characteristics of a resonant tunneling diode are discussed next. Resonant tunneling through a double barrier has been extensively investigated by many researchers.[19–23] Most of these investigations, however, assumed that a Fabry-Pèrot type enhancement of the transmission is operational in such structures. But when the phase coherence of the electrons wave is destroyed by scattering, such transmission enhancement can be considerably weakened, and the electrons must be viewed as tunneling through the barriers "sequentially". Because scatterings are random processes, it is very difficult to quantitatively correlate them with wavefunctions at resonance. In the paper, we employed the Fabry-Pèrot model and Monte Carlo simulation to study the scattering effects on the transmission characteristics of a RTD. At the same time, we also employed the QMWI method to give a quantitative description on whether the tunneling mechanism is coherent tunneling or sequential tunneling. Our approaches can easily include the three-dimensional effect. As we can see in the paper, the three-dimensional effect is important and has to be considered for the broadening of the transmission spectrum.

## 2. Energy Band-Pass Filter

Figures 1(a) and (b) are the schematics of the proposed structures that give energy band-pass filter characteristics. $a$ and $b$ are the widths of the wells and the barriers, respectively and $L$ is the total length of the superlattice. The first structure (Fig. 1(a)) can be considered as a regular superlattice but with the potential modulated by a Gaussian function. The Gaussian function is expressed by $\exp(-x^2/\sigma_s^2)$, where $x$ is the coordinate in the direction normal to the superlattice and $\sigma_s/\sqrt{2}$ is the standard deviation of the Gaussian function. The potential profile can be obtained, for example, by gradually changing the mole fraction in GaAs/AlAs/InGaAs material system. Figure 1(b) shows an alternative way to obtain a similar Gaussian potential profile. The period, $a + b$, is kept constant throughout the structure but the ratio $a/a + b$ is varied according to a modulated Gaussian function. This structure, unlike the first one, has constant barrier heights but variable barrier width. So it can be much more easily realized by expitaxial growth techniques. From the basic quantum theory,[24] we know that when the electrons are moving in a region where the spatial variation of potential is small compared with the electron wavelength, the reflection is expected to be small. By combining a slowly varying potential with a periodic superlattice which exhibits miniband structures, we thereby obtain an energy band-pass filter.

Consider one of the examples with the structure shown in Fig. 1(a). The superlattice is composed of 40 layer-pairs with barrier width $a = 32$ Å and a well width $b = 32$ Å. Thus, the total length of the superlattice $L$ is 2560 Å. The width $\sigma_s$ of the modulating Gaussian function is taken to be $L/4$, and the barrier height $V_0$

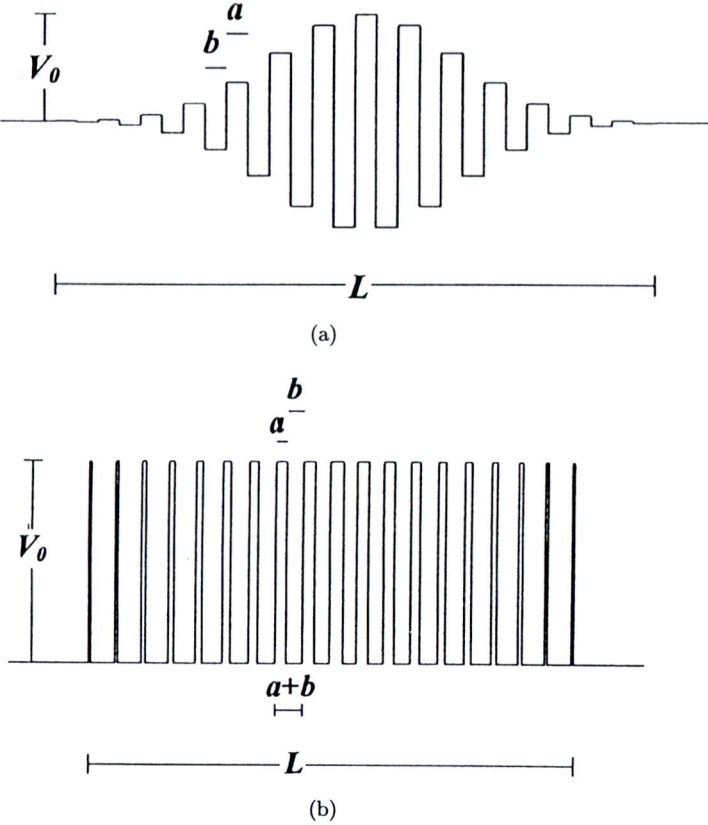

Fig. 1. Schematic conduction-band edge diagram of two different types of EBPFs. (a) The barrier height $V_0$ is modulated by a Gaussian function, (b) The ratio $a/a + b$ is varied according to a modulated Gaussian function.

is 0.45 eV. The effective mass is assumed to be 0.067 $m_0$ throughout the structure, where $m_0$ is the free-electron mass. Figure 2(a) plots the transmission probability calculated by the QMWI method (solid line) which is identical to the one calculated by the transfer-matrix method (circle). This figure shows nearly total transmission when the electron energy is in the range between 0.7 to 1.0 $V_0$ and above 1.7 $V_0$, while the transmission probability is zero when the electron energy lies outside these ranges. The bands are flat and the boundary between the passbands and stopbands are abrupt. This superlattice structure behaves like an energy band-pass filter (EBPF), which is similar to the frequency band-pass filter in circuit theory. This is quite different from the transmission characteristics of other types of superlattice structures. To make a comparison with regular superlattices, we calculate the transmission probability of a rectangular MQWs (multiple quantum wells) superlattice with 40 layer-pairs. The barrier height used here is 0.4 eV, the widths of both barriers and wells are 40 Å. Figure 2(c) shows the calculated transmission probability versus energy. It indicates the existence of allowed minibands. But the transmission probability is not uniformly equal to one within each band. It is obvious that these conventional rectangular MQBs do not have flat passbands as the EBPF does.

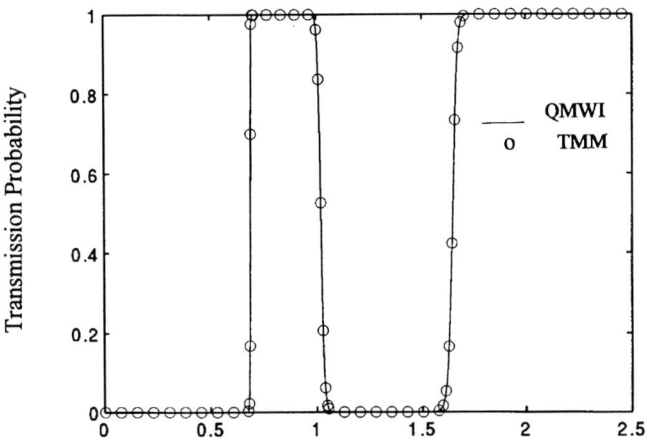

Normalized Incident Electron Energy, ($E/ V_0$)

(a)

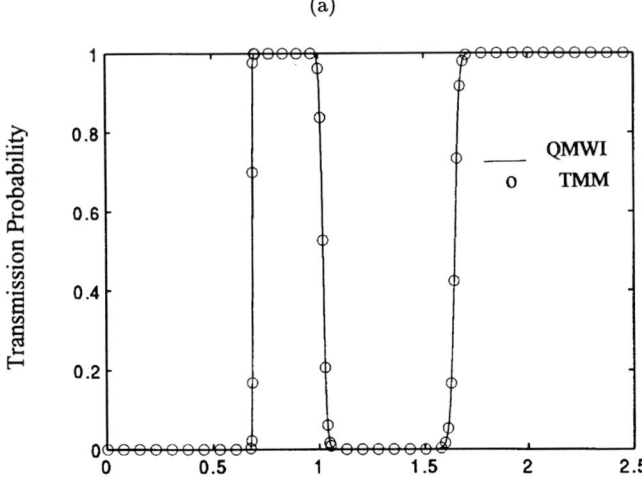

Normalized Incident Electron Energy, ($E/ V_0$)

(b)

Fig. 2. Plot of the transmission probability as a function of normalized incident electron energy for (a) the structure shown in Fig. 1(a), with 40 layer-pairs, (b) the structure shown in Fig. 1(b), where $a + b = 50$ Å, $V_0 = 0.25$ eV, and periods $= 61$, (c) the transmission probability of a conventional MQWs for comparison.

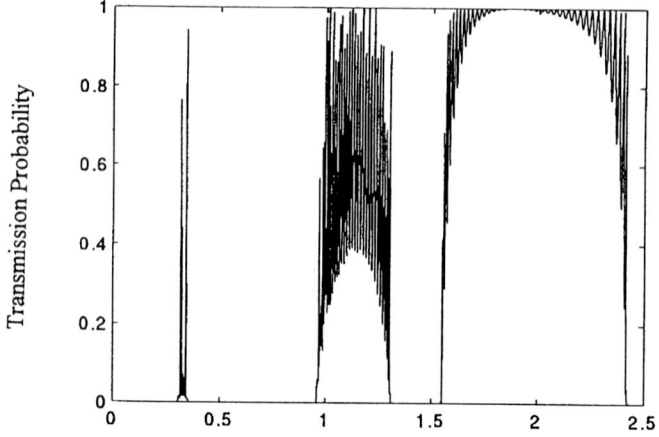

Normalized Incident Electron Energy, $(E/V_0)$

(c)

Fig. 2. (*Continued*)

For the structure shown in Fig. 1(b), we consider a superlattice composed of 61 layer-pairs with a barrier height $V_0 = 0.25$ eV. The period $a+b$ is equal to 50 Å, and the total length of the structure $L$ is 3050 Å. The barrier width is varied gradually according to a Gaussian function $a_i = [(a+b)/2]\exp[-(i-31)^2/2\sigma_x^2]$, where $a_i$ is the width of the $i$th barrier, and $\sigma_x$ is chosen to be 10. The calculated transmission probability by the QMWI method is plotted as a function of the electron energy and is shown in Fig. 2(b). This figure shows nearly total transmission when the electron energy is in the range between 0.5 $V_0$ to 0.8 $V_0$ and above 1.8 $V_0$, while the transmission probability is zero when the electron energy lies outside these ranges. Flat passbands and stopbands also result. So, the second proposed structure can also be used as an energy band-pass filter for electrons.

## 3. Time Evolution of Electron Wavepacket Through EBPF

To further check the concept discussed above, the time evolution of electron wave packet propagating through the first proposed structure is calculated by numerically solving the Schrödinger differential equation.[25] The time-dependent wave equation for a system governed by a time-independent potential $V(x)$ is:

$$-\frac{\hbar^2}{2m}\frac{\partial^2\Psi}{\partial x^2} + V(x)\Psi(x,t) = i\hbar\frac{\partial\Psi}{\partial t}, \qquad (1)$$

where $\Psi(x,t)$ is the electron wave function, $m$ is the effective mass of electron, and $\hbar$ is the Planck's constant. For ease of writing, we work in a system of units in which the mass $m = 1/2$ and $\hbar = 1$. Then Eq. (1) becomes

$$-\frac{\partial^2 \Psi}{\partial x^2} + V(x)\Psi(x,t) = i\frac{\partial \Psi}{\partial t}. \tag{2}$$

It should be noted that the unit for potential energy $V(x)$ now has to be multiplied by the factor $2m/\hbar^2$. Equation (2) can be transformed into a set of differential equations:

$$\Psi_{j+1}^{n+1} + \left(i\frac{2\varepsilon^2}{\delta} - \varepsilon^2 V_j - 2\right)\Psi_j^{n+1} + \Psi_{j-1}^{n+1}$$

$$= -\Psi_{j+1}^n + \left(i\frac{2\varepsilon^2}{\delta} + \varepsilon^2 V_j + 2\right)\Psi_j^n - \Psi_{j-1}^n, \tag{3}$$

where

$$n = 1, 2, 3, \ldots N,$$

$$\Psi_j^n = \Psi(x_j, t_n),$$

$$V_j = V(x_j),$$

$$\delta = t_n - t_{n-1} \quad \text{for all } n,$$

$$\varepsilon = x_j - x_{j-1} \quad \text{for all } j,$$

$$j = 1, 2, 3, \ldots J.$$

The differential equation is then rewritten in the form of a difference equation in a finite space-time grid. This difference equation is stable and unitary, but implicit. Equation (3) is solved with the initial condition:

$$\Psi(x,0) = e^{ik_0 x}e^{-(x-x_0)^2/2\sigma_0^2}.$$

We see that this packet is centered about $x = x_0$ with a spread in $x$ governed by $\sigma_0$. The factor $e^{ik_0 x}$ makes our initial wave function move to the right with an average momentum $\hbar k_0$, where $k_0$ is equal to $\sqrt{2mE}/\hbar$ and $E$ is the average energy of the electron wavepacket. We imagine that the physical system with which we work is situated in a large (one-dimensional) "bot", and that the wave function for the system must vanish on the "walls" of the box. Thus our boundary conditions may be stated in the form

$$\Psi_0^n = \Psi_j^n = 0 \quad \text{for all } n.$$

The criteria for a suitable choice of input parameters are given by Goldberger et al.[25] Figure 3(a) shows the time series of a Gaussian wavepacket impinging upon the first proposed EBPF which have the same structure as that used for Fig. 2(a).

117

The average incident energy of the wavepacket is chosen to be 0.425 $V_0$, and the spread of the packet, $\sigma_0$ is 400 Å, which corresponds to an energy uncertainty of about 0.023 eV. From Fig. 2(a) we know that the energy of the wavepacket lies within the stopband of the EBPF. Figure 3(a) shows clearly that the wavepacket

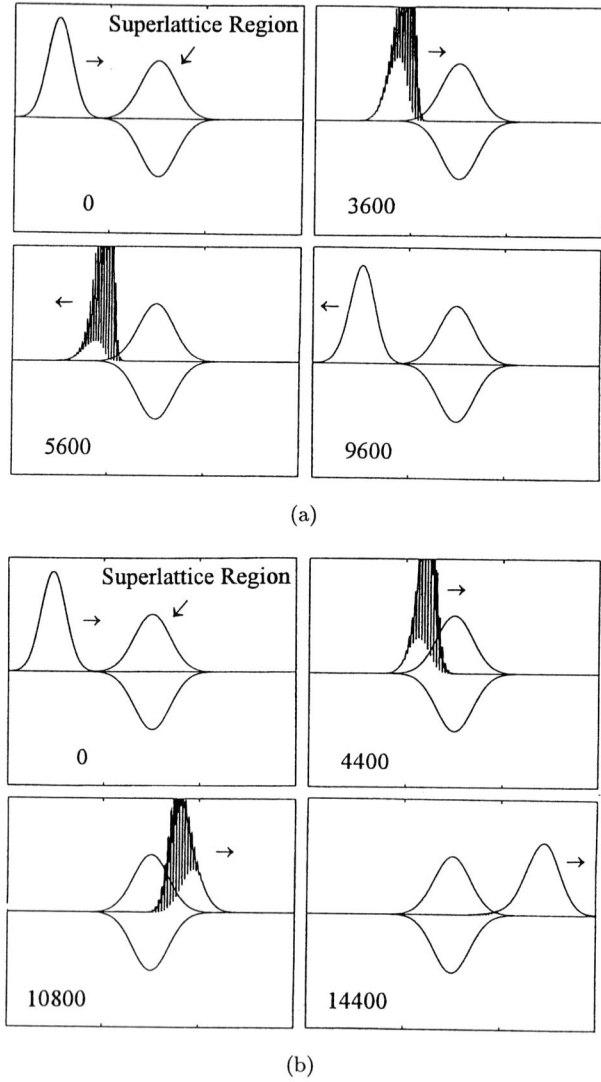

(a)

(b)

Fig. 3. Time evolution of a Gaussian wavepacket scattering from the first proposed structure with the layer parameters used in Fig. 2(a). (a) The average electron incident energy is 1.25 $V_0$, (b) The average electron incident energy is 0.85 $V_0$. The region enclosed by the positive and negative Gaussian function is the superlattices as shown in Fig. 1(a). (c) Scattering from a conventional MQWs for comparison. The average electron incident energy is 1.15 $V_0$. The region enclosed by rectangle is the MQWs. Numbers in each configuration denote the time in the unit of $2.316 \times 10^{-17}$ sec.

118

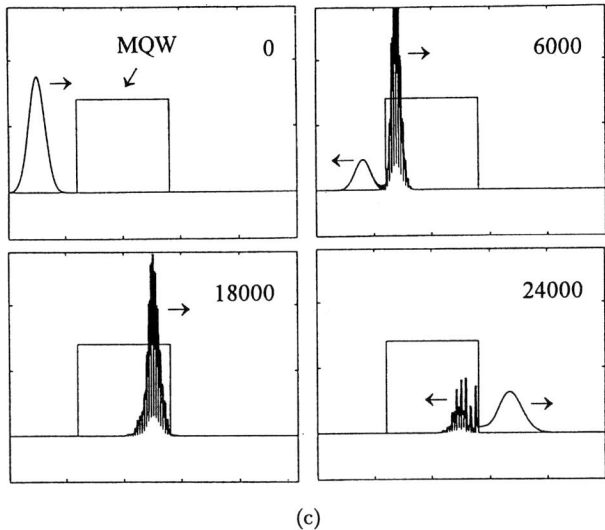

(c)

Fig. 3. (*Continued*)

is totally reflected. If the initial wavepacket moves to the right with an incident energy $E = 0.85 V_0$ and the same width of 400 Å, (this corresponds to an energy uncertainty of about 0.0325 eV), that is, when the incident energy lies in the pass-band of the EBPF, the time evolution of the wavepacket, shown in Fig. 3(b), is totally different. Complete transmission takes place and no noticeable reflection is detected. Although the scattering strength is strong when the wavepacket is moving within the superlattice, there is no distortion for the transmitted wave except for the spreading of the wavepacket. To make a comparison between EBPF and the conventional rectangular MQW, we also simulated the scattering of a Gaussian wavepacket by a rectangular MQWs with the transmission characteristics shown in Fig. 2(c). The wavepacket has an incident energy of $1.15 V_0$ with a width of 0.036 eV (the energy spreading again corresponds to a spatial width of 400 Å) which lies within the miniband of the MQWs. The time evolution of the wavepacket moving through such a structure is shown in Fig. 3(c). As expected, partial reflection and transmission are observed even when the energy of the wavepacket is within the miniband of the MQWs. From the numerical results presented here, it is clear that the proposed structure can really serve as an energy band-pass filter for electrons.

## 4. Quantum-Mechanical Wave Impedance (QMWI)

The generalized concept of quantum-mechanical wave impedance (QMWI) was first introduced by Khondker *et al.*[15] This concept is analogous to the impedance in the well-developed transmission line theory. The quantum-mechanical transmission probability can be easily calculated using this method. The QMWI at any plane $x$

can be defined as

$$Z(x) = \frac{2\hbar}{jm(x)} \frac{\Psi'(x)}{\Psi(x)}, \tag{4}$$

where $Z(x)$ is the wave impedance looking into the positive $x$ direction, $j = \sqrt{-1}, m(x)$ is the effective mass of electron at $x, \Psi(x)$ and $\Psi'(x)$ are the electron wave function and its spatial derivative, respectively, for the potential problem of interest. For an arbitrarily-shaped potential, we can approximate the potential and effective mass by multi-step functions with a sequence of $N$ segments. Thus, if $x_i$ and $x_{i+1}$ are the boundaries of segment $i$, the QMWI at $x_i$ can be calculated by

$$Z(x_i) = Z_{0i} \frac{Z(x_{i+1}) \cosh(\gamma_i l_i) - Z_{0i} \sinh(\gamma_i l_i)}{Z_{0i} \cosh(\gamma_i l_i) - Z(x_{i+1}) \sinh(\gamma_i l_i)}, \tag{5}$$

where

$$\gamma_i = j\sqrt{(2m_i/\hbar^2)(E - V_i)},$$
$$l_i = x_{i+1} - x_i, \tag{6}$$

and

$$Z_{0i} = \frac{2\gamma_i \hbar}{jm_i} \tag{7}$$

is the characteristic impedance of the medium. Equation (5) expresses the QMWI at $x_i$ in terms of the QMWI at $x_{i+1}$, and $\gamma_i, l_i$, and $Z_{0i}$. Once the $Z(x_i)$ is calculated, we can repeat the process for segment $i-1$ to calculate $Z(x_{i-1})$ using $\gamma_{i-1}, l_{i-1}$, and $Z_{0i-1}$. Repeatedly using Eqs. (5), (6), and (7), we can evaluate the total input impedance of EBPF and treat the whole superlattice structure as an equivalent load impedance $Z_{EBPF}$. Thus the reflection coefficient $\rho_x(E)$ for the wave amplitude can be calculated as

$$\rho(E) = \frac{Z_{EBPF} - Z_0}{Z_{EBPF} + Z_0}, \tag{8}$$

where $Z_0$ is the characteristic QMWI of the bulk semiconductor outside the EBPF, and the transmission probability is given by

$$T(E) = 1 - |\rho(E)|^2. \tag{9}$$

We have used Eq. (9) to calculate the transmission probability for the two proposed EBPF structures. The result is the same as that calculated by transfer-matrix method and has been shown in Fig. 2.

From transmission line theory[26] we know that a matched condition occurs when the load impedance is equal to the characteristic impedance of the line. Under such a condition, the reflection coefficient $\rho_x(E)$ in Eq. (8) should be zero and the transmission probability $T(E)$ in Eq. (9) should be equal to 1. Figure 4(a) shows the QMWI $Z_{EBPF}$ and $Z_0$ as a function of energy of the first proposed EBPF with the same structure parameters in Fig. 2(a). It clearly demonstrates that when the incident energy lies in the passband, $Z_{EBPF}$ matches $Z_0$ completely, while outside the passband, a large impedance mismatch exists there. The result is in good agreement with that calculated in Fig. 2(a). Figure 4(b) shows the calculated QMWI $Z_{MQW}$ and $Z_0$ as functions of energy for a rectangular MQW, which has the structure parameters similar to those used in Fig. 2(c). The figure demonstrates that impedance mismatch exists everywhere, even in the minibands. This explained why a rectangular MQW structure does not have the property of total transmission for a Gaussian wavepacket.

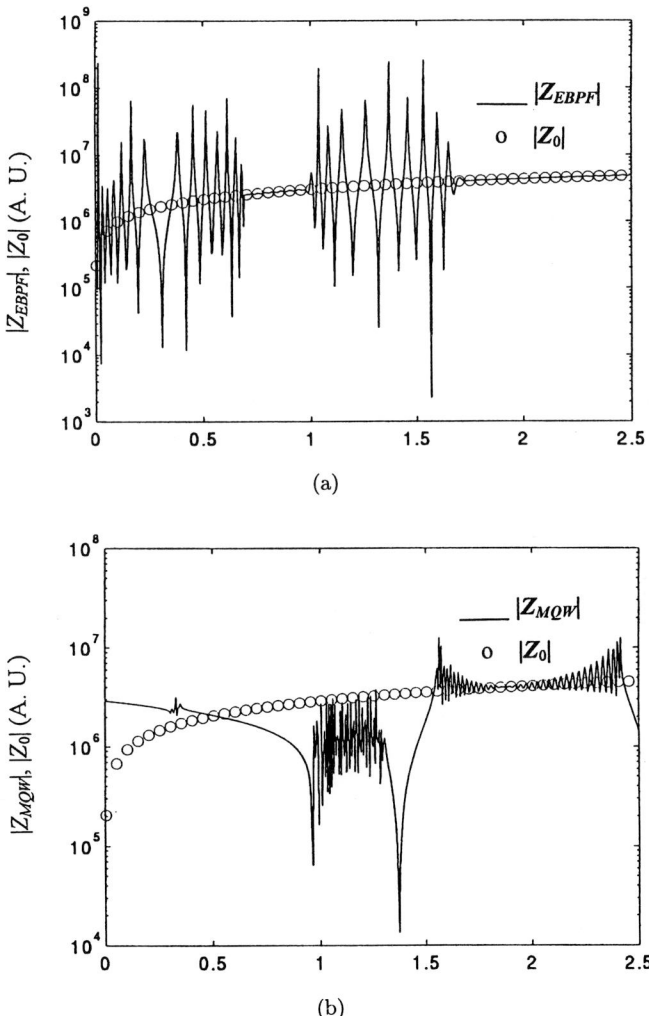

(a)

(b)

Fig. 4. The absolute values of quantum-mechanical wave impedance (QMWI) (a) $Z_{EBPF}$ and $Z_0$ of the first proposed EBPF, (b) $Z_{MQW}$ and $Z_0$ of a conventional MQWs as a function of normalized incident electron energy with the structure parameters used in Fig. 1(a).

## 5. Scattering Effects on Resonant Tunneling Diode

Although the description of electron transport through a resonant tunneling diode (RTD) may seem like a simple problem, the modeling of devices based on this structure has not been fully successful. For example, the calculated peak to valley ratios in the current versus voltage curves are much larger than what has been measured. One reason behind the failure of theories is that the mechanism for tunneling might be sequential rather than Fabry-Pèrot like. Due to scattering, the resonant enhancement of transmission is absent. Another difficulty faced in establishing such a theory lies in the fact that the scattering effects are three-dimensional in nature, while energy and momentum are not conserved in each direction. But most analyses are one-dimensional (which assume that the perpendicular momentum of the electron is left unchanged).

The resonant tunneling diode acts like a Fabry-Pèrot resonator for the electron wave.[7] The total tunneling transmission can be calculated as the sum over multiple scattered waves. As shown in Fig. 5, for an incident wave $\Psi_{in}$ in the emitter region, owing to the multiple reflection, the following wave components are generated:

$$\Psi_{tn} = \Psi_{in} t_1 (r_2 r_1 \exp(i2\theta))^{n-1} t_2 \exp(i\Phi_{tn}), \tag{10}$$

where $\theta = L\sqrt{2m^*_{well}E}/\hbar \cdot L$ and $m^*_{well}$ are the width and the electron effective mass of the well and $E$ is the electron incident energy. $t_1(t_2)$ and $r_1(r_2)$ are the transmission and reflection coefficient of the first (second) barrier, respectively. $\Phi_{tn}$ is the phase shift caused by phase breaking and is zero when the scatterers in the well are absent. In this work, we use the Monte Carlo (MC) method[27] to obtain $\phi_{tn}$. The total transmission probability is obtained as

$$T_{total} = \frac{\langle k_{out}\rangle}{k_{in}} |(\Psi_{t1} + \Psi_{t2} + \ldots)/\Psi_{in}|^2, \tag{11}$$

where $\langle k_{out}\rangle$ is the ensemble average of the momentum for the electrons tunneling out of the quantum well. $\langle k_{out}\rangle$ can be obtained in the following way. First, we evaluate the time, $\tau_{well}$, that the electrons stay in the well. The electron dwelling time, $\tau_{well}$, based on the QMWI can be expressed in an integral[17]:

$$\tau_{well} = 2 \int_0^L \frac{dx}{R(x)},$$

where $R(x)$ is the real part of the QMWI of the RTD. Thanikasalam *et al.*[18] have used this method and derived an analytical expression for $\tau_{well}$. The calculated $\tau_{well}$ is then used as the total simulation time for Monte Carlo simulation. The electron experiences different scattering according to the scattering rate. At the end of simulation, the final electron wave vector is $k_{out}$. The ensemble average wave vector $\langle k_{out}\rangle$ is obtained if we sum up all the $k_{out}$ and divide it by the number of trials.

(a)

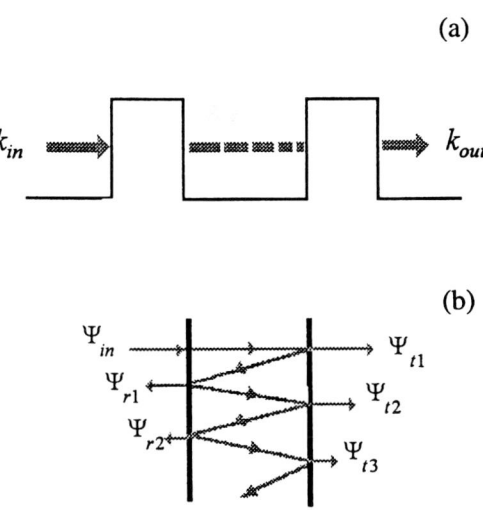

(b)

Fig. 5. (a) Graphical representation of the electron tunneling through the resonant tunneling diode, (b) The two barriers of RTD can be replaced by two semitransparent reflectors and the total transmission probability can be expressed by a infinite series of wavefunction.

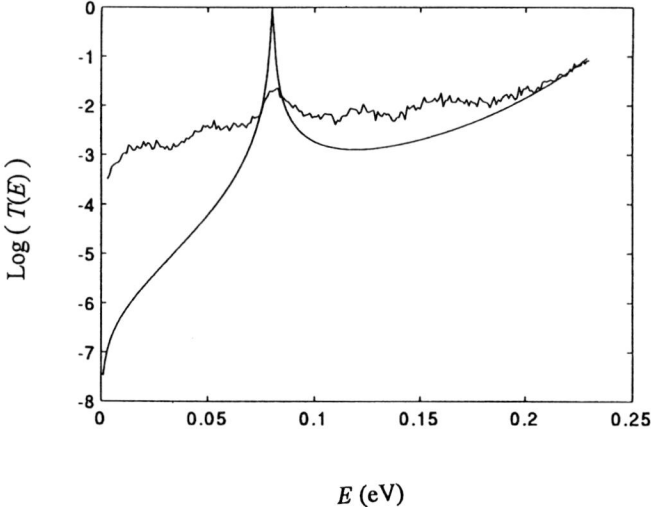

Fig. 6. Plot of transmission probability as a function of electron energy for a 50 Å/50 Å/50 Å AlGaAs/GaAs double-barrier heterostructure at the lattice temperature of 300 K. Also shown is the transmission probability in the absence of scattering (smooth line).

The test diode we study here is a 50 Å/50 Å/50 Å AlGaAs/GaAs double-barrier RTD. The acoustic phonon scattering, the polar optical phonon scattering, and the impurity scattering are considered in the calculation. Figure 6 shows the equilibrium (no bias) transmission coefficient $T(E)$ versus $E$ for the test diode at a lattice temperature of 300 K. Also shown is the transmission coefficient in the absence of scattering (smooth line). Many different transmission peaks are observed. The main peak centered upon the energy $E \approx 85$ meV, which is about 4 meV shift of the main resonant transmission peak relative to the one observed in the absence of scattering, i.e. $E \approx 81$ meV. It is clear that the transmission peak is lowered by scattering. The first peak to the right of the main peak is centered around 120 meV, which corresponds to the resonant tunneling associated with the emission of a phonon (phonon energy $\approx 35$ meV).[28] The first peak to the left of the main peak is centered around 50 meV corresponding to the resonant tunneling assisted by the absorption of a phonon. The other peaks found in the transmission spectrum are due to multi-phonon processes. If we approximately recognize the peak-to-valley current ratio of a RTD as being proportional to the transmission probability, we find from Fig. 6 that the ratio is about 4 which is in agreement with the experimental results.[29]

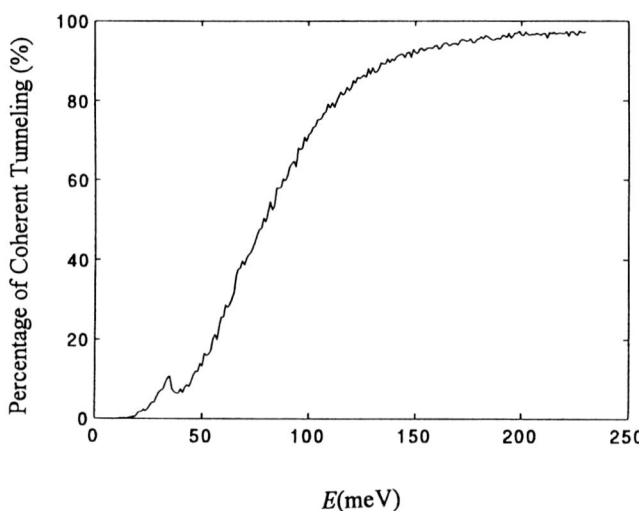

$E(\text{meV})$

Fig. 7. Plot of percentage of coherent tunneling as a function of electron energy for a RTD with the same structure parameters used in Fig. 6. The small kink is due to the fact that a threshold energy $\hbar\omega_0 \approx 35$ meV exists for the phonon emission process.

Figure 7 shows the plot of percentage of coherent tunneling as a function of electron energy for a RTD with the same structure parameters used in Fig. 6. If the scattering time $\tau_s$ (= reciprocal of the scattering rate) is shorter than the resonant time $\tau_{well}$, the scattering will destroy the phase coherence and reduce the probability for coherent tunneling. By using QMWI, we can easily calculate $\tau_{well}$ and compare it with $\tau_s$. From the result, we can give a quantitative description about the effects of scattering on the coherent tunneling and the sequential tunneling. When the electron energy is low, the calculated $\tau_{well}$ is much larger than $\tau_s$. So, before the coherently tunneling electron stream reaches its maximum value, the scattering events prohibit further coherent tunneling. These electrons will then tunnel out of the quantum well in a separate (incoherent) process. On the other hand, if the electron energy is high enough, the calculated $\tau_{well}$ is much smaller than $\tau_s$, phase coherence can be built up quickly and electrons can tunnel out of the well without experience much scattering. The small kink observed in Fig. 7 is due to the fact that a threshold energy $\hbar\omega_0 \approx 35$ meV exists for the phonon emission process.

## 6. Conclusion

We have described the design of two artificial quantum-mechanical energy band-pass filters (EBPF) using superlattice structures with a Gaussian envelop profile or gradually changing barrier and well width. Flat transmission bands and reflection bands are obtained by properly choosing the layer parameters. Simulations of the time evolution of wavepacket traveling through such structures clearly demonstrate the band passing characteristics of EBPF. The phenomenon of total transmission can be successfully explained by using the concept of wave impedance analogous to that in the transmission line theory. By combining the Fabry-Pèrot model, the QMWI method, and the Monte Carlo method, we have studied the scattering effects on the transmission spectrum of a RTD. The results indicate: the spectrum is broadened, the peak amplitude is decreased, the peak position is shifted, and the phonon assisted tunneling was initiated. Finally, we used the calculated $\tau_{well}$ (obtained from QMWI method) to give a quantitative description about the effects of scattering on coherent and sequential tunneling of a RTD.

## Acknowledgment

This work is supported by the National Science Council of the Republic of China under contract No. NSC 86-2215-E-009-010.

## References

1. L. L. Chang, L. Esaki, and R. Tsu, "Resonant tunneling in semiconductor double barriers", *Appl. Phys. Lett.* **24** (1974) 593–595.
2. Y. H. Lee, B. Tell, K. Brown-Goebeler, J. L. Jewell, and J. V. Hove, "Top surface-emitting GaAs four quantum well lasers emitting at 0.85 um", *Electron. Lett.* **26** (1990) 710–711.
3. K. Kishino, M. S. Unlu, J. I. Chyi, J. Reed, L. Arsenault, and H. Morkoc, "Resonant cavity-enhancee(RCE) photodetectors", *IEEE J. Quantum Electron.* **27** (1991) 2025–2034.
4. J. M. Hammer, "High-speed electro optic waveguide grating modulator using epitaxial ZnO", *IEEE J. Quantum Electron.* **11** (1975) 138–144.
5. T. Nakagawa, N. Kawai, K. Ohta, and M. Kawashima, "Time evolution of electron wavepackets in modulated superlattices and at their boundaries", *Superlatt. and Microstr.* **1** (1983) 217–221.
6. R. V. Schmidt, "Narrow-band grating filters for thin-film optical waveguides", *Appl. Phys. Lett.* **25** (1974) 651–653.

7. I. H. Tan, G. L. Snider, and E. L. Hu, "Fabry-Pèrot analysis of resonant tunneling structures", *Superlatt. & Microstr.* **10** (1991) 67–72.
8. L. Easki and R. Tsu, "Superlattice and negative differential conductivity in semiconductors", *IBM J. Res. Develop.* **14** (1970) 61–65.
9. V. K. Tripathi and P. K. Bhatacharya, "Electron energy states and miniband parameters in a class of non-uniform quantum well and superlattice structures", *Superlatt. & Microstr.* **1** (1985) 73–79.
10. R. Dingle, *Advances in Solid State Physics*, vol. XV, ed. H. J. Queisser, Pergamon Vieweg, 1975.
11. K. Iga, H. Uehara, and F. Koyama, "Electron reflectance of multiple quantum barrier (MQB)", *Electron. Lett.* **22** (1986) 1008–1010.
12. F. Capasso, K. Mohammed, and A. Y. Cho, "Resonant tunneling through double barriers, perpendicular quantum transport phenomena in superlattices, and their device applications", *IEEE J. Quantum Electron.* **22** (1986) 1853–1869.
13. S. T. Yen, C. M. Tsai, C. P. Lee, and D. C. Liu, "Enhancement of electron wave reflection by superlattices with multiple stacks of multi-quantum barriers", *Appl. Phys. Lett.* **64** (1994) 1108–1110.
14. D. Mukherji and B. R. Nag, "Band structure of semiconductor superlattices", *Phys. Rev.* **B-12** (1975) 4338–4345.
15. A. N. Khondker, M. R. Khan, and A. F. M. Anwar, "Transmission line analogy of resonance tunneling phenomena: The generalized impedance concept", *J. Appl. Phys.* **63** (1988) 5191–5193.
16. A. F. M. Anwar and M. M. Jahan, "Traversal time in an asymmetric double-barrier quantum-well structure", *IEEE J. Quantum Electron.* **31** (1995) 3–7.
17. A. F. M. Anwar, A. N. Khondker, and M. R. Khan, "Calculation of the traversal time in resonant tunneling devices", *J. Appl. Phys.* **65** (1989) 2761–2765.
18. P. Thanikasalam, R. Venkatasubramanian, and M. Cahay, "Analytical expression for tunneling time through single and double barrier structures", *IEEE J. Quantum Electron.* **29** (1993) 2451–2458.
19. M. Jonson and A. Grincwaig, "Effect of inelastic scattering on resonant and sequential tunneling in double barrier heterostructures", *Appl. Phys. Lett.* **51** (1987) 1729–1731.
20. J. A. Stovneng, E. H. Hauge, P. Lipavsky, and V. Spicka, "Tight-binding approach to resonant tunneling with electron-phonon coupling", *Phys. Rev. B* (1991) 13595–13602.
21. P. Roblin and W. R. Liou, "Three-dimensional scattering-assisted tunneling in resonant-tunneling diodes", *Phys. Rev. B* **47** (1993) 2146–2161.
22. Y. Hu and S. P. Stapleton, "Double-barrier resonant tunneling transport model", *IEEE J. Quantum Electron.* **29** (1993) 327–339.
23. K. Furuya, N. Machida, and Y. C. Kang, "Analysis of phase breaking in resonant tunneling diodes using correlation function", *Jpn. J. Appl. Phys.* **33** (1994) 2511–2512.
24. M. Lundstrom, *Fundamentals of Carrier Transport*, Addison-Wesley, Reading, MA, 1990, pp. 10–11.
25. A. Goldberg, H. M. Schey, and J. L. Schwartz, "Computer-generated motion pictures of one-dimensional quantum-mechanical transmission and reflection phenomena", *Am. J. Phys.* **35** (1967) 177–186.
26. D. K. Cheng, *Field and Wave Electromagnetics*, Addison-Wesley, Reading, MA, 1983, pp. 390–395.
27. C. Moglestue, *Monte Carlo Simulation of Semiconductor Devices*, Chapman & Hall, 1993.
28. B. K. Ridley, *Quantum Processes in Semiconductors*, Clarendon Press, 1993.

29. T. C. L. G. Sollner, W. D. Goodhue, P. E. Tannenwald, C. D. Parker, and D. D. Peck, "Resonant tunneling through quantum wells at frequencies up to 2.5 Thz", *Appl. Phys. Lett.* **43** (1983) 588–590.

International Journal of High Speed Electronics and Systems, Vol. 8, No. 4 (1997) 703–717

# THE PERFORMANCE OF $Hg_{0.8}Cd_{0.2}Te$ PHOTODETECTORS BY USING PHOTO SURFACE TREATMENT

Y. K. SU

*Department of Electrical Engineering, National Cheng Kung University, Tainan, Taiwan, R.O.C.*


C. T. LIN

*Vanguard International Semiconductor Corporation, Taiwan, R.O.C.*

The principal aim of this paper is to propose an easy, vapor phase, and reproducible photo surface treatment method to improve the device performance of the $Hg_{0.8}Cd_{0.2}Te$ photoconductive detector. Experimental results, including Auger electron spectroscopy (AES), MIS leakage current, $1/f$ noise voltage spectrum, $1/f$ *knee* frequency, responsivity $R_\lambda$, and specific detectivity $D^*$ for stacked photo surface treatment and ZnS or CdTe passivation layers are presented. By using this method, we found that there is no accumulation of Hg in the oxide/HgCdTe interface regions. Since the photo chemical vapor native oxidation is a dry oxidation method deposited at a low temperature, it can effectively suppress the Hg enhancement and the Cd depletion effects and thus obtain a high quality interface. We also found that the photo surface treatment in combination with thermally evaporated ZnS or CdTe layer would shift the $1/f$ *knee* under 100Hz in an electrical field under 50 V/cm, reduce the noise power spectrum, and achieve a lower surface recombination velocity $S$ of 300 cm/sec as well as a high $D^*$ of $3 \times 10^{10}$ cm $Hz^{\frac{1}{2}}$/w for blackbody radiation. It was also found that HgCdTe photoconductor passivated with stacked layers shows improved interface properties when compared to the photoconductor passivated with a single passivation layer.

## 1. Introduction

HgCdTe photoconductor arrays have become an accepted standard in high-resolution thermal imaging systems in the $3 \sim 5$ $\mu$m and $8 \sim 14$ $\mu$m spectral regions. Unlike other IR materials such as InSb, one can easily change the composition ratio between Hg and Cd to adjust the bandgap energy of HgCdTe and thus to adjust the corresponding wavelength. Also, because of its intrinsic property, a HgCdTe photo detector has a long carrier life time and a small thermal generation rate that is important for high temperature operation. Unfortunately, the yield rate and device stability of HgCdTe still cannot reach the demands of mass production. The most important drawback of a HgCdTe IR array is that it is a defective material since the Hg atoms have a tendency to deviate from its stoichiometry even at a low temperature. It has been pointed out that the Hg vacancies and rapid diffusion of Hg may result in serious difficulties during processing and it will also degrade its device performance.

Current surface passivations[1] used for HgCdTe include native oxide,[2] native sulfides, CdTe[3] and ZnS. All the materials and related deposition procedures have been intensively studied by a number of groups over the last several years. However, no standard passivation material and method have been established yet. Due to its poor thermal stability, it is difficult to obtain a stable passivation layer on top of HgCdTe so as to improve the performance of the HgCdTe IR detector. For the same reason, to fabricate a HgCdTe detector, all process steps should be performed at low temperature particularly for surface passivation. Since Hg atoms tend to deviate from stoichiometry even at a modest temperature, an appropriate surface preparation procedure must be used in order to improve the quality of the interface. As pointed out by Professor Y. Nemirovsky;[4] "I believe that the native sulfides passivation as well as the native oxide passivation can be upgraded significantly with an appropriate vapor phase heat treatment that will improve the stoichiometry." A new temperature and vapor phase passivation method is necessary so as to achieve a high quality surface passivation layer.

In this study, we choose photo native oxidation, using a low temperature vapor phase process for surface passivation. By using this novel oxidation technique, we can avoid the large fixed positive charges contained in the anodic oxide and a strong accumulation on the surface of $n$-type HgCdTe photoconductor which occurs frequently for wet anodic oxidation.[5] We also call the photo native oxidation process as photo surface treatment, since the photo native oxide can form a better interface as the first stage. In the following sections, we will use the stacked photo surface treatment and insulator passivations to fabricate HgCdTe photoconductors. We will describe in detail for the first time, the relation between the passivants and the $1/f$ noise. For the far IR focal plane arrays, the performance of the photoconductive detectors would be dominated by the low frequency $1/f$ noise and the surface recombination centers. It has been generally recognized that photoconductive detectors with a poorly passivated layer exhibit a large amount of surface recombination centers and a large $1/f$ noise. In this paper, we will show that by improving the surface passivation, we can reduce the $1/f$ noise and $1/f$ knee frequency to a considerable degree. We will also show that detectors with the photo surface treatment will have a significantly improved $1/f$ noise and specific detectivity $D^*$ compared to detectors without the photo surface treatment.

## 2. Surface Treatment and Detector Fabrication Technology

The surface treatment used in this work involves the formation of a thin photo oxide layer on top of HgCdTe wafers before the deposition of the thick insulator layers; such as ZnS and CdTe. The photo oxide layer is formed by sending the HgCdTe wafers into a direct photo chemical vapor deposition system (direct photo-CVD system) with a deuterium ($D_2$) lamp, which radiates strong vacuum ultra violet (VUV) and ultra violet (UV) light within the 100 to 200 nm wavelength regions. The $O_2$ gas, which was sent into the photo CVD system, absorbs strongly

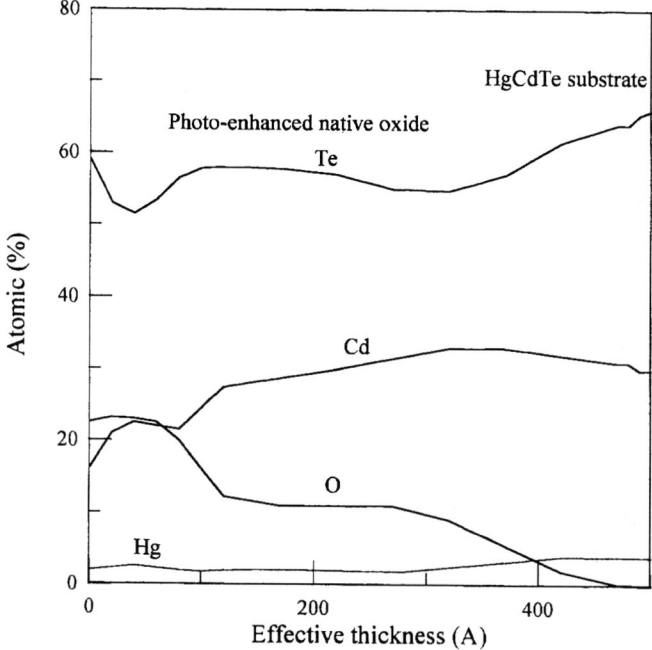

Fig. 1. Auger sputter profile of 400 Å thick photo native oxide deposited on HgCdTe. There is no Hg-rich effect in the interface regions.

in the wavelength region between 133 and 175 nm. Therefore, the $D_2$ lamp is a suitable light source that can effectively excite $O_2$ into excited oxygen atoms at low temperature;[6]

$$O_2 \rightarrow O(^3P) + O(^1d), \quad 133 < \lambda < 175 \text{ nm}. \tag{1}$$

These excited oxygen atoms would react with the components of the HgCdTe surface to form a photo native oxide layer. It is expected that a good quality native oxide film can be formed by using such a low temperature vapor phase process. Figure 1 shows an AES depth profile of a 400 Å photo-enhanced native oxide. From Fig. 1, we can see that, there is no significant Hg enhancement layer on the substrate side of the interface. It is very important that the Hg, HgTe, and Te particles have been observed at the anodic oxide/HgCdTe interface. These particles, which exhibited behavior associated with fixed charges, will tend to shunt the applied voltage, enhance energy band bending and serve as a source of carriers. From Fig. 1, in contrast to the anodic oxide and UV light oxide, neither the enhancement of Hg nor the depletion of Cd was found in our photo native oxide layer. For our photo-enhanced native oxidation, the saturated thickness of photo native oxides is about 40 nm at low temperature condition ($< 50°C$). This thickness is enough to improve the interface properties. However, since the photo native oxide is too thin to provide isolation, we deposited a high resistivity ZnS or CdTe layer as the second stage to protect the photo native oxide. According to our previous papers,[7,8] the MIS device fabricated through this method has near flat-band condition, a lower interface trap density and a lower hysteresis.

Four different kinds of MIS diodes were fabricated. Before device fabrication, the HgCdTe wafers were cleaned by using the two step treatment. The first step is to polish the sample in solvents; methanol, acetone, and TCA at 40°C. Next, the wafer were lightly etched with 1.8% bromine in methanol and again followed by a solvent cleaning. Photo surface treatment were performed immediately after the surface preparation was completed. The parameters used for photo surface treatment were described as follows: growth temperature was lower than 50°C, the chamber pressure was lower than $3 \times 10^{-6}$ Torr and the growth pressure was 10 Torr, the $O_2$ gas flow was 5 sccm, and the growth time was 2 h. After photo surface treatment, insulators, such ZnS or CdTe, were deposited on top of the HgCdTe wafers. After that, ohmic contacts were made by immersing $n$-type HgCdTe in 10% $H(AuCl_4)3H_2O$ solution for 5 s. Finally, these samples were rinsed in deionized water for 5 min and blown dry by pure $N_2$. Samples without the photo surface treatment were also prepared, i.e. four different kinds of insulators, including ZnS, ZnS/photo-enhanced native oxide, CdTe, and CdTe/photo-enhanced native oxide, were prepared in this study. For comparison, all samples were fabricated with the same growth conditions and physical dimensions. The leakage current-voltage

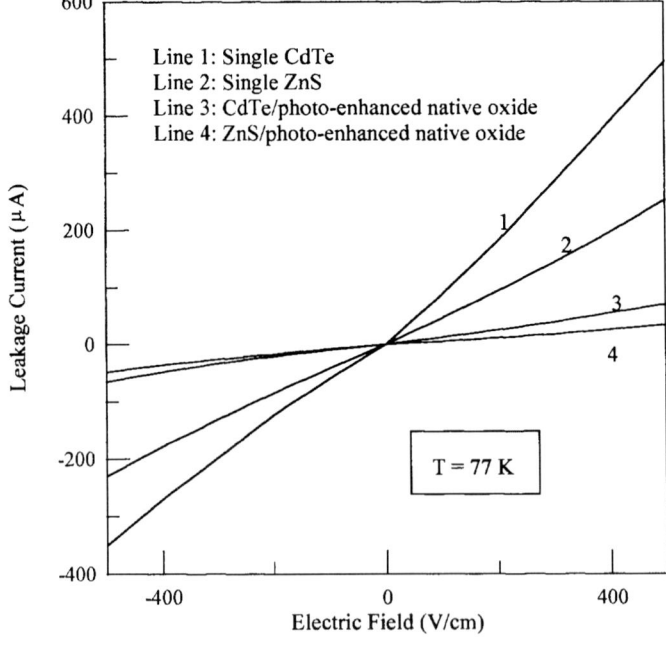

Fig. 2. The leakage current of different HgCdTe MIS devices passivated with different insulators.

(I-V) characteristics of these MIS diodes are shown in Fig. 2. From Fig. 2, we can see that, in the same electrical field, the leakage current of HgCdTe MIS devices can be reduced by a factor of $5 \sim 6$ by inserting a thin photo native oxide layer between ZnS or CdTe, and the HgCdTe substrate. This leakage current reduction again indicates that by using photo surface treatment, one can improve the electrical properties of the interface.

## 3. Theoretical Performance of HgCdTe Photoconductive Detectors

### 3.1. *Responsivity* ($R_\lambda$)

Consider the photo responsivity $R_{BB}(V/W)$ for black body radiation in steady state

$$R_{BB} = \frac{S}{E \times A_d}, \qquad (2)$$

where $S$ is signal of response voltage, $E$ is the incident optical power, and $A_d$ is the absorption area. The formula of $E$ could be written as follows

$$E = \varepsilon \sigma T^4 \frac{d^2}{4D^2}, \qquad (3)$$

where $\sigma$ is the Boltzmann's constant, $T$ is the temperature of the blackbody, and $D$ is the distance between the detector and the blackbody. In our paper, the responsivity characteristics were measured by using blackbody radiation. Therefore, one technique is to determine $R_\lambda$ by first measuring $R_{BB}$. The spectral distribution of the blackbody is

$$g = \frac{R_\lambda}{R_{BB}} = \frac{\eta(v_s)}{v_s} \left[ \int_{v_c}^{\infty} \frac{\eta(v)M(v,T_2)dv}{R_{BB}\, v} \right]^{-1}, \qquad (4)$$

where $v_s$ is the frequency of the signal power, and $T_2$ is the ideal blackbody temperature. According to (4), the value of $g$ depends only on blackbody temperature and cutoff frequency; for example, with $T = 500$ K and $\lambda c = 12$ $\mu$m, g $\approx 3.5$. $R_\lambda$ can be derived by combining (2) and (4). Consider the photo responsivity $R_\lambda(V/W)$ for monochromatic radiation in steady state;[9]

$$R_\lambda = \eta \frac{\lambda}{hc} e r_d \frac{\mu_e E_b}{l} \tau_{eff}, \qquad (5)$$

where $\eta$ is the quantum efficiency, $\lambda$ is the cutoff wavelength, $r_d$ is the detector resistance, $\mu_e$ is the electron mobility, $\tau_{eff}$ is the effective carrier lifetime, and $E_b$ is the electric field bias. The quantum efficiency $\eta$ can be written as unity. Assuming that surface recombination velocity at the upper and lower semiconductor surfaces can be modeled by an average surface recombination velocity, $S$ and the sidewall surfaces recombination velocity were neglected.[10] The effective minority carrier lifetime can be written as

$$\tau_{eff} = \left( \tau_{A1}^{-1} + \tau_R^{-1} + \frac{2S}{d} \right)^{-1}, \qquad (6)$$

where $d$ is the photoconductive detector thickness, $\tau_A$ is the Auger-1 lifetime, and $\tau_R$ is the radiative lifetime. It has been shown that the Auger-1 process forms the dominant mechanism in $n$-type HgCdTe and the extrinsic lifetime for the Auger-1 process can be expressed as

$$\tau_{A1} = \frac{2n_i^1}{(n_0 + P_0)n_0}\tau_{A1}^{(i)},$$

(7)

where $n_0$ and $P_0$ are the thermal equilibrium concentration for electrons and holes, $n_i$ is the intrinsic concentration, and $\tau_{A1}^{(i)}$ is the intrinsic Auger-1 lifetime. Combining Eqs. (6) and (7), these expressions show that the maximum effective minority carrier lifetime is close to the extrinsic Auger-1 lifetime. For example, the extrinsic Auger-1 lifetime in our paper was calculated to be about $10^{-6}$ sec. If the effective minority carrier lifetime is close to the extrinsic Auger-1 lifetime, the average surface recombination velocity $S$ is typically of the order of 500 cm/s. From the responsivity measurement, the effective minority carrier lifetime can be extracted by using Eq. (5). We select the HgCdTe photoconductive detector, with photo surface treatment, as an example. The responsivity characteristics of photodetector were measured with blackbody radiation at 500 K, background temperature at 300 K, and operating frequency at 270 Hz. As we have pointed out before, we have calculated the average surface recombination velocity $S$ of 300 cm/sec.

### 3.2. *Noise*

Considering the total noise voltage, the full assessment of photoconductor performance was accomplished. For a typical HgCdTe photoconductor, the total noises were given by

$$V_t^1 = V_J^2 + V_{g-r}^2 + V_{1/f}^2 + V_a^1,$$

(8)

where $V_t$ is the total noise, $V_J$ is the Johnson noise, $V_{g-r}$ is the generation and recombination noise, $V_{1/f}$ is the $1/f$ noise, and $V_a$ is the amplifier noise. Since the $V_J$ and $V_a$ are much smaller than the total noise spectral density at 77 K, we can neglect the $V_J$ and $V_a$. To the best of our knowledge, background $g-r$ noise is directly proportional to the effective carrier lifetime, and the $1/f$ noise behavior can be fairly complex. It is believed that most $1/f$ noise mainly result from two mechanisms; one consists of the carrier interactions with the interface traps, and the other is the surface mobility fluctuations between the HgCdTe and passivation.[11] $1/f$ noise and $g-r$ noise in semiconductors are mainly based on the existence of surface traps. According to this viewpoint, both $1/f$ noise and $V_{g-r}$ are determined with the trap centers within the interface. According to the empirical results, both noises are obviously improved by photo surface treatment. The following empirical relation has been found to apply

$$V_{1/f}^2 \cong (K_0/f)V_{g-r}^3,$$

(9)

where $K_0$ is a constant.

$f_0$ is the $1/f$ *knee* frequency, which is defined as the frequency at which the $1/f$ noise power equals the $g - r$ noise power, and the $1/f$ *knee* frequency is readily determined to be

$$f_0 = K_1 V_{g-r} \,, \tag{10}$$

where $K_1$ is a constant. Equation (10) states that $1/f$ *knee* frequency increases with $g - r$ noise. The electrical spectrum of the detectivity was controlled by $1/f$ *knee* frequency at the low end parameter. The lower $1/f$ *knee* frequency will give the more broad operating frequency bandwidth under the background limited condition. This conclusion is a key which decreasing the surface traps will effectively reduce noise and increase operating frequency bandwidth. If the operating frequency was near the $1/f$ *knee* frequency, the noise was wholly dominated by $g - r$ noise

$$V_n = \sqrt{V_{g-r}^2} \,. \tag{11}$$

By using (2) and (11) the specific detectivity $D^*$ for blackbody radiation can be written as

$$D_{BB}^* = \frac{R_{BB}}{V_n}(lw\Delta f)^{1/2} \,. \tag{12}$$

Thus, it is possible to calculate and compare the detectivity of the photoconductor deposited with different passivations.

## 4. Experimental Results and Discussions

A simple and stable technology which is appropriate for fabricating HgCdTe IR arrays is presented. Consider the simple photoconductive detectors illustrated in

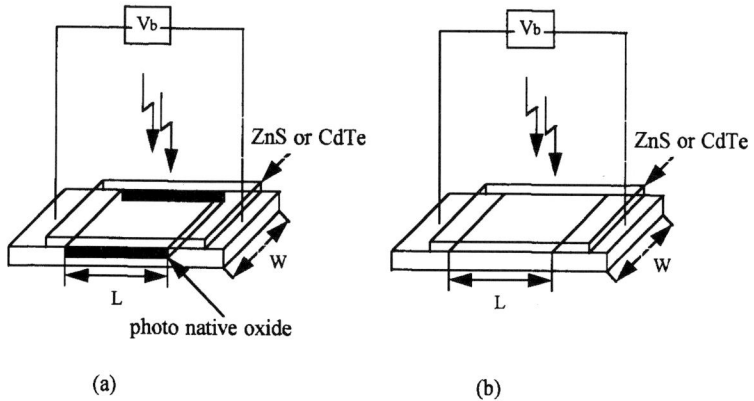

(a)          (b)

Fig. 3. Schematic illustration of a photoconductive detectors defining the various surface and geometrical parameters. By using photo-CVD, the HgCdTe surface would grow a thin photo native oxide layer.

Fig. 3, made from $n$-type bulk $Hg_{0.8}Cd_{0.2}Te$, with different passivations. The basic idea behind the improved fabrication procedure is using photo surface treatment before the insulator is deposited. First, the $Hg_{0.8}Cd_{0.2}Te$ wafers were cleaned by using the two step treatment. The first step is to polish the sample in solvents; methanol, acetone, and TCA under heat at 40°C, in succession. Next, a light etch with 1/8% bromine in methanol was applied, again followed by solvent cleaning. Photo surface treatment was done as soon after surface preparation as possible. The photo surface treatment conditions are described as follows: growth temperature was lower than 50°C, the chamber was evacuated below $3 \times 10^{-6}$ Torr and growth pressure was 10 Torr, the $O_2$ gas flow rate was 5 cubic centimeters per minute (sccm), and growth time was 2 h. As mentioned above, photo surface treatment is an easy, low temperature and vapor phase process. After photo surface treatment, insulators, such as CdTe or ZnS, were deposited on top of the HgCdTe wafers. The array was delineated using a photolithographic process and etching. After that, ohmic contacts were made by immersing $n$-type HgCdTe in 10% $H(AuCl_4)\cdot3H_2O$ solution for 5 s. Finally, these samples were rinsed in deionized water for 5 min and blown dry using pure $N_2$.

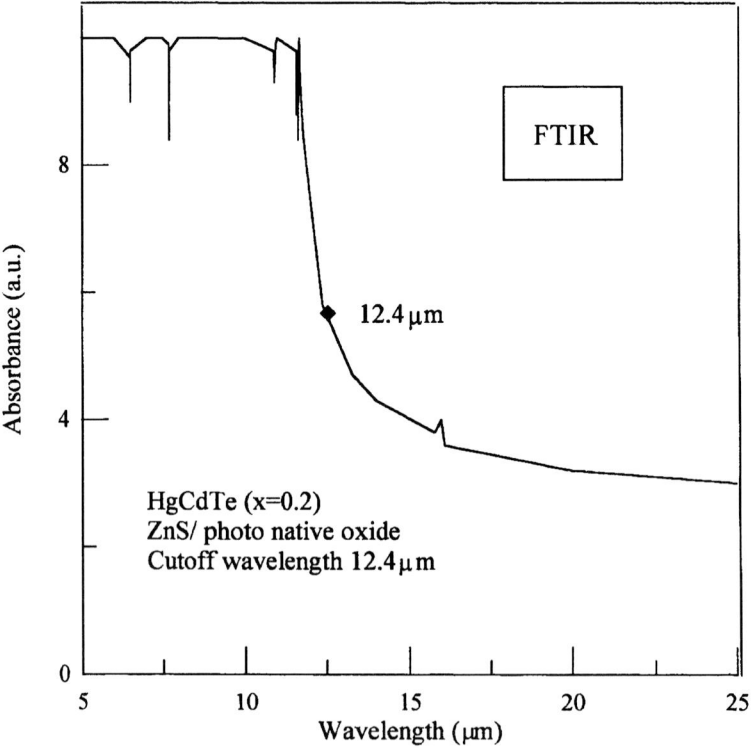

Fig. 4. The FTIR absorption spectrum of the photoconductive detector passivated stacked ZnS/ photo-enhanced native oxide layers.

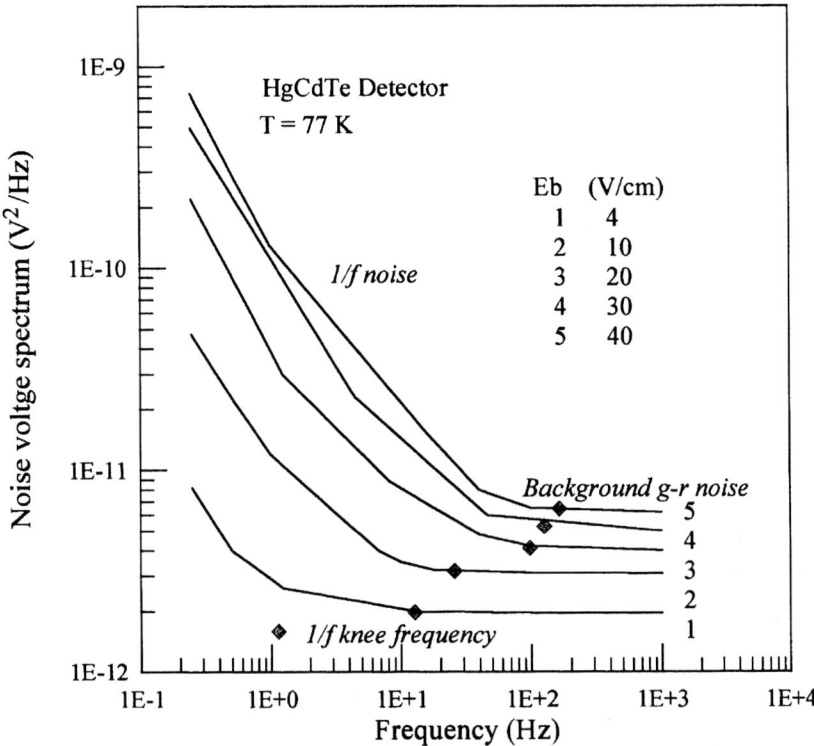

Fig. 5. Measured noise voltage as a function of frequency. These lines are drawn to present the $1/f$ noise at low frequency and the background $g - r$ noise level at high frequency. The star points represent the $1/f$ *knee* frequency.

Figure 4 is the FTIR measurement, and it obviously indicates that the cutoff wavelength of $\lambda_c$ is about 12.4 $\mu$m. The first important parameter which needs to be considered for any detector is the noise performance of the detector. Some noise components will appear at frequency spectrum; the measured detector PC-9601A was deposited on the ZnS with photo surface treatment at 77 K, as shown in Fig. 5. If the noise voltage spectrum is plotted on log–log paper, the resulting graph will approach a straight line at low frequency. It has been demonstrated that the relative $1/f$ noise in a semiconductor resistor could be represented by[12]

$$\frac{S_I(f)}{I^2} = \frac{\alpha_H}{f^\gamma N},\qquad(13)$$

where $I$ is the bias current, $f$ is the frequency, the exponent $\gamma$ is close to unity, and $\alpha_H$ is the Hooge parameter. The frequency exponent $\gamma$ of the $1/f^\gamma$ spectrum for three different passivations are listed in Table 1.

We now discuss how $\alpha_H$ can be determined experimentally. Equation (13) can be directly transformed, and frequency $f$ was set as 1 Hz;

$$\alpha_H = \frac{f^\gamma S_I(f)N}{I^2} = \frac{S_I(1)N}{I^2},\qquad(14)$$

Table 1. Parameters of HgCdTe photoconductive detectors passivated with different passivation.

| Passivation Type | ZnS | ZnS+photo Surface Treatment | CdTe+photo Surface Treatment |
|---|---|---|---|
| Optical Area ($\mu$m$\times\mu$m) | $40 \times 10$ | $40 \times 10$ | $40 \times 10$ |
| Blackbody Temperature (°C) | 500 | 500 | 500 |
| Background Temperature (K) | 300 | 300 | 300 |
| $\gamma$ | 1.1 | 1.1 | 0.96 |
| $\alpha_H$ | $2 \times 10^{-3}$ | $5 \times 10^{-5}$ | $7.5 \times 10^{-5}$ |
| $S/N$ | 1040 | 2434 | 650 |
| $D^*$ for blackbody radiation(cmHz$^{1/2}$W$^{-1}$) | $14 \times 10^{10}$ | $3 \times 10^{10}$ | $8.6 \times 10^{9}$ |

where $\alpha_H$ is the Hoog parameter. From Fig. 5, we can determine that the value $\alpha_H$ of this device in the $1/f$ noise region was $\alpha_H = 5 \times 10^{-5}$. In the same method, $\alpha_H$ can be identified with different passivation layers, each resulting in a characteristic value for $\alpha_H$, shown in Table 1. For HgCdTe photoconductive detectors, $\alpha_H$ depends on the process involved. If photo surface treatment was used, we can reduce the $\alpha_H$ significantly. In Fig. 5, the $1/f$ *knee* frequency was measured around $1 \sim 150$ Hz under electrical field bias of 50 V/cm. The background $g - r$ noise is equal to the $1/f$ noise at vicinal $1/f$ *knee* frequency, and the noise voltage spectrum was flat toward high frequency as well as proportional to the electrical field bias. Based on the above results, we can confirm that the detector, with photo surface treatment, has broad operating frequency bandwidth satisified with background $g - r$ noise limited performance.

Next, we compare the $1/f$ noise spectral density and $1/f$ *knee* frequency curves obtained from different passivations, as shown in Fig. 6. Figure 6(a) shows the $1/f$ noise versus electrical field bias at operating frequency of 1 Hz. Figure 6(a) indicates that, with photo surface treatment, the noise was reduced by a factor of 100 and irrespective of whether ZnS or CdTe forms the second stage has the near noise spectral intensity. Figure 6(b) shows the $1/f$ *knee* frequency versus electrical field bias for different passivations. The photo surface treatment offers the lowest $1/f$ *knee* frequency at all values of electrical field bias. An important observation that the HgCdTe surface properties were indeed improved by photo surface treatment, can be made from previous data.

In the present case, we may select an operating frequency to avoid $1/f$ noise and we have measured the $g - r$ noise and responsivity for the following condition:

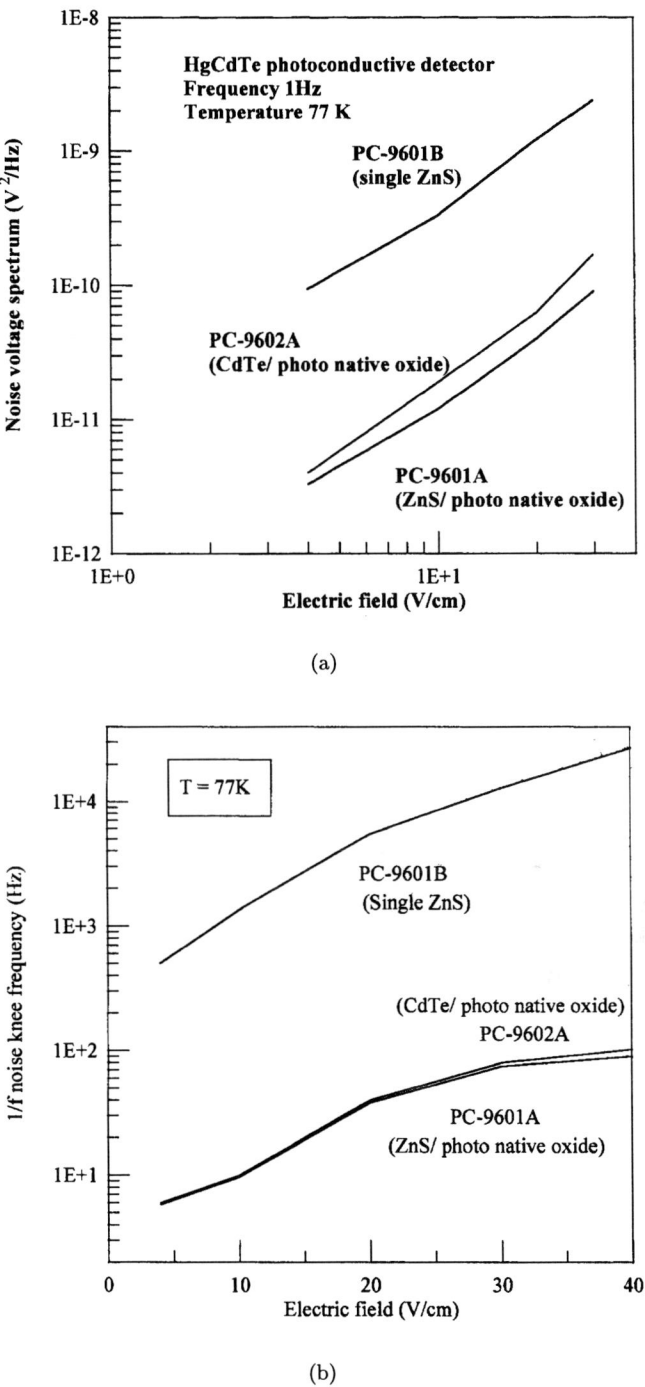

Fig. 6. (a) $1/f$ noise voltage versus electrical field at 1 Hz, showing linear dependence at log–log plot, (b) $1/f$ knee frequency versus electrical field. The $1/f$ knee frequency strongly depends on passivated method and photo surface treatment could improve the $1/f$ noise and $g - r$ noise.

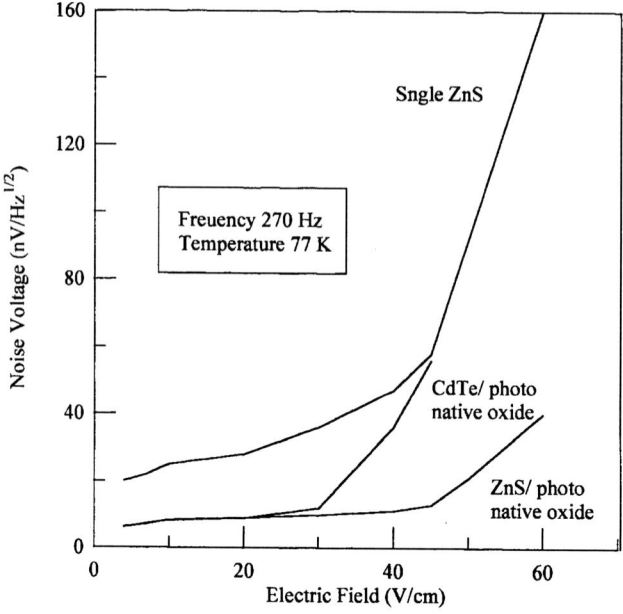

Fig. 7. Noise of HgCdTe photoconductive detectors deposited with different passivations versus electrical field.

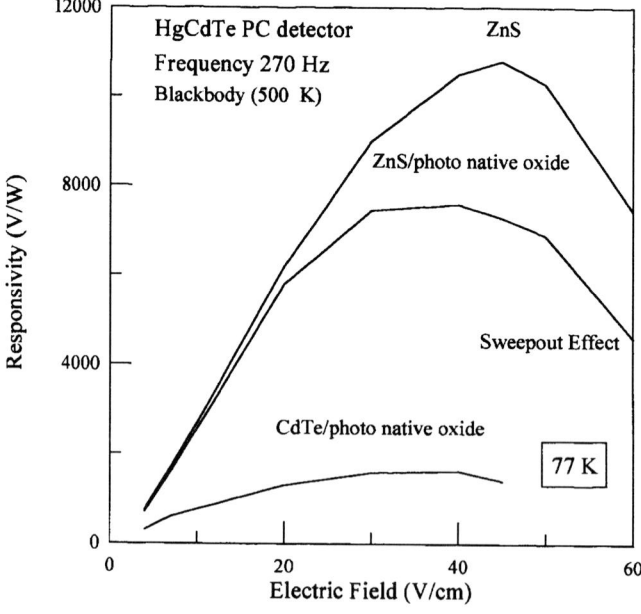

Fig. 8. Responsivity of HgCdTe detectors with different passivations versus electrical field. The sweepout effect would obviously occur when electrical field value of 40 V/cm.

operating at central frequency 270 Hz with 60 Hz bandwidth at 77 K. Then, we compare different surface passivations: CdTe/photo-enhanced native oxide, ZnS/photo-enhanced native oxide, and ZnS to find their effect on $g - r$ noise and responsivity. Figure 7 shows the measured noise as a function of electric field bias. Pictorially, we can illustrate the improvment of $g - r$ noise due to photo surface treatment. Figure 8 shows the responsivity of HgCdTe photoconductive detectors, which were deposited with different passivations, versus applied electrical field bias measurement. By comparing the three curves, we can clearly see that the responsivity of the detector with photo surface treatment is lower than the detector without photo surface treatment; meanwhile, the responsivity of the detector with CdTe deposited as second stage is obviously lower than the detector with ZnS deposited. To demonstrate these results, we consider two factors: IR reflection and IR absorption effects. In the first instance, there are some IR reflection that would happen in the stacked passivations structure. After some mathematical manipulation, the amount of IR reflection is found about 30%. The thickness of ZnS or CdTe can be adjusted as AR coating to prevent IR reflection in practical device fabrication. Secondly, it has been found that the energy band-gaps of CdTe and ZnS are about 1.6 eV and 3.4 eV, respectively. The responsivity of CdTe passivation would be worse than the responsivity of ZnS passivation, since some incident photo energy is absorbed within the CdTe and photo native oxides regions. Both

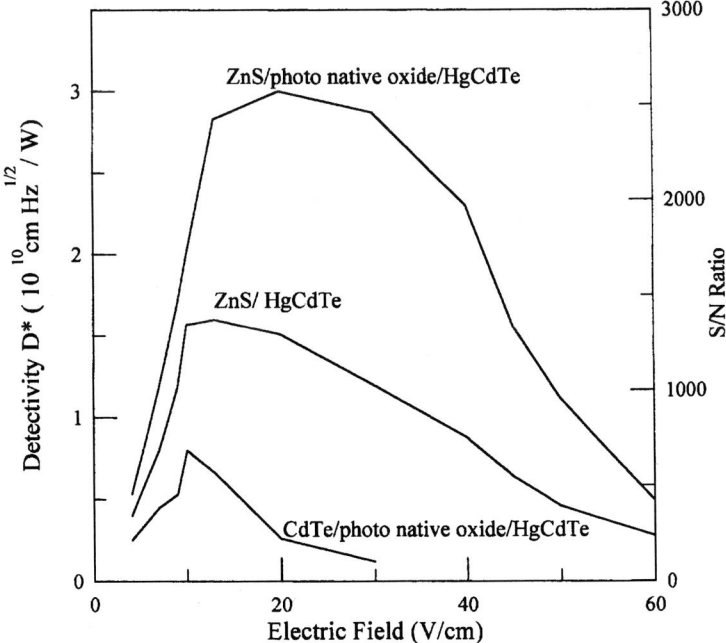

Fig. 9. Measured $D^*$ as a function of electrical field for blackbody radiation and background temperature 300 K.

IR reflection and absorption effects reduce the total number of steady state excess carriers, so the responsivity would be reduced. Based on the above statement, photo surface treatment seems to promote low responsivity. However, photo surface treatment would obviously improve the noise characteristics. Low responsivity is not itself an insurmountable problem; it is always possible to increase signal levels by adding amplifiers to the signal processing. Signal to noise ratio $S/N$ does describe the "clean-liness" of a given signal level. Finally, to characterize our $Hg_{0.8}Cd_{0.2}Te$ photoconductive detectors, the specific detectivity $D^*$ values can be calculated according to Eq. (12). The signal to noise ratio $S/N$ and the specific detectivity $D^*$ versus different external bias are presented in Fig. 9. By comparing the three curves shown in Fig. 9, we can see that the specific detectivity $D^*$ are increased with electrical field bias until a sweepout effect is reached. Furthermore, the specific detectivity $D^*$ of detector passivated stacked ZnS/photo native oxide passivations, due to its relative low value of $g - r$ noise, would have increased two times as the single ZnS detector passivated. Recently, deposition of CdTe on HgCdTe surfaces emerged as a very promising method by MBE or MOCVD. Especially, these techniques enable direct growth of high quality CdTe on top of HgCdTe in a single run. However, owing to the IR absorption effect, the optical proprties of CdTe is worse than ZnS. In our photoconductors, the maximum specific detectivity $D^*$ and signal to noise ratio are about $3 \times 10^{10}$ cm $Hz^{1/2}W^{-1}$ and 2434 for blackbody radiation, respectively.

## 5. Conclusion

Using the conventional approach to fabricate $Hg_{0.8}Cd_{0.2}Te$ photoconductive detector arrays leaves a Hg rich effect and an unstable interface. An improved detector fabrication technology called photo surface treatment is an easy, vapor phase, and reproducible process. It has been shown that photo surface treatment would improve electrical and optical properties of the $Hg_{0.8}Cd_{0.2}Te$ detector by experiments, involving Hall measurement, MIS leakage current, noise, responsivity, and specific detectivity in this paper. These improvements are attributed to the excellent interface between photo native oxide and the HgCdTe substrate. Finally, we expect that the technology of the surface treatment will be applied in the HgCdTe photovoltaic detector and will lead to a much better results in future research.

## Acknowledgment

This work is supported by the Chung Institute of Science and Technology under contract number: NSC. 85-2623-D-006-004 and National Science Council, Republic of China, under Contract No. NSC. 85-2215-E-006-004.

## References

1. Y. Nemirovsky and G. Bahir, "Passivation of mercury cadmium telluride surfaces", *J. Vac. Sci. Technol.* **A7**, 2 (1989) 450–459.

2. Y. Nemirovsky and I. Kidron, "The Interface between $Hg_{1-x}Cd_xTe$ and its native oxide", *Solid State Electronics* **22** (1979) 831–837.

3. G. Bahir, V. Ariel, V. Garber, D. Rosenfeld, and A. Sher, "Electrical properties of epitaxially grown CdTe passivation for long-wavelength HgCdTe photodiodes", *Appl. Phys. Lett.* **65**, 21 (1994) 2725–2727.

4. Y. Nemirovsky, "Passivation with II-VI compounds", *J. Vac. Sci. Technol.* **A8**, 2 (1990) 1185–1187.

5. Nili Mainzer, Eliezer Weiss, Daniel Laser, and Michael Shaanan, "Effect of anodic fluoro-oxide on the thermal stability of $Hg_{1-x}Cd_xTe$ photoconductive arrays", *J. Vac. Sci. Technol.* **A7** 2 (1989) 460–463.

6. J. D. Lin, Y. K. Su, S. J. Chang, M. Yokoyama, and F. Y. Juang, "Passivation with $SiO_2$ on HgCdTe by direct photochemical-vapor deposition", *J. Vac. Sci. Technol.* **A12**, 1 (1994) 7–11.

7. C. T. Lin, Y. K. Su, H. T. Huang, S. J. Chang, G. S. Chen, T. P. Sun, and J. J. Luo, "Electrical properties of the stacked ZnS/Photo-enhanced native oxide passivation for long wavelength HgCdTe Photodiodes", *IEEE Photon. Techno. Lett.* **8** (1996) 676–678.

8. Yan-Kuin Su, Chung-Te Lin, Hsin-Tien Huang, Shoou-Jinn Chang, Tai-Ping Sun, Gin-Shiang Chen, and Jiunn-Jye Luo, "Electrical properties of high-quality stacked CdTe/photo-enhanced native oxide for long HgCdTe passivation", *Jpn. J. Appl. Phys.* **35**, 1, 2B (1996) 107–109.

9. J. F. Siliquini, C. A. Musca, B. D. Nener, and L. Faraone, "Temperature dependence of $Hg_{0.68}Cd_{0.32}Te$ infrared photoconductor performance", *IEEE Trans. Electron Devices* **42** (1995) 1441–1448.

10. E. Finkman and S. E. Schacham, "Surface recombination velocity of anodic sulfide and ZnS coated p-HgCdTe", *J. Vac. Sci. Technol.* **A7**, 2 (1989) 464–468.

11. Jose L. Melendez and Jeff Beck, "The role of the insulator in determining $1/f$ noise in $Hg_{1-x}Cd_xTe$ integrating MIS devices", *J. of Electron. Mat.* **22**, 8 (1993) 993–998.

12. Xi-Chen Zhu, Xiaolan Wu, A. Van Der Ziel, and E. G. Kelso, "The Hooge parameters for $n$-and $p$-type $Hg_{1-x}Cd_xTe$", *IEEE Trans. Electron Devices* **ED-32**, 7 (1985) 1353–1354.

International Journal of High Speed Electronics and Systems, Vol. 8, No. 4 (1997) 719–732

# ELECTRO-OPTIC CHARACTERIZATION OF MICROWAVE STANDING WAVES IN A GaAs TRANSMISSION LINE BY USING A NOVEL PHASE ANALYZING TECHNIQUE

CI-LING PAN, GONG-RU LIN, JIA-MIN SHIEH, CHIA-WEN TSAI, and S.-C. WANG

*Institute of Electro-optical Engineering,*
*National Chiao Tung University,*
*Hsinchu, Taiwan 300, R.O.C.*

HSIAO-HUA WU

*Department of Physics, Tunghai University, Taichung, Taiwan 407, R.O.C.*

We demonstrate an accurate, non-contact and compact characterization technique for measuring both the amplitude and phase component of microwave standing-wave patterns in a GaAs microstrip transmission line. A laser-diode-based optoelectronic phase lock loop was employed as a phase-referencing scheme. Key parameters such as voltage standing-wave ratio and reflection coefficient for a GaAs microstrip transmission line were determined up to 16 GHz. Dispersion characteristics were found in good agreement with selected theoretical models.

## 1. Introduction

The standing wave pattern of guided microwave or millimeter waves in monolithic microwave integrated circuits (MMIC's) can provide a wealth of information on guided wave structures. Properties and parameters such as dispersion characteristics, impedance mismatch between waveguide transitions or discontinuities, and properties of the guided modes can be deduced. Conventional slotted line techniques become impractical at high microwave frequencies due to the influence of the contact probe which introduces unwanted parasitic impedance. While the electro-optic sampling and related techniques[1,2] have been extensively employed for ultrafast transient measurements, relatively less attention has been paid to their applications in noncontact microwave standing wave measurements. Previously, one of the authors (C.-L. Pan) and co-workers have reported direct and non-invasive probing of standing waves in GaAs coplanar waveguides at frequencies up to 20.01 GHz. Compressed YAG laser pulses and the electro-optic harmonic mixing technique were employed.[3,4] In these early experiments, only scalar measurements were made and the S/N's of the data were relatively poor. Some measurement results of standing waves in microstrip lines have also been reported by Weingarten *et al.*[5] The characteristics of even and odd modes of a coupled slot line were also investigated by the electro-optic standing wave measurement technique.[6]

However, little attention was paid to the phase components in these earlier measurements. Lately, we have successfully developed laser-diode-based optoelectronic phase-tracking techniques for electro-optic and photoconductive sampling.[7-10] Using this scheme, the waveform of free-running microwave signals up to 20 GHz with ultralow root-mean-square (rms) phase fluctuation was reported.[11] Since this is a frequency-domain technique, it also allows phase-tracking and sampling at frequencies well beyond the 3dB bandwidth of the gain-switched laser diode pulses. Taking advantage of the excellent sensitivity for this phase measurement scheme, we report for the first time accurate and non-contact vector measurements of standing-wave patterns using a laser-diode-based system in this paper. A GaAs microstrip transmission line (MTL) was characterized by analyzing the phase data of the standing waves in the range of 4 to 16 GHz. Our experimental results are in good agreement with selected theoretical models.

## 2. Basic Principles

Our technique is based on the optoelectronic phase lock loop (OEPLL). It consists of an optoelectronic harmonic mixer (OEHM) and a conventional electronic phase lock loop. A generic OEPLL is shown schematically in Fig. 1. In this approach, a sample of the microwave signal, $f_m$, is heterodyned with the $M$th harmonic of an optical pulse train at a repetition frequency of $f_0$. This is illustrated in Fig. 2. The OEHM generates an output at the intermediate frequency (IF), $f_{IF} = M f_0 - f_m$. This is filtered, amplified, and fed to a phase detector (PD) where it is compared in phase with a reference signal from a signal source synchronized to the optical pulse train. The output of the PD is then sent to a voltage-controlled-oscillator (VCO) for tracking the optical pulse train. In reality, the microwave signal might be free-running and originate from a MMIC. We employ gain-switched laser diodes

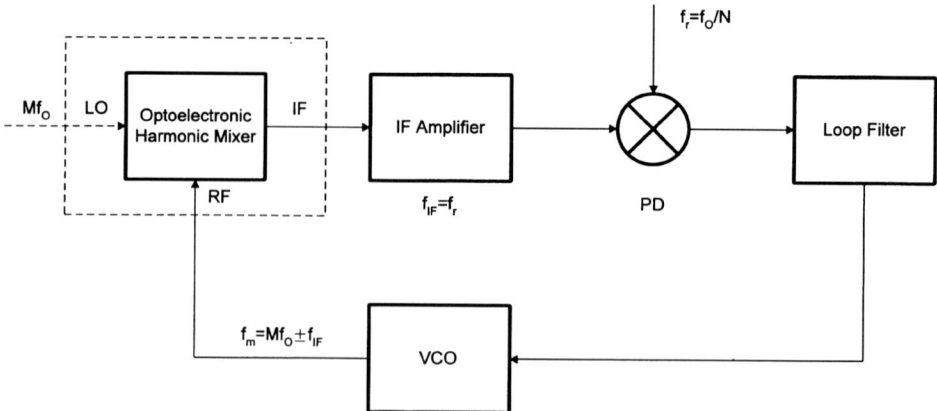

Fig. 1. The block diagram of a generic OEPLL — LO: local oscillator; IF: intermediate frequency; VCO: voltage-controlled oscillator.

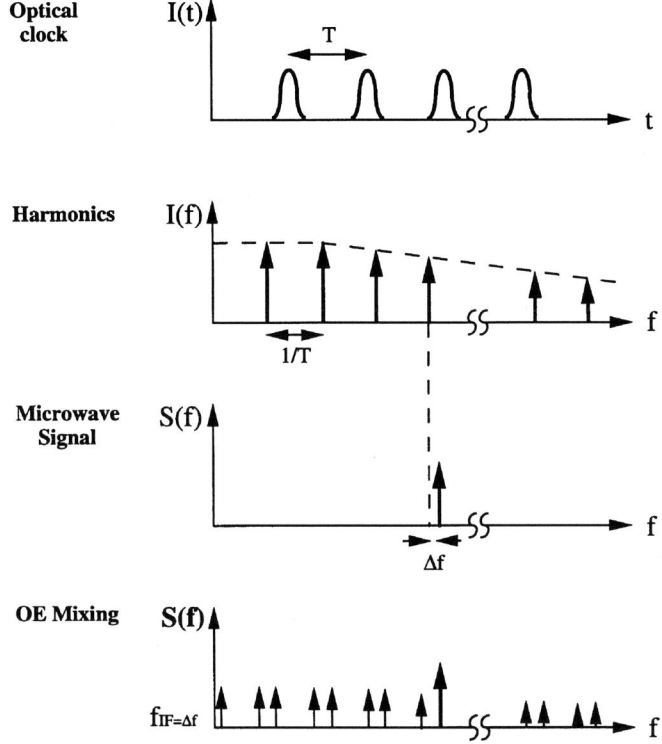

Fig. 2. A schematic illustrating the basic principle of optoelectronic harmonic mixing.

(GSLD's) as optical local oscillators. These can be driven by the VCO for tracking the free-running oscillator (FRO) as the repetition frequency of GSLD can be varied easily.

The key component of the OEPLL is the OEHM. In this work, we employed a microwave-biased photoconductor as the OEHM, as shown in Fig. 3. It consists of a high-speed photoconductor incorporated into a transmission line. The microwave signal traveling down the transmission is interrupted by the photoconductive gap, where it mixes with the harmonic frequency components of the optoelectronically generated electrical pulse train. It can be shown that the IF photocurrent is

$$i_{photon} = \frac{R_{pc} I_0 \tau \sqrt{\pi/\ln 2}}{2T} \sum_{n=1}^{\infty} \exp^{-(n\omega_0\tau)^2/16\ln 2} \sin[n\omega_0 - \omega_m], \qquad (1)$$

where $R_{pc}$ is the photoresistance of the photoconductor; $I_0$, $\tau$, $T$, $\omega_0$, are respectively the peak intensity, pulse width, period, and angular frequency of the laser while $\omega_m$ is the angular frequency of the microwave signal. The conversion loss is given by

$$\frac{P_{in}}{P_{out}} = \frac{R_{pc}}{R_L}, \qquad (2)$$

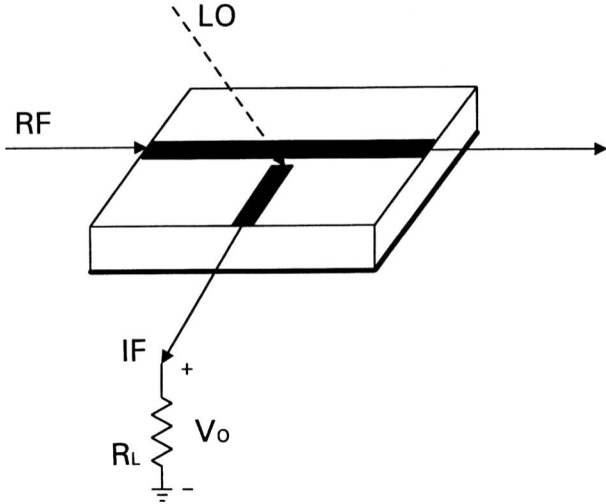

Fig. 3. The photoconductive switch as an OEHM: $R_L$ is the load resistance at the IF port.

where $P_{in}$ and $P_{out}$ are microwave and IF power respectively, and $R_L$ is the load resistance at the IF port. In the short-noise limit, the signal-to-noise ratio of the OEHM is

$$\frac{S}{N} = \frac{V_m(R_{pc} + R_L)}{2\sqrt{2}qBR_{pc}^2},$$  (3)

where $V_m$ is the peak value (in volts) of the microwave signal biasing the photo-conductor; $q$ is the electronic charge; and $B$ is the IF bandwidth.

## 3. Experimental

The experimental apparatus is shown in Fig. 4. It consists of two sub-systems: an optoelectronic phase locked loop (OEPLL) for phase-tracking and a reflection-mode electro-optic sampler (EOS). A sweep oscillator (HP8350B mainframe with HP83592B plug-in) operating in the cw mode simulates as the free-running oscillator (FRO). The typical variation of the FRO output frequency, $f_m$, was $\approx \pm 200$ kHz to $\pm 600$ kHz over a period of 10 minutes for $f_m$ in the range of 4–20 GHz. For phase tracking of the free-running microwave signal, a laser-diode-based OEPLL[4] was employed. In the OEPLL, a gain-switched laser diode, GSLD1 ($\lambda = 0.8$ $\mu$m) driven by a voltage-controlled oscillator (VCO, a HP8640B operated in the FM mode) at $f_0 \approx 500$ MHz, functioned as the optical local oscillator. The average optical power was 0.3 mW and the laser pulsewidth was 45 ps. A GaAs:Cr photoconductive switch with a 10 $\mu$m gap was used as the optoelectronic harmonic mixer (OEHM). It was used for intermixing the microwave signal and higher-order harmonics of

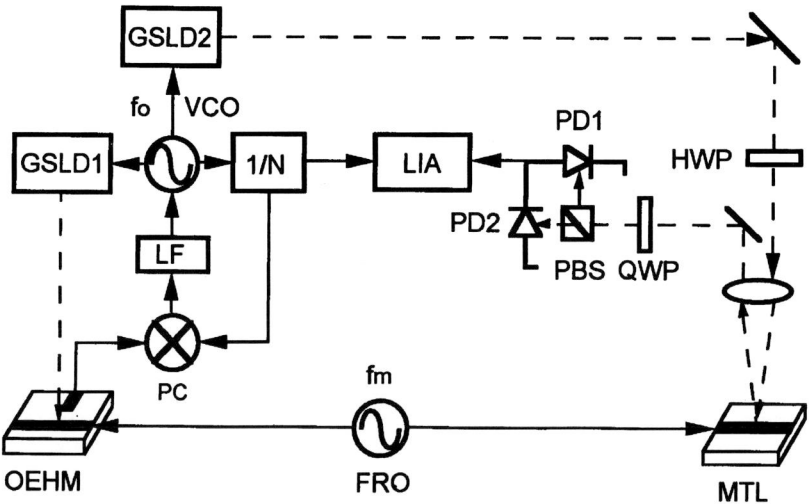

Fig. 4. Schematic diagram of the OEPLL based electro-optic standing wave measurement system. FRO: free-running oscillator; LF: low-pass filter; PC: phase comparater; LIA: lock-in amplifier; PD1 and PD2: photodiodes; PBS: polarization beam splitter; QWP: quarter-wave plate; HWP: half-wave plate.

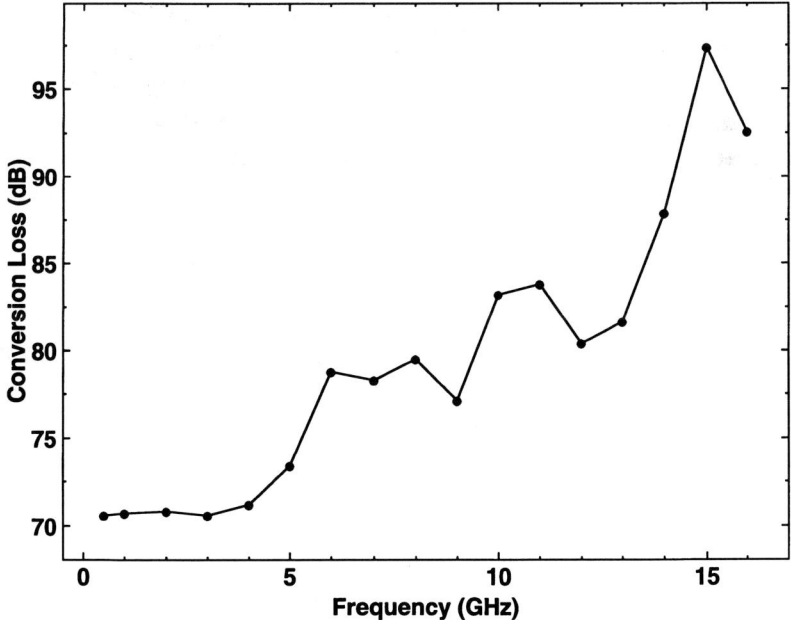

Fig. 5. Conversion loss of the GaAs optoelectronic harmonic mixer as a frequency of the microwave frequency.

the laser pulse train to generate a desired intermediate frequency (IF) signal. The intermediate frequency is $f_{IF} = Mf_0 - f_m$, where $M$ is an integer and corresponds to the order of the harmonics generated. The phase of the IF signal was then compared with that of the IF reference signal $f_{ref}$ using an analog phase comparator (PC, EXAR model XR-2208). The IF reference signal was derived from the VCO through a frequency divider (i.e. $f_{ref} = f_0/N$, where $N$ is integer). The error signal generated from the phase comparator was then fed back to the VCO via an active loop filter (LF). The OEPLL achieves stable phase tracking of optical pulse trains from GSLD1 to the free-running oscillator (FRO) at frequencies, $f_m \approx Nf_0 \pm f_{IF}$, beyond 20 GHz.[11] A typical single-side-band (SSB) phase noise of this OEPLL phase-tracked to the microwave signal of $f_m = 16$ GHz was about $-70$ dBc/Hz at 1 kHz offset from the carrier frequency. The conversion loss (defined as the power ratio of the microwave to IF signal) of the OEHM is shown in Fig. 5. At 16 GHz, the loss was $\approx -39$ dB. The S/N ratio was 58 dB. The 3 dB IF band width was in excess of 200 kHz.

For electro-optic measurement of the standing wave pattern, we employed a reflection-mode electro-optic sampler modified to take advantage of improved S/N (by a factor of 2) of the differential detection scheme. The optical probe pulse was provided by another gain-switched laser diode (GSLD2, $\lambda = 1.3$ $\mu$m) driven by the same phase-locked VCO. Its average power was 0.5 mW and the pulsewidth was 40 ps. The laser beam from GSLD2 through a halfwave plate was focused and scanned along the edge of the planar waveguide. The reflected signal was intensity-modulated by the electric field of the standing waves along the transmission line. A pair of InGaAs photodiodes (PD1 and PD2), a polarizing beam splitter (PBS), and a quarter wave plate (QWP), completed the rest of the optical detection system. For signal processing, we employed a lock-in amplifier (LIA) with an external reference source at the intermediate frequency, $f_{IF}$, derived from the phase-locked VCO. This system allows measurement of both phase and amplitude of the standing wave pattern simultaneously and accurately.

## 4. Results and Analysis

We have characterized a GaAs microstrip transmission line (MTL) by using this technique. The MTL has a strip width of 0.76 mm and thickness of 0.975 mm. The strip was connected in series with a standard 50 $\Omega$ SMA connector by using a standard ribbon bonding process.

Figure 6 shows the magnitude and phase of the standing wave pattern on the MTL with open termination ($f_m = 16$ GHz). Note that the S/N of the phase data of the standing wave (Fig. 6(b)) is significantly better than that of the amplitude data (Fig. 6(a)). This indicates that the OEPLL technique can provide excellent phase tracking capability. We attribute the difference in S/N for Figs. 6(a) and 6(b) partly to minor variations in the lateral position of the beam with respect to the microstrip line during the scan. To verify this, we have measured the amplitude and

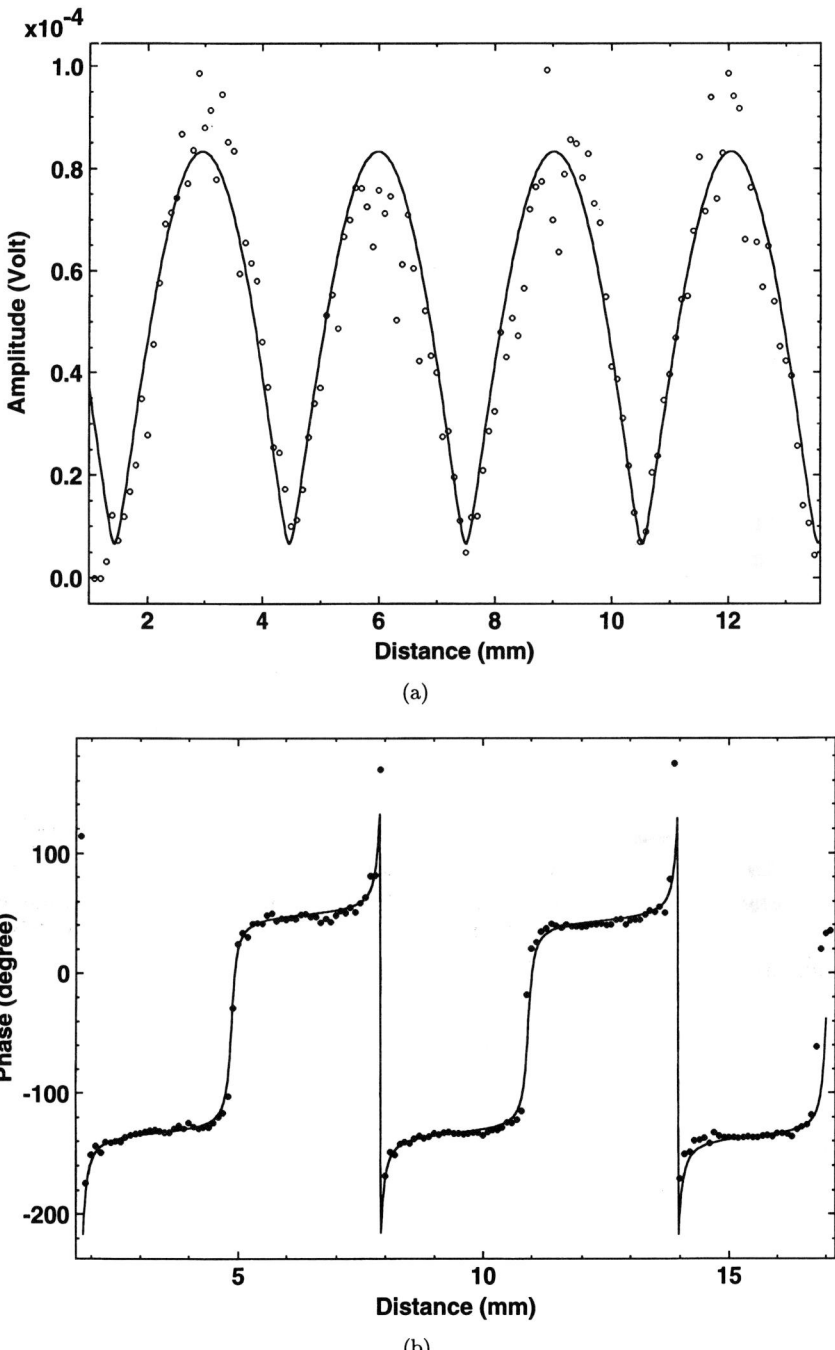

Fig. 6. (a) Magnitude and (b) phase of the standing wave pattern of 16 GHz microwave signals in a GaAs microstrip transmission line with an open terminal. The open circles are data points. The solid lines are the theoretical fits using Eqs. (4) and (5).

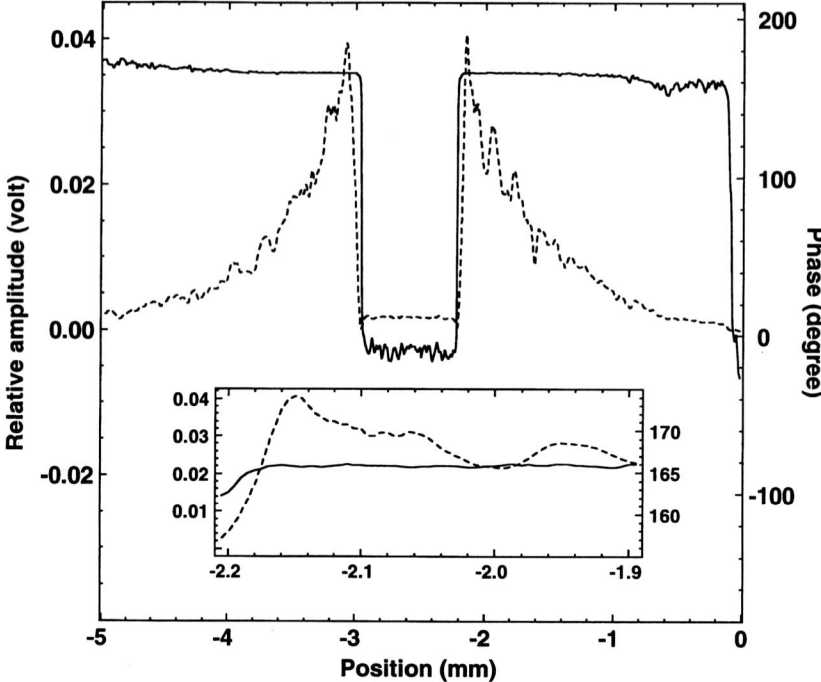

Fig. 7. The amplitude and phase components of the microwave electric field distributed along the transverse direction of the GaAs transmission line.

phase distribution of the electric field transverse to the propagation direction of the transmission line, as shown in Fig. 7. The amplitude component of the microwave signal decays almost exponentially away from the strip along the transverse direction. The phase component, on the other hand, remains almost constant. This can be understood as follows: The laser probed the lateral fringe field region along the edge of the transmission line. The amplitude of the electro-optic signal can vary significantly (up to 30%) even with a lateral displacement of the probe spot as small as tens of microns in magnitude. In comparison, the corresponding phase fluctuation is typically 0.5° or less. The above result suggests that the phase data of the standing wave pattern should be less susceptible to ptical misalignment during the scan. Furthermore, the phase data is relatively insensitive to the amplitude noise of the microwave signal as well as the intensity noise of the laser. This is demonstrated in Fig. 8, in which we have plotted the long-term amplitude and phase noise of the electro-optic sampler. For a microwave signal with power of 12.5 dBm at $f_m = $ 16 GHz, the electro-optic signal measured by the LIA was $\approx$ 70 $\mu V_{rms}$ with a rms noise density of about 5.5 $\mu V/\sqrt{Hz}$, or S/N $\approx$ 16. The corresponding rms phase fluctuation was 0.025 radians (or 1.5°) for a noise bandwidth of 1 Hz, or S/N $\approx$ 500.

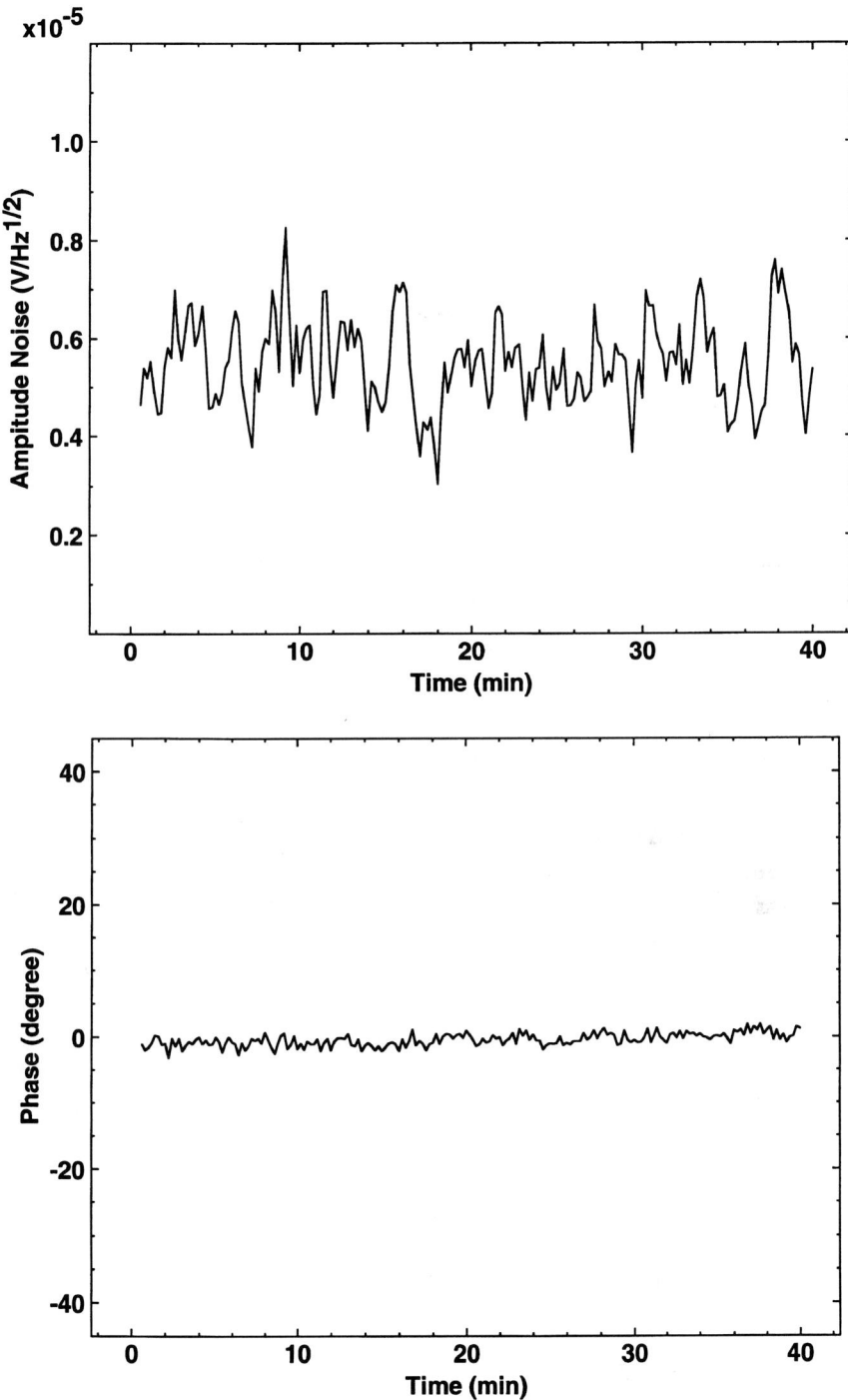

Fig. 8. Long-term stabilities of the amplitude and phase of the electro-optic probe signal.

Key parameters of the MTL can be deduced by analyzing the standing wave pattern in either Figs. 6(a) or 6(b). The amplitude of the standing-wave patterns in a microwave transmission line can be expressed as[12]

$$|V| \propto \sqrt{1 + \Gamma_2 + 2\Gamma \cos\left(\frac{4\pi n_f}{\lambda_o}\right)} L, \qquad (4)$$

where $\Gamma$ is the reflection coefficient and $n_f$ is the effective refractive index of the MTL. The phase of the standing wave, on the other hand, is a transcendental function given by:

$$\theta = \tan^{-1}\left[\left(\frac{1 + |\Gamma|}{1 - |\Gamma|}\right)^{-1} \tan\left(\frac{2\pi n_f}{\lambda_0}L\right)\right]. \qquad (5)$$

The solid lines in Figs. 6(a) and 6(b) are the best fitted curves using Eqs. (4) and (5) by fine adjustment of the parameters $\Gamma$ and $n_f$. Although either the amplitude or the phase component of the standing wave pattern can be used in determination of $\Gamma$ and $n_f$, clearly the phase data would be much more sensitive to these parameters due to the transcendental functional dependence. The phase measurement can thus provide more accurate determination of both $\Gamma$ and $n_f$. Furthermore, only a half cycle of the standing-wave pattern is needed for the phase fitting process. This also facilitates measurements at longer wavelengths on relatively short transmission lines. For the data shown in Fig. 6(b), we obtained $\Gamma = 0.86$ and $n_f = 3.092$ for the GaAs MTL structure. The normalized errors are $\Delta\Gamma/\Gamma \leq 1\%$ and $\Delta n_f/n_f < 0.3\%$ respectively. The corresponding voltage-standing-wave-ratio (VSWR) is about 13.3. In comparison, we can only obtain a cursory evaluation of the $\Gamma$ and VSWR of about $0.86 \sim 0.94$ and $13.3 \sim 33.3$ with significantly larger error bar of $\Delta\Gamma/\Gamma \approx 4.5\%$ from the fitting of the amplitude data in Fig. 6(a). In Fig. 9, we show the standing wave pattern for the MTL terminated with 50 $\Omega$. The solid curves are best-fit curves using Eqs. (4) and (5). We find that $\Gamma \approx 0.24$ as opposed to zero for a purely resistive matched load. To the best of our knowledge, this is the first time that characteristic parameters of microwave planar waveguides are determined in this manner.

By varying the microwave frequency, we also obtain the dispersion characteristics of the microstrip transmission line structure. In Fig. 10(a), we show the dependence of $n_f$ as a function of frequency for the MTL. The dispersion data are in good agreement with theoretical predictions calculated using a full-wave mode-matching method[13] and an approximate dispersion formula by Yamashita et al.[14] Fitting with other models such as the Hewlett-Packard Libra software were found to be less than satisfactory. The experimentally determined reflection coefficients are plotted as a function of frequency in Fig. 10(b). For comparison, we also measure by using the conventional network analyzer the $\Gamma$'s of an unconnected (open-terminated) SMA connector identical to the one used in MTL termination. This is illustrated as the

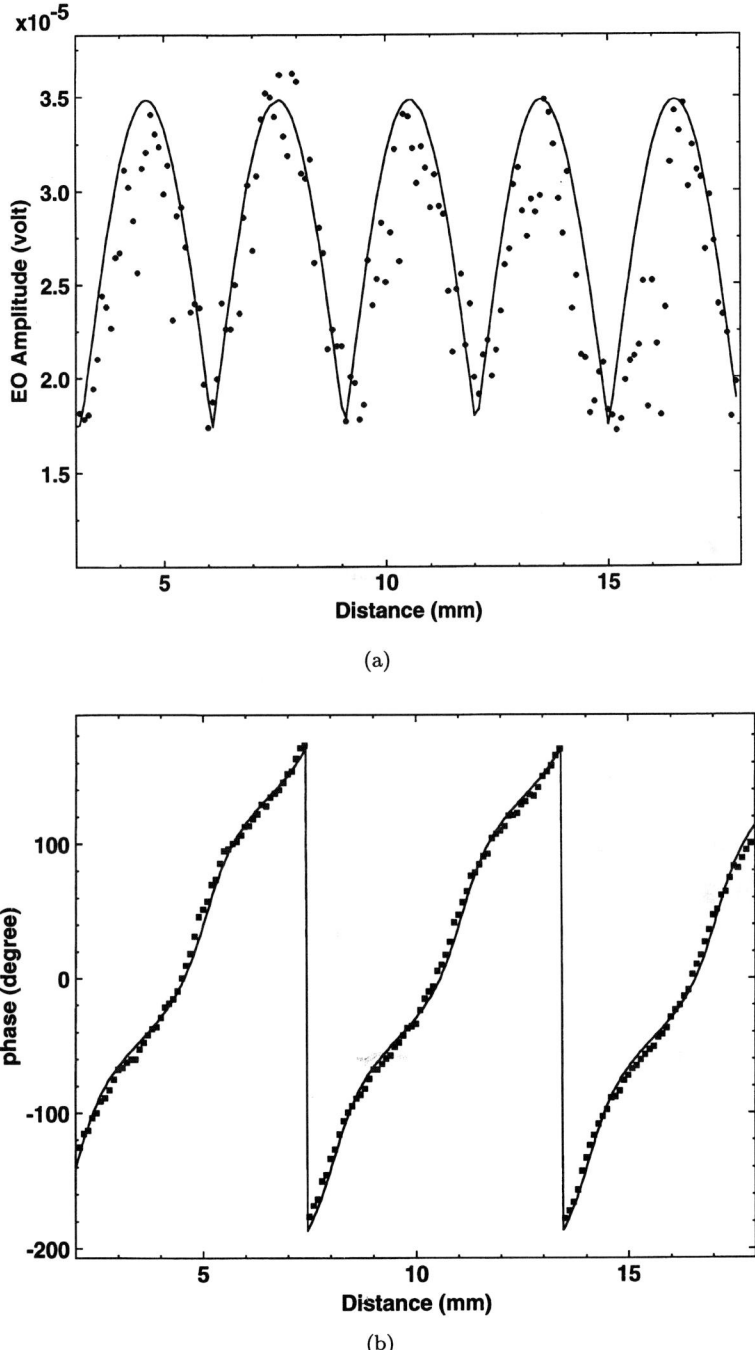

(a)

(b)

Fig. 9. (a) Magnitude and (b) phase of the standing wave pattern of 16 GHz microwave signals in a GaAs microstrip transmission line with 50 Ω termination. The open circles are data points. The solid lines are the theoretical fits using Eqs. (4) and (5).

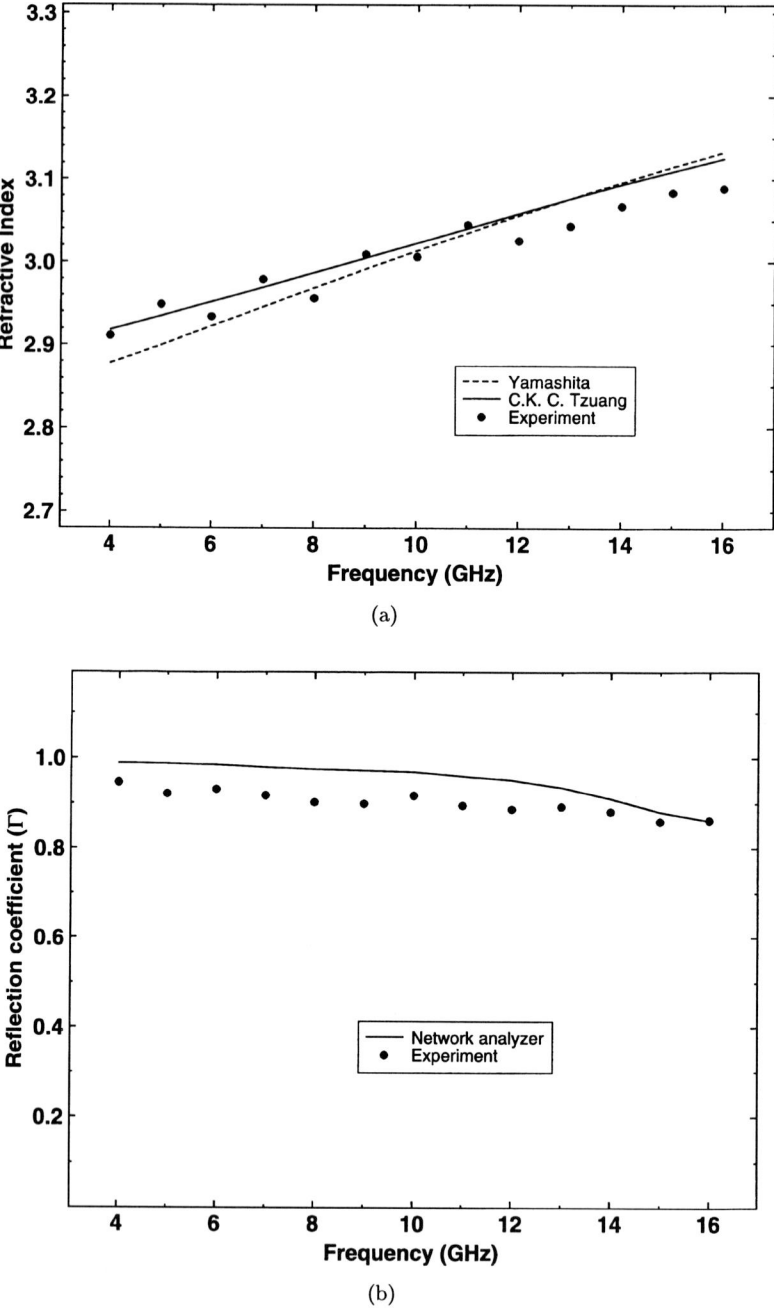

(a)

(b)

Fig. 10. (a) Dispersion of the MTL deduced from standing wave measurement. The solid circles are experimental data. The solid and dashed curves are theoretical values calculated using models presented in Refs. 13 and 14, respectively. (b) Reflection coefficients of the open-ended MTL are plotted as a function of frequency. The solid curve plotted data for the SMA connector terminating the MTL as determined by conventional network analysis techniques.

solid curve in Fig. 10(b). The data for the SMA terminating the end of a calibrated semi-rigid coaxial cable were utilized here to illustrate the discrepancy between the GaAs MTL and the standard coaxial cable associated with the network analyzer. Note that the data obtained from either the network analyzer or our measuring technique reveals the same frequency-dependent trend.

It is also interesting to compare the present technique with previous time-domain approaches for optoelectronic measurements of dispersion characteristics of microwave transmission lines.[15,16] The laser-diode-based system is much more compact and accurate. Furthermore, our technique also has several additional merits such as: (1) phase locking at the frequency beyond the 3dB bandwidth of the OEHM; (2) phase tracking of a free-running oscillator through easy tuning of the repetition rate of the gain-switched laser diode; (3) insensitive to amplitude noise and hence better S/N; (4) frequency-domain operation and no fourier transform of the time-domain data is required.

## 5. Summary

We report for the first time a novel phase-analyzing technique for direct and non-invasive vector measurement of microwave standing-wave patterns on microstrip transmission line at frequencies up to 16 GHz by using a laser-diode-based optoelectronic phase tracking and electro-optic sampling system. Dispersion characteristics for a GaAs microstrip transmission line were also determined and found in good agreement with selected models. Other key parameters, e.g. voltage standing-wave ratios and reflection coefficients can be more accurately deduced by utilizing this technique. As laser diodes generating ultrashort pulses and high-speed photoconductive switches become available, the extension of these measuring and analyzing techniques to higher microwave and millimeter-wave frequencies should be straightforward.

## Acknowledgments

This work was supported by the National Science Council of the ROC. The sweep oscillator was on loan from Prof. K. Tai. Data for Fig. 9 was taken by Mr. Dai-Sen Tsai.

## References

1. J. A. Valdmanis, "Electro-optic measurement techniques for picosecond materials, devices and integrated circuits", in *Measurements of High Speed Signal in Solid State Devices, Semiconductors and Semimetals*, vol. 28, eds. K. J. Weingarten and R. B. Marcus, Academic Press, New York, 1990, pp. 136–219.
2. K. J. Weingarten, M. J. W. Rodwell, and D. M. Bloom, "Picosecond optical sampling of GaAs integrated circuits", *IEEE J. Quantum Electron.* **24** (1988) 198–220.
3. Z. H. Zhu, C.-L. Pan, Y. H. Lo, M. C. Wu, S. Wang, B. H. Kolner, and S. Y. Wang, "Electro-optic measurement of standing waves in a GaAs coplanar waveguide", *Appl. Phys. Lett.* **50** (1987) 1228–1230.

4. Z. H. Zhu, M. C. Wu, Y. H. Lo, C.-L. Pan, S. Y. Wang, and S. Wang, "Measurements on standing waves in GaAs coplanar waveguide at frequencies up to 20.1 GHz by electro-optic probing", *J. Appl. Phys.* **64** (1988) 419–421.

5. K. J. Weingarten, M. J. W. Rodwell, J. L. Freeman, S. K. Diamond, and D. M. Bloom, in *Ultrafast Phenomena*, eds. V. G. R. Fleming and A. E. Siegman, Springer, New York, 1986.

6. R. Majdi-Ahy, K. J. Weingarten, M. Riaziat, B. A. Auld, and D. M. Bloom, "Electro-optic sampling measurement of coplanar waveguide (coupled slot line) modes", *Electron. Lett.* **23** (1987) 1262–1263.

7. H.-H. Wu, C.-S. Chang, and C.-L. Pan, "Optoelectronic phase-locking of microwave signals up to 18 GHz by a laser-diode-based GaAs:Cr photoconductive harmonic mixer", *IEEE Microwave Guided Wave Lett.* **2** (1992) 11–13.

8. C.-L. Pan and H.-H. Wu, "Synchronization of electrical and optical signals by using an optoelectronic timing discriminator in a phase-lock loop", *IEEE. Photon. Technol. Lett.* **4** (1992) 1298–1301.

9. H.-H. Wu, C.-S. Chang, and C.-L. Pan, "Electro-optic sampling of optoelectronically phase-locked 10.0 GHz microwave signals using semiconductor laser diodes", *Electron. Lett.* **27** (1991) 1622–1623.

10. H.-H. Wu, C.-S. Chang, and C.-L. Pan, "A laser-diode-based photoconductive harmonic mixer for microwave waveform and spectrum measurements," *IEEE Microwave Guided Wave Lett.* **2** (1992) 273–275.

11. H.-H. Wu, G.-R Lin, and C.-L. Pan, "Optoelectronic phase tracking and electrooptic sampling of free-running microwave signals up to 20 GHz in a laser-diode-based system", *IEEE Photon. Technol. Lett.* **7** (1995) 670–672.

12. R. E. Collins, *Foundation of Microwave Engineering*, McGraw-Hill, New York, 1996.

13. The calculations were performed by the group of C.-K. C. Tzuang. See, for example, C.-K. C. Tzuang, C.-C. Tien, and K.-K. Chan, "Full-wave investigation of leakage from a covered microstrip line with finite strip conductivity and thickness", *Proc. European Microwave Conf.*, 1990, pp. 543–548.

14. E. Yamashita, K. Atsuki, and T. Ueda, "An approximate dispersion formula of microstrip lines for computer-aided design of microwave integrated circuits", *IEEE Trans. Microwave Theory Tech.* **MTT-27** (1979) 1036–1038.

15. S.-L. L. Huang, Chi H. Lee, and Hing-Loi A. Hung, "Real-time linear time-domain network analysis using picosecond photoconductive mixer and samplers", *IEEE Trans. Microwave Theory Tech.* **MTT-43**, 6 (1995) 1281–1289.

16. D. E. Cooper, "Picosecond optoelectronic measurement of microstrip dispersion", *Appl. Phys. Lett.* **47**, 1 (1985) 33–35.

International Journal of High Speed Electronics and Systems, Vol. 8, No. 4 (1997) 733–748
© World Scientific Publishing Company

# REAL-TIME SHIFT-INVARIANT OPTICAL
# PATTERN RECOGNITION

YIH-SHYANG CHENG

*Institute of Optical Sciences, National Central University,*
*Chungli, Taiwan 32054, R.O.C.*

Shift invariance is an asset of the VanderLugt correlator, from which the location of
the identified object is automatically specified. The development of filters which possess
two or three types of invariance (shift, rotation, size, and distortion) simultaneously is
reviewed. Various real-time implementation of VanderLugt as well as joint-transform
correlators by utilizing spatial light modulators are also reviewed.

## 1. Introduction

Optical pattern recognition by complex spatial filtering was introduced by
VanderLugt[1] in 1964. The interferometrically constructed frequency-plane mask
can effectively control both the amplitude and phase of a transfer function although
it consists only of the pattern of absorption. This type of coherent optical processing has the potential to perform 2D pattern recognition at extremely high speed.
Hence, various techniques and different algorithms were developed.

To avoid the synthesis and alignment problem of the complex spatial filter in the
VanderLugt correlator (VLC), the joint-transform correlator (JTC) was proposed
by Weaver and Goodman[2] and independently by Rau[3] shortly after the introduction
of the VLC. However, due to the lack of efficient interface devices, little progress on
JTC was reported. In 1984, Yu and Lu[4] realized that using a magneto-optic device
as the input programmable object and a liquid crystal light valve as the real-time
readout device, the JTC can become a real-time programmable correlator. Since
then, development of the JTC has speeded up.

In optical pattern recognition, there are basically two approaches which are the
correlation approach and the neural network approach. Recent review of optical
neural network can be found in Refs. 5 and 6. In this paper, we focus our attention
on the development of the correlation approach, particularly in the development of
the shift-invariant correlator.

## 2. Comparison Between VLC and JTC

There are two major types of correlators for optical pattern recognition which are
the VLC and the JTC. The correlator with frequency plane complex matched spatial
filtering is known as the VLC while that using spatial domain filtering is the

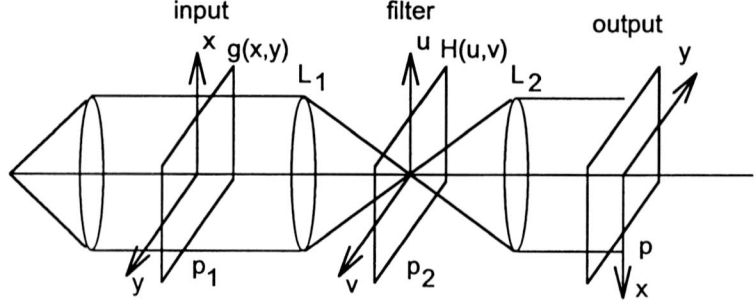

Fig. 1. VanderLugt correlator (VLC).

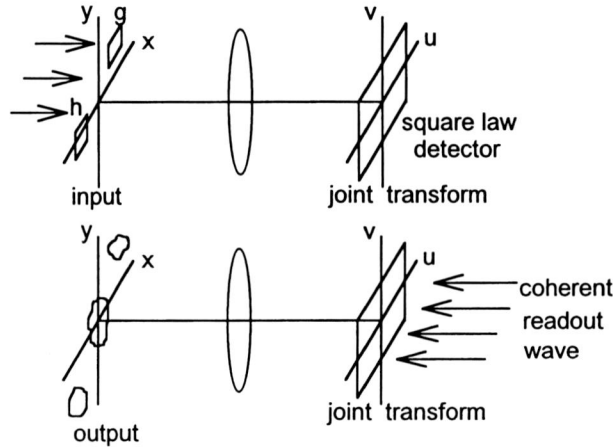

Fig. 2. A joint-transform correlator (JTC).

JTC. Figure 1 shows the usual 4-f coherent optical processing system. Light from a laser source is collimated before shining on the input object $g(x, y)$. The filter $H(u, v)$ is situated at the frequency plane. The object spectrum $G(u, v)$, carried by the laser light, is modified by the amplitude transmittance function of the filter. The resulted function $G(u, v)H(u, v)$ is then inverse Fourier transformed to the output plane $p$. If the filter function is the complex conjugate of the object spectrum, a bright autocorrelation spot will appear in the output plane. When the object is shifted laterally, the correlation spot would be shifted correspondingly. This shift-invariant characteristic is an asset of the optical correlator. Figure 2 shows a joint-transform correlator. Again, collimated laser light is utilized to illuminate the input object plane. Reference object $h(x, y)$ as well as the input object $g(x, y)$ are placed side by side in the object plane. A square law converter in the frequency plane detects the joint power spectrum (JPS) and converts it to be an amplitude transmittance function to be read out by a collimated wave. This amplitude transmittance function is then Fourier transformed by the final lens to the output plane. Both Fourier transforms (FT) may be carried out by a single lens with a beam splitter to guide the light to the output plane. When the reference object is identical with the input object, two autocorrelation spots appear symmetrical with respect to the origin of the output plane. The distance of the correlation spot from the origin of the coordinate system is the separation between two objects. The relative orientation of the correlation spots is the same as that between two objects. Hence, the shift-invariant property is also preserved in the JTC.

VLC relies on the prefabricated filter on the frequency plane. Once the filter is in position, each input object to be identified runs through the filter independently at the speed of light. In JTC, instead of the need for a matched filter $H(u, v)$, a spatial domain impulse response $h(x, y)$ is required. Although the JTC avoids the filter synthesis and alignment problems, it suffers from the problem of low detection efficiency in the situation of multi-object recognition or target imbedded in intensive noise.[7]

A conventional joint-transform correlator has some advantages including a high space-bandwidth product, a low carrier frequency, a higher degree of modulation, and suitability for real-time implementation. However, it also has some drawbacks which include inefficient usage of the illuminating light, requirement for large Fourier transform lens, stringent spatial coherence requirement, and overall small size of the joint-transform spectrum.[8] A nonconventional JTC[9] utilizing a small FT lens for the input object and the other for the reference object was proposed to eliminate the requirement for large lens. Based on the replication of the joint-transform power spectrum (JTPS) on a spatial light modulator (SLM) after the detection by CCD, a high efficiency JTC[10] was demonstrated. By using partial coherent readout wave with coherent width equal to the bandwidth of the Fourier spectrum, the correlation peak intensity would be increased to $[1 + NN]$ times that of the JTC, where $N$ is the number of repetitions for the JTPS. The coherent artifacts can also be suppressed leaving a correlation peak with a much better signal-to-noise ratio. To increase the effective focal length and hence enlarge the JTPS, a FT lens followed by a concave lens to form a Gallilean telescope[11,12] was proposed. This method can alleviate the problem of the oversmall size of the Joint transform spectrum.

## 3. Filter Design in VLC

Although the VLC can perform matched filtering at an extremely high speed, it is very sensitive to distortion of the input pattern from the reference pattern. The sensitivity depends on parameters such as the shape and the spatial frequency bandwidth of the object. For a moderate 30 $\mu$m resolution aerial image, a dramatic and disastrous loss in signal-to-noise ratio (SNR) from 30 to 3 dB occurs for a small 2 percent scale change or a 3.5° rotation.[13] By utilizing the scale-invariant property of the Mellin transform and noting that the Mellin transform can be performed as a FT of a stretched input, a way to achieve scale-invariant pattern recognition was demonstrated. If the object is presented in a rectangular form of polar coordinates[14] with the center chosen for the polar coordinate system coinciding with the center of rotation of the object, rotation by an angle $\theta$ causes the object to be shifted by $\theta$ if the angle coordinate is allowed to cover two or more times of $2\pi$. The above approaches were taken by Casasent and Psaltis[13] to achieve simultaneous scale and rotation invariance. A 2D object is stretched by logarithmic transformation before entering into the optical system. The matched filter is made under the same coordinate transformation to which the input object is subjected. The output correlation peak will maintain the same value for either scale or rotational change of the input object except for the fact that its position translates with rotation. The shift-invariant property of the conventional VLC is then lost.

Multiple spatial filters of the object to be recognized at different scale changes and rotational angles can be synthesized and placed in the frequency plane for pattern identification. This method would give a lower correlation peak intensity which is inversely proportional to the square of the number of the coded filters. It is desirable to make each filter as powerful as possible to increase the system performance and possibly minimize the number of filters required. In the following, we discuss some filter design techniques which preserve the shift-invariant property of the VLC.

CIRCULAR HARMONIC FILTER: This important technique in shift and rotational-invariant pattern recognition was proposed by Hsu and Arsenault.[15,16] The basic theory is presented below. A 2D function $g(r,\theta)$, expressed in polar coordinates, is naturally periodic in the variable $\theta$, with a period $2\pi$. Hence, it may be expressed in Fourier series in the angular variable,

$$g(r,\theta) = \sum_{m=-\infty}^{\infty} g_m(r)\, e^{jm\theta}\,, \tag{1}$$

where the $m$th Fourier coefficient is given by

$$g_m(r) = \frac{1}{2\pi} \int_0^{2\pi} g(r,\theta)\, e^{-jm\theta}\, d\theta\,. \tag{2}$$

A rotated version of the function $g(r,\theta)$ can similarly be expressed as

$$g(r,\theta-\alpha) = \sum_{m=-\infty}^{\infty} g_m(r)\, e^{jm(\theta-\alpha)}\,. \tag{3}$$

The correlation output, at the origin, between the function $g(r,\theta)$ and its rotated version $g(r,\theta-\alpha)$ is

$$R_\alpha = \int_0^\infty r\left[\sum_{m=-\infty}^{\infty} g_m^*(r) \int_0^{2\pi} g(r,\theta-\alpha)\, e^{-jm\theta}\, d\theta\right] dr \tag{4}$$

162

Utilizing the identity (from Eq. (3))

$$\frac{1}{2\pi} \int_0^{2\pi} g(r, \theta - \alpha) \, e^{-jm\theta} \, d\theta = g_m(r) \, e^{-jm\alpha} ,$$

we then have

$$R_\alpha = 2\pi \sum_{m=-\infty}^{\infty} e^{-jm\alpha} \int_0^{\infty} r |g_m(r)|^2 \, dr . \tag{5}$$

The above equation shows that, for each circular harmonic (CH) component, the correlation output undergoes a different phase shift $-m\alpha$. If a filter consisting of only one CH component, say the $M$th, is inserted in the frequency plane of the VLC, then the correlation output would be

$$R_\alpha = 2\pi \, e^{-jM\alpha} \int_0^{\infty} r |g_M(r)|^2 \, dr . \tag{6}$$

From this equation, we can determine the rotation angle $\alpha$ of the input object from the exponent. Or, since a detector generally detects the output intensity, the phase in the above equation is then lost after detection giving the same output correlation intensity for object at any angle of rotation. The CH expansion of a function depends on the particular point chosen for the center of that expansion. The quality of the correlation peaks obtained depends on the proper choice of the expansion center. Procedures for determining an appropriate center is given by Sheng and Arsenault.[17]

Although pattern recognition with a single CH filter (CHF) provides rotational invariance, the discrimination capability may not be good since may CH components are discarded. By combining a few CH components, it is extended to the case with limited rotational invariance.[18] Other methods using multiple CH components and analyzing the resulting multiple correlation output by statistical pattern-recognition method were also proposed.[19,20] Phase-only CHF (POCHF) and binary POCHF were demonstrated[21–23] to increase the light efficiency, correlation peak sharpness, and discrimination ability. However, it is noisy under a noisy environment because of its high-pass nature. Using wavelet transform technique for only one CH component,[24] the discrimination capability can also be improved together with suppression of high-frequency noise. A method combining CH filtering and automatic scale searching by light of different wavelengths to achieve simultaneous rotation, scale, and shift invariance was suggested using a white-light source.[25] A filter called minimum average correlation energy (MACE) filter[26] was also introduced to produce sharp correlation peaks at origin. This type of filter is further utilized in color pattern recognition.[27]

MELLIN RADIAL HARMONIC FILTER: This is a simple filter design technique which allows simultaneous shift and scale invariant pattern recognition.[28] We present the basic theory in the following. A 2D function $g(r, \theta)$ may be decomposed into the combination of a set of functions which is invariant to scale change,

$$g(r, \theta) = \sum_{m=-\infty}^{\infty} g_m(\theta)\, r^{i2\pi m - 1}\,. \tag{7}$$

By restricting the function $r^{i2\pi m - 1}$ to exist in a region between $r_0$ and $R$, where $r_0$ and $R$ satisfy the relation $\ln R - \ln r_0 = L$ and $L$ is an integer, the $m$th coefficient of the Mellin radial harmonic (MRH) is found to be

$$g_m(\theta) = \frac{1}{L} \int_{r_0}^{R} g(r, \theta)\, r^{-i2\pi m - 1}\, r\, dr\,. \tag{8}$$

The correlation output, at the origin, between the $M$th radial harmonic and a scaled object (scaled by a factor $\beta$, where $\beta$ smaller than unity means the object pattern is enlarged and vice versa) is

$$R(\beta) = \int_{r=r_0}^{R} \int_{\theta=0}^{2\pi} \left[ g_M^*(\theta)\, r^{-i2\pi M - 1} \right] g(\beta r, \theta)\, r\, dr\, d\theta\,. \tag{9}$$

Substituting an identity similar to Eq. (7) for the scaled object into the above equation, we then have

$$R(\beta) = \frac{e^{i2\pi M \ln \beta}}{\beta} R(1)\,. \tag{10}$$

From the above equation, we notice that the correlation intensity at the origin is scaled by $\beta^{-2}$ times, correspondingly (i.e. if the object is linearly enlarged by two times, the energy transmitted through the object is four times larger and similarly the correlation peak intensity is increased by four times). Although the RHF is capable of producing correlation peaks for objects with different sizes, the correlation peaks do not have equal height. For objects which are significantly different in scale, the correlation peak may be smaller than the side lobes of other correlation output and may not be recognized. To alleviate this problem, a technique with logarithmic radial harmonic (LRH) filter was introduced[29] to equalize the correlation peak intensity for input objects of different sizes and to increase the discrimination ability among similar objects. By considering the correlation expression in the frequency plane, the phase-only LRH filter function was proposed. The correlation peak variation is less than 20% within a scale range of 4. Another technique based on wavelet transform, which has good discrimination ability and is more suitable under noisy environment, was attempted.[30] By using a MRH of the wavelet transformed object as the filter, the ratio of the correlation peaks (CP) is made proportional to the linear scale ratio $\beta$ of the object and the CP for a similar object becomes vanishingly small. Another method was also introduced[31] to improve the behavior of the MRH filter. An algorithm, based on the construction and later maximization of a modified energy function of the target, is proposed to obtain the proper expansion center and optimal order of the MRH of an object. The procedure consists of the suppression of the non-discriminant uniform background in the energy function of the target. The real filter for scale-invariant pattern recognition[32] was also reported.

Image moments are also used for pattern recognition. The low-order image geometrical moments are useful for determining image position, orientation, and scale. The Fourier–Mellin moments feature vectors together with the weighted distance criterion were proposed for scale- and rotational-invariant pattern recognition.[33,34] Recently, based on the method by choosing a RH for an object to decompose into a logarithmic harmonic set and then selecting one harmonic component as the filter,[35-37] simultaneous scale-, projection, and shift-invariant pattern recognition was achieved.

SYNTHETIC DISCRIMINANT FUNCTIONS (SDF): This method was based on the earlier work done by Braunecker and Lohmann[38,39] and Caulfield and Haimes.[40] Casasent and his coworkers[41,42] suggested the use of a linear combination of reference images to create a composite image and then correlating the input object with this composite image. The weights for the linear combination are selected so that the cross-correlation output at the origin is the same for all images belonging to one class. In the following, we present the basic theory of this SDF approach. A certain "training set" of images in which the members may be the scaled versions and/or rotated versions of a single object, or they may be more generally distorted versions of that object, or they may be some of other objects for which we desire their filter output to be zero.

Let the training set of $N$ images be represented by $\{g_n(x,y)\}$ where $n = 1, 2, \ldots, N$. This set is divided into two subsets $\{g_n^c\}$ and $\{g_n^i\}$. The correct set $\{g_n^c\}$ is expected to give unity correlation output while the incorrect set $\{g_n^i\}$ is desired to produce zero output. In order to produce a filter impulse $h(x,y)$ with desired behavior, we expand it in a series using the training images as basis functions,

$$h(x,y) = \sum_{n=1}^{N} c_n\, g_n(x,y)\,. \tag{11}$$

Correlation, at the origin, for any one member, say $g_m(x,y)$, of the training set with the filter function can be written as

$$a_m = \int_{-\infty}^{\infty} \int_{-\infty}^{\infty} g_m^*(x,y)\, h(x,y)\, dx\, dy = \sum_{n=1}^{N} c_n \int_{-\infty}^{\infty} \int_{-\infty}^{\infty} g_m^*(x,y)\, g_n(x,y)\, dx\, dy\,, \tag{12}$$

where Eq. (11) is utilized and $a_m$ is either unity or zero depending on which class the input object belongs to. Denoting the correlation between $g_m$ and $g_n$ by $R_{mn}$, Eq. (12) becomes

$$a_m = \sum_{n=1}^{N} c_n R_{mn} .$$

(13)

By considering all members of the training set, we then have a set of $N$ linear equations in the $N$ unknowns $c_n$. Let $\overset{\leftrightarrow}{R}$ be a $N \times N$ square matrix with $R_{mn}$ as the element in the $m$th raw and the $n$th column and let $\vec{a}$ and $\vec{c}$ be $N$-dimensional column vectors. We then have

$$\vec{a} = \overset{\leftrightarrow}{R} \vec{c} .$$

(14)

By inverting the matrix $\overset{\leftrightarrow}{R}$ and multiplying the inverse by the vector $\vec{a}$, the unknown vector $\vec{c}$ can be found

$$\vec{c} = \overset{\leftrightarrow}{R}^{-1} \vec{a} .$$

(15)

Substituting the elements $c_n$ in the above equation into Eq. (11), the filter impulse can thus be constructed.

Variants of the SDF have been developed which include the optimal linear discriminant function filter,[43] the minimum average correlation energy (MACE) SDF,[44] and the minimum-variance (MV) SDF.[45] A generalized SDF formulation[46] was also proposed. The disadvantage of straightforward application of MVSDF and generalized SDF would be the requirement to solve for the inverse of a huge matrix $(N \times N)$. However, the variants of the SDF would probably be the most powerful filter formulations ever developed. Caelli and Liu[47] used an adaptive approach to demonstrate that the number of templates needed for efficient pattern recognition is considerably lower than previously thought. Experiments was also demonstrated.[48] The idea of using composite training images[49] allows more images to be included in the construction of SDF without increasing the size of the training-set was suggested. A tutorial survey of composite filter designs was given by VijayaKumar.[50] Interested readers can find lots of references on filter design techniques in that paper. A recent attempt in applying the idea of SDF to CH of objects with four different sizes was reported[51,52] which shows the capability of performing shift, rotation, and limited scale invariant pattern recognition.

## 4. Real-Time Implementation

Real-time implementation of optical correlator is critical if it would have practical applications. This depends very much on the advancement of the devices called spatial light modulators (SLM) which modulate either the amplitude or/and the phase of the light in real-time. There are many different SLM technologies as can be seen in the book by Efron[53] and the article by Neff, Athale, and Lee.[54] Liquid crystal SLM (liquid crystal light valve, liquid crystal television, and ferroelectric liquid crystal SLM), magneto-optical SLM, deformable mirror SLM, multiple-quantum-well SLM, and acoustical-optical Bragg cell are considered as the most important SLM technologies. SLM can limit the performance, particularly in space-bandwidth product, speed, and modulation fidelity, of the optical correlator. There are basically two kinds of SLM's which are the electrically addressed SLM's and the optically addressed SLM's. A recent review is given by Ichioka, Iwaki, and Matsuoka.[55]

(A). REAL-TIME VLC: In the VLC, once the designed filter is in position, the time lapse for a correlation process, in an optical system which is 60 cm long, is about 2 pico seconds. So, the main factor which slows down the speed of the correlation process would be the process in getting the information into and out of the optical system. Gara demonstrated a real-time tracking system for a moving object[56] based on the above principle and took advantage of the shift-invariant property of the VLC. However, the performance depends on the response time of the transducer which would blur the input image if the object is moving too fast. A portable real-time coherent optical correlator was introduced by Upatnieks[57] using a liquid crystal image converter followed by laser diodes as incoherent-to-coherent converter to real-time input the object into the optical system. A LCTV with low quality polarizers and diffuser taken out and immersed in a liquid gate[58] was also suggested as the input device. In principle, any kind of SLM can serve as the real-time input device. The most challenging task would be the implementation of real-time spatial filter by the SLM at the frequency plane. An SLM cannot simultaneously modulate the light amplitude as well as the phase accurately as required by the filter function. Computer generated hologram techniques, such as the detour phase method,[59] can be used to generate the required phase and amplitude of the filter by amplitude modulation on the light beam. However, for a SLM with a few hundred pixels in one direction, only objects with very low resolution can be used. Furthermore, the diffraction efficiency is low for this SLM filter, hence most of the light is wasted in the unwanted zero-order. For better light efficiency, one would like to implement the phase-only filter (POF) by the SLM since the light is not attenuated by the filter. The space-bandwidth product can also be saved because no carrier frequency is required in the in-line situation. Horner and Gianino[60] showed that the correlation peak for POF is considerably sharper than that for conventional matched filtering. This is due to the inherent high-pass nature on the POF. A more convenient way to implement POF on an SLM is to binarize the phase although the light efficiency and the correlation SNR are higher for analog POF.[61] Flannery and coworkers[62] used a $48 \times 48$-element electrically addressed magnetooptic SLM to implement the first BPOF on a real-time correlator. The resulting speed (4 frames per second) is limited by the controlling microcomputer rather than the SLM's. BPOF correlation using a deformable mirror device[63] was also reported. This is a $128 \times 128$-element device which is capable of continuous phase modulation. Frame rates for this device can be as high as 8 kHz although it was limited by the computer interface hardware to address 180 filter patterns per second. BPOF implementation using LCTV[64] and LCLV[65] was also demonstrated. Recently, binary POCHF implementation using a LCTV in the frequency plane was demonstrated.[66] Optical disk-based VLC setups were suggested by Psaltis, Neifeld, and Yamamura[67] to vastly increase the correlation speed. The optical disk (OD) is characterized by large information-storage capacity and high readout speed. The first system proposed massive storage of computer generated Fourier-transform holograms in the OD, which is situated in the frequency plane of an optical system. In the second system, massive reference images (spatial domain patterns) are stored in the OD. The input object is first Fourier transformed by a lens and is recorded as an off-axis Fourier transform (FT) hologram at the frequency plane by a photorefractive crystal. Then, light is illuminated on the OD to read out the reference images which are FT by the same lens and run through the FT hologram sequentially. By rotating the disk and relatively translating the disk with respect to the optical system, an input object can be made to correlate with the reference-image bank at a speed of 40,000 image correlations/sec. We note that if the reference images on OD are replaced by the impulse of the invariant filter (i.e. function in spatial domain), described in Sec. 3, the pattern recognition speed can be increased by many times. Research on increasing the speed of correlation by using photorefractive GaAs[68] was also reported. Using four-wave mixing in polyacetylene film,[69] the system allows the correlation speed to reach 1 pico second. A recent interest is to develop a relatively low cost programmable real-time optical correlator system[70] in which LCTV's (Epson model VP-100PS, $320 \times 164$ pixels) are used not only in the input plane (amplitude modulation) but also in the frequency plane (phase modulation). They demonstrated that it is not necessary to implement more than four phase levels in the second LCTV. Certainly, the future development of SLM and photorefractive material would further improve the speed and the quality of the optical correlator. Finally, we note that holographic associative memory can also be used in real-time pattern recognition.[71]

(B). REAL-TIME JTC: Pichon and Huignard[72] demonstrated a real-time correlation experiment by using photorefractive BSO crystal (The use of four-wave mixing in photorefractive medium for real-time correlation was demonstrated by Pepper et al.[73]) to record the JPS in the JTC. Argon laser line at 488 nm is used in the recording process and a low power He–Ne laser is used for the read-out process. They also suggested the use of light valves as the real-time input device. The introduction of the spatial light modulators into both the input plane and the frequency plane was proposed by Yu and Lu.[4] Since then the research on joint-transform correlator has been extensive.[74-86] A JTC with low cost LCTV's in both the input plane and the frequency plane was reported.[87] The object and the reference pattern can be imaged by a TV (or CCD) camera or generated by a microcomputer onto the input LCTV side-by-side. The joint power spectrum (JPS) detected by TV camera is sent to another (or the same) LCTV for another Fourier transformation. The appearance and the location of the correlation spot tells that not only the desired object is present but also where it is. Reference patterns can be dynamically changed which is an advantage over the traditional

VLC in which dynamical implementation of the complex filter is difficult. In parallel to the OD-based VLC, a scheme in JTC was suggested.[88] Massive reference patterns are recorded on the OD in either binary or grey scale (area modulation) form. More than 27,000 reference images can be recorded on a single 12 cm diameter OD. These images are sequentially accessed and each produces JPS with the object. The JPS is detected by an optically addressed ferroelectric liquid crystal SLM. This system is capable of performing more than 6400 correlations per second. Rajbenbach *et al.*[89] proposed a compact photorefractive correlator which is potentially more suitable for industrial use, particularly the use for parts identification on the production lines. This system is composed of mini-YAG lasers and liquid crystal SLM, in conjunction with an updatable holographic BSO crystal. An Epson video projector model LC-500 containing $320 \times 264$ pixel elements was used as input device. The BSO crystal with response time between 35 and 100 ms at intensity level of approximately $10 \text{ mW/cm}^2$ is used as the recording medium (resolution much better than that for liquid crystal SLM) for JPS. The resulted speed is 100 ms per correlation which is limited by the BSO crystal. It is clear that the pattern recognition speed for such a system depends very much on the continuous improvement of the speed of the SLM and the photorefractive crystal. The capability of this type of JTC can further be improved if the impulse of the filter, such as the rotational, projection, scale invariant filters, or SDF (described in Sec. 3), are utilized in this system. This system was recently applied to fingerprint identification[90] by connecting with a PC-based image processing board.

## 5. Conclusions

The shift-invariant property is an asset of the VanderLugt correlator, by which the location of the detected object is automatically specified. Since the input scene propagates at the speed of light, it generally takes only in the order of pico seconds to reach the output plane. However, if the object is different from the reference object (stored in the frequency plane as a Fourier transform hologram) in scale, orientation, or other types of distortion by some degree, the correlation peak vanishes. Hence, the ability to design a filter which is capable of detecting objects with two or more (rotational, size, projection, or distortion) invariance properties constitutes an important part in the development of a real-time optical correlator. The circular harmonic filter, radial harmonic filter, logarithmic radial harmonic filter, and synthetic discriminant function filter are suitable candidates for these purposes.

The factor which slows down the speed of correlation in the VLC is the speed of getting the information into and out of the optical system. Hence, the speed of the spatial light modulator is important in the development of a real-time VLC. Historical implementation of real-time VLC is reviewed. To avoid the waste of light in the unwanted zero-order and to save the space-bandwidth product, phase-only filtering is generally preferred. One proposed system which can vastly increase the

169

correlation speed is based on the characteristics of high-storage capacity and high readout speed of an optical disk.

The joint-transform correlator was proposed to avoid the filter synthesis and alignment problems. In addition to the implementation using LCTV as the input and the square-low detecting devices, a system with photorefractive crystal as the real-time recording medium (high resolution) seems to be practical for industrial tracking. If the dynamically changed filters (in spatial domain) are replaced by those designed to have many simultaneous invariances, the capability of JTC can be further increased.

Future development of the SLM's and the photorefractive crystals together with the development of versatile filters and algorithms would constantly improve the speed and the capability of the optical correlator.

Finally, I apologize for the possibility of omission of some significant work in this field of shift-invariant optical pattern recognition.

## Acknowledgment

This work was sponsored by the National Science Council, Taiwan, through grant NSC 85-2215-E-008-005.

## References

1. A. VanderLugt, "Signal detection by complex spatial filtering", *IEEE Trans. Inform. Theory* **IT-10** (1964) 139–145.
2. C. S. Weaver and J. W. Goodman, "A technique for optically convolving two functions", *Appl. Opt.* **5** (1966) 1248–1249.
3. J. E. Rau, "Detection of differences in real distributions", *J. Opt. Soc. Amer.* **56** (1966) 1490–1494.
4. F. T. S. Yu and X. J. Lu, "A real-time programmable joint-transform correlator", *Opt. Commun.* **52** (1984) 10–16.
5. F. T. S. Yu and S. Jutamulia, *Optical Signal Processing, Computing and Neural Networks*, John Wiley, New York, 1992, Chap. 9.
6. F. T. S. Yu and D. A. Gregory, "Optical pattern recognition: architectures and techniques", *Proc. IEEE* **84** (1996) 733–752.
7. F. T. S. Yu, Q. W. Song, Y. S. Cheng, and D. A. Gregory, "Comparison of detection efficiencies for VanderLugt and joint-transform correlators", *Appl. Opt.* **29** (1990) 225–232.
8. F. T. S. Yu and S. Jutamulia, *Optical Signal Processing, Computing and Neural Networks*, John Wiley, New York, 1992, Chap. 2.
9. F. T. S. Yu, C. Zhang, Y. Jin, and D. A. Gregory, "Nonconventional joint-transform correlator", *Opt. Lett.* **14** (1989) 922–924.
10. F. T. S. Yu, E. C. Tam, and D. A. Gregory, "High-efficiency joint-transform correlator", *Opt. Lett.* **15** (1990) 1029–1031.
11. J. A. Davis, M. A. Waring, G. W. Bach, R. A. Lilly, and D. M. Cottrell, "Compact optical correlator design", *Appl. Opt.* **28** (1989) 10–11.
12. F. T. S. Yu, S. Wu, S. Rajan, and D. A. Gregory, "Compact joint-transform correlator with a thick photorefractive crystal", *Appl. Opt.* **31** (1992) 2416–2418.

13. D. Casasent and D. Psaltis, "New optical transforms for pattern recognition", *Proc. IEEE* **65** (1977) 77–83.

14. O. Bryngdahl, "Geometrical transformation in optics", *J. Opt. Soc. Am.* **64** (1974) 1092–1099.

15. Y. N. Hsu and H. H. Arsenault, "Rotational invariant digital pattern recognition using circular harmonic expansion", *Appl. Opt.* **21** (1982) 4012–4015.

16. Y. N. Hsu and H. H. Arsenault, "Optical pattern recognition using circular harmonic expansion", *Appl Opt.* **21** (1982) 4016–4019.

17. Y. Sheng and H. H. Arsenault, "Method for determining expansion centers and predicting sidelobe levels for circular-harmonic filters", *J. Opt. Soc. Am.* **A4** (1987) 1793–1797.

18. H. H. Arsenault, C. Ferreira, M. P. Levesque, and T. Szpolik, "Simple filter with limited rotation invariance", *Appl. Opt.* **25** (1986) 3230–3234.

19. R. Wu and H. Stark, "Rotation-invariant pattern recognition using a vector reference", *Appl. Opt.* **23** (1984) 838–840.

20. Y. N. Hsu and H. H. Arsenault, "Pattern discrimination by multiple circular harmonic components", *Appl. Opt.* **23** (1984) 841–844.

21. H. F. Yau and C. C. Chang, "Phase-only circular harmonic matched filtering", *Appl. Opt.* **28** (1989) 2070–2074.

22. J. Rosen and J. Shamir, "Circular harmonic phase filters for efficient rotation-invariant pattern recognition", *Appl. Opt.* **27** (1988) 2895–2899.

23. L. Leclerc, Y. Sheng, and H. H. Arsenault, "Rotation invariant phase-only and binary phase-only correlation", *Appl. Opt.* **28** (1989) 1251–1256.

24. Y. S. Cheng and T. C. Liang, "Rotational invariant pattern recognition using a composite circular harmonic and 2D isotropic Mexican wavelet filter", *Opt. Commun.* **112** (1994) 9–15.

25. K. Mersereau and G. M. Morris, "Scale, rotation and shift invariant image recognition", *Appl. Opt.* **25** (1986) 2338–2342.

26. D. Casasent, A. Iyer, and G. Ravichandran, "Circular harmonic function MACE filters", *Appl. Opt.* **30** (1991) 5169–5175.

27. J. Garcia, J. Campos, and C. Ferreira, "Circular-harmonic minimum average correlation energy filter for color pattern recognition", *Appl. Opt.* **33** (1994) 2180–2187.

28. D. Mendlovic, E. Maron, and N. Konforti, "Shift and scale invariant pattern recognition using Mellin radial harmonic", *Opt. Commun.* **67** (1988) 172–176.

29. J. Rosen and J. Shamir, "Scale invariant pattern recognition with logarithmic radial harmonic filters", *Appl. Opt.* **28** (1989) 240–244.

30. Y. S. Cheng and B. Wang, "Shift and scale invariant pattern recognition using Mellin radial harmonics and wavelet transform", *Proc. Photonics/Taiwan '96*, Hsin Chu, Taiwan, Dec. 1996, pp. 50–52.

31. A. Moya, E. Tajahuerce, J. Garcia, D. Mendlovic, and C. Ferreira, "Method for determining the proper expansion center and order for Mellin radial harmonic filters", *Opt. Commun.* **103** (1993) 39–45.

32. E. Tajahuerce, A. Moya, J. Garcia, and C. Ferreira, "Real filter based Mellin radial harmonics for scale-invariant pattern recognition", *Appl. Opt.* **33** (1994) 3086–3093.

33. Y. Sheng and L. Shen, "Orthogonal Fourier-Mellin moments for invariant pattern recognition", *J. Opt. Soc. Am.* **A11** (1994) 1748–1757.

34. L. Shen and Y. Sheng, "Noncentral image moments for invariant pattern recognition", *Opt. Engin.* **34** (1995) 3181–3186.

35. D. Mendlovic, N. Konforti, and E. Marom, "Shift and projection invariant pattern recognition using logarithmic harmonics", *Appl. Opt.* **29** (1990) 4784–4789.

36. D. Mendlovic, Z. Zalevsky, J. Garcia, and C. Ferreira, "Logarithmic harmonics proper expansion center and order for efficient projection invariant pattern recognition", *Opt. Commun.* **107** (1994) 292–299.

37. D. Mendlovic, Z. Zalevsky, I. Kiryuschev, and G. Lebreton, "Composite harmonic filters for scale-, projection-, and shift-invariant pattern recognition", *Appl. Opt.* **34** (1995) 310–316.

38. B. Braunecker, R. Hauck, and A. W. Lohmann, "Optical character recognition based on non redundant correlator measurements", *Appl. Opt.* **18** (1979) 2746–2753.

39. H. J. Caulfield and R. Haimes, "Generalized matched filtering", *Appl. Opt.* **19** (1980) 181–183.

40. D. Casasent, "Unified synthetic discriminant function computational formalism", *Appl. Opt.* **23** (1984) 1620–1627.

41. D. Casasent and W. T. Chang, "Correlation synthetic discriminant functions", *Appl. Opt.* **25** (1986) 2343–2350.

42. B. Braunecker and A. W. Lohmann, "Character recognition by digital holography", *Opt. Commun.* **11** (1974) 141–143.

43. V. Sharma and D. Casasent, "Optimal linear discriminant functions", *Proc. SPIE* **519** (1984) 50–55.

44. A. Mahalanobis, B. Kumar, and D. Casasent, "Minimum average correlation energy filters", *Appl. Opt.* **25** (1987) 3633–3640.

45. B. Kumar, "Minimum-variance synthetic discriminant functions", *J. Opt. Soc. Am.* **A3** (1986) 1579–1584.

46. Z. Bahri and B. Kumar, "Generalized synthetic discriminant functions", *J. Opt. Soc. Am.* **A5** (1988) 562–571.

47. T. M. Caelli and Z. Q. Liu, "On the minimum number of templates required for shift, rotation and size invariant pattern recognition", *Patt. Recog.* **21** (1988) 205–216.

48. D. Casasent and R. Ye, "Optical laboratory realization of distortion invariant filters", *Proc. SPIE* **939** (1988) 105–120.

49. J. D. Brasher and M. Woodson, "Composite training images for synthetic discriminant functions", *Appl. Opt.* **35** (1996) 314–317.

50. B. V. K. VijayaKumar, "Tutorial survey of composite filter designs for optical correlators", *Appl. Opt.* **31** (1992) 4773–4801.

51. H. F. Yau, Y. OuYang, and S. W. Wang, "Shift, rotation and limited scale invariant pattern recognition using synthetic discriminant functions", *Opt. Rev.* **2** (1995) 266–269.

52. H. F. Yau, Y. Ouyang, and P. W. Chen, "Optical demonstration of shift-, rotational- and limited size invariant pattern recognition using a circular harmonic SDF filter", *Opt. and Quantum Electronics* **28** (1996) 1543–1550.

53. U. Efron (ed.), *Spatial Light Modulator Technology*, Marcel Dekker, New York, 1994.

54. J. A. Neff, R. A. Athale, and S. H. Lee, "Two-dimensional spatial light modulators: a tutorial", *Proc. IEEE* **78** (1990) 826–855.

55. Y. Ichioka, T. Iwaki, and K. Matsuoka, "Optical information processing and beyond", *Proc. IEEE* **84** (1996) 694–719.

56. A. D. Gara, "Real-time tracking of moving objects by optical correlation", *Appl. Opt.* **18** (1979) 172–174.

57. J. Upatnieks, "Portable real-time coherent optical correlator", *Appl. Opt.* **22** (1983) 2798–2803.

58. D. A. Gregory, "Real-time pattern recognition using a modified liquid crystal television in a coherent optical correlator", *Appl. Opt.* **25** (1986) 467–469.

59. G. R. Brawn and A. W. Lohmann, "Complex spatial filtering with binary masks", *Appl. Opt.* **6** (1966) 967–969.
60. J. L. Horner and P. D. Gianino, "Phase-only matched filtering", *Appl. Opt.* **23** (1984) 812–816.
61. H. Bartelt and J. L. Horner, "Improving binary phase correlation filters using iterative techniques", *Appl. Opt.* **24** (1985) 2894–2897.
62. D. L. Flannery, A. M. Biernacki, J. S. Loomis, and S. L. Cartwright, "Real-time coherent correlator using binary magnetooptic spatial light modulators at input and Fourier planes", *Appl. Opt.* **25** (1986) 466.
63. J. M. Florence and R. O. Gale, "Coherent optical correlator using a deformable mirror device spatial light modulator in the Fourier plane", *Appl. Opt.* **27** (1988) 2091–2093.
64. T. H. Barnes, T. Eiju, K. Matsuda, and N. Ohyama, "Phase-only modulation using a twisted nematic liquid crystal television", *Appl. Opt.* **28** (1989) 4845–4852.
65. J. A. Davis, G. M. Heissenberger, R. A. Lilly, D. M. Cottrell, and M. F. Brownell, "High efficiency optical reconstruction of binary phase-only filters using the Hughes liquid crystal light valve", *Appl. Opt.* **26** (1987) 929–933.
66. J. P. Drolet, L. Leclerc, Y. Sheng, and H. H. Arsenault, "Real-time binary phase-only circular harmonic filters using a liquid crystal television in the Fourier plane of an optical correlator", *Opt. Eng.* **31** (1992) 939–946.
67. D. Psaltis, M. A. Neifeld, and A. Yamamura, "Image correlators using optical memory disks", *Opt. Lett.* **14** (1989) 429–431.
68. D. T. H. Liu and L. J. Cheng, "Real-time VanderLugt optical correlator that uses photorefractive GaAs", *Appl. Opt.* **31** (1992) 5675–5679.
69. P. D. Foote, G. M. Proudley, G. S. Beddard, G. G. McFadyen, G. D. Reid, L. M. Connors, M. Bell, T. J. Hall, and K. Powell, "Picosecond optical correlation using dynamic holography in polyacetylene', *Appl. Opt.* **32** (1993) 174–178.
70. C. Gorecki, B. Trolard, and L. Oriat, "Real-time pattern recognition by VanderLugt correlator using amplitude and phase modulation properties of the Epson liquid-crystal TV", *Opt. Rev.* **3** (1996) 171–176.
71. E. G. Paek and A. V. Lehmen, "Real-time holographic associative memory for identifying words in a continuous letter string", *Opt. Eng.* **28** (1989) 519–525.
72. L. Pichon and J. P. Huignard, "Dynamic joint-Fourier-Transform correlator by Bragg diffraction in photorefractive Bi12SiO20 crystals", *Opt. Commun.* **36** (1981) 277–280.
73. D. M. Pepper, J. Au Yeung, D. Fekete, and A. Yariv, "Spatial convolution and correlation of optical fields via degenerate four-wave mixing", *Opt. Lett.* **3** (1978) 7–9.
74. F. T. S. Yu, M. Lu, G. Lu, S. Yin, T. D. Hudson, and D. K. McMillan, "Optimum target detection using a spatial domain bipolar composite filter with a joint-transform correlator", *Opt. Eng.* **34** (1995) 3200–3207.
75. G. Lu, Z. Zhang, and F. T. S. Yu, "Phase-encoded input joint-transform correlator with improved pattern discriminability", *Opt. Lett.* **20** (1995) 1307–1309.
76. F. T. S. Yu, G. Lu, M. Lu, and D. Zhao, "Application of position encoding to a complex joint-transform correlator", *Appl. Opt.* **34** (1995) 1386–1388.
77. F. T. S. Yu and Y. S. Cheng, "White-light joint-transform correlator", *Opt. Lett.* **15** (1990) 192–194.
78. Y. S. Cheng, "Analysis of a white-light joint-transform correlator with application to color-object detection", *Opt. Commun.* **99** (1993) 252–263.
79. F. Cheng, F. T. S. Yu, and D. Gregory, "Multitarget detection using spatial synthesis joint-transform correlation", *Appl. Opt.* **32** (1993) 6521–6526.
80. D. Mendlovic, Z. Zalevsky, and N. Konforti, "Joint transform correlator with incoherent output", *J. Opt. Soc. Am.* **A11** (1994) 3201–3205.

81. D. Mendlovic, M. Deutsch, C. Ferreira, and J. Garcia, "Single-channel polychromatic pattern recognition by the use of a joint-transform correlator", *Appl Opt.* **35** (1996) 6382–6389.
82. P. Erbach, D. A. Gregory, and X. Yang, "Optical wavelet transform by the phase-only joint-transform correlator", *Appl. Opt.* **35** (1996) 3117–3126.
83. R. K. Wang, L. Shang, and C. R. Chatwin, "Modified fringe-adjusted joint-transform correlation to accommodate noise in the input scene", *Appl. Opt.* **35** (1996) 286–295.
84. G. Keryer and J. L. D. Delatocnaye, "A multichannel joint-transform correlator", *Opt. Commun.* **118** (1995) 102–113.
85. L. Bigue, M. Fraces, and P. Ambs, "Experimental implementation of a joint-transform correlator using synthetic discriminant functions", *Opt. and Laser in Eng.* **23** (1995) 93–111.
86. J. Khoury, J. S. Kane, G. Asimellis, M. Croningolomb, and C. Woods, "All-optical nonlinear joint Fourier-transform correlator", *Appl. Opt.* **33** (1994) 8216–8225.
87. F. T. S. Yu, S. Jutamulia, T. W. Lin, and D. A. Gregory, "Adaptive real-time pattern recognition using liquid crystal TV based joint-transform correlator", *Appl. Opt.* **26** (1987) 1370–1372.
88. F. T. S. Yu, Taiwei Lu, E. C. Tam, E. Nishihara, and T. Nishikawa, "Optical disk based joint-transform correlator", *Appl. Opt.* **30** (1991) 915–916.
89. H. Rajbenbach *et al.*, "Compact photorefractive correlator for robotic applications", *Appl. Opt.* **31** (1992) 5666–5674.
90. J. Rodolfo, H. Rajbenbach, and J. P. Huignard, "Performance of a photorefractive joint-transform correlator for fingerprint identification", *Opt. Eng.* **34** (1995) 1166–1171.

International Journal of High Speed Electronics and Systems, Vol. 8, No. 4 (1997) 749–765

# A HOLOGRAPHIC MEMORY FOR DIGITAL DATA STORAGE

C. P. YANG, S. H. LIN, M. L. HSIEH, K. Y. HSU,* and T. C. HSIEH[†]

*Institute of Electro-Optical Engineering,*
[†]*Department of Electrophysics,*
*National Chiao Tung University,*
*Hsin-Chu, Taiwan, R.O.C.*
*\* E-mail: ken@cc.nctu.edu.tw*

A read-only holographic memory for digital data storage is experimentally demonstrated. Techniques for coding and decoding of optical signals, and the interface techniques between the optical memory and a personal computer are described. The performance of the optical memory and the techniques for improving the bit error rate (BER) are presented.

## 1. Introduction

The information storage device is one of the main components in computers. Currently, popular storage media include magnetic hard disks and optic disks. These devices store digital data in a planar medium with a track format, i.e. the data bits are recorded and read out bit by bit in a sequential procedure from the tracks. The data access rate of this method is mainly determined by the mechanical moving speed of the read/write head with respect to the storage medium. With the present day technology, the data access rate is limited to the order of 10 Mbits/s. Furthermore, since the data bits are stored in a planar medium, the memory capacity is limited by the available area of the storage medium. In order to overcome the bottleneck of the data access rate and to increase the memory capacity of the system, it is interesting to explore a new technology for data storage.

Optical holography has been proposed to be a potential technique for information storage since the 1960s.[1–3] In recent years, attributed to the advances in spatial light modulator technologies and in photorefractive crystal growth, much research effort has been attracted to holographic memories.[4–8] The most unique characteristics of this kind of memory are its parallel readout of the recorded image and the potential of high storage capacity. In the recording stage, a two-dimensional (2D) light patterns (called the object beam) interfaces with a reference beam (which could be a plane wave, spherical wave, or a phase-encoded wave). The interference fringes of the object beam and the reference beam are recorded in the storage medium, which is called a hologram. In the reading stage, the reference beam illuminates the hologram and the whole page of the original 2D pattern is reconstructed at the instant of illumination. If the bright and dark pixels of the 2D patterns represent 1 and 0 bits of a digital data file, respectively, then one page of the digital file is obtained on the illumination of a reading beam. The data rate can be very fast. Assuming that each data page has $480 \times 440$ bits binary signals and an acousto-optical scanning method is used to address the reading beam at a speed of 100 $\mu$s, then the data rate is about 2 Gbits/s, which is at least two orders of magnitude higher than that of the conventional storage techniques. In addition, by using multiplexing techniques for recording holograms, thousands of images can be stored in a volume of single crystal. Based on the diffraction limited estimation, the storage density of volume holographic memories can reach up to $10^{12}$ bits/cm$^3$. In a recent experiment, 10,000 pages of information have been stored in a single crystal. Each of these pages measured 320 by 220 bits, thus the total capacity amounted to 100 megabytes. If multiple locations in the crystal were used, then the storage capacity could be much higher.

Research on holographic memory covers a wide range of interesting topics,[9] such as the materials for volume holograms, the multiplexing techniques for multiple page storage, the display and detection devices of 2D data pages, the encoding and decoding techniques for the optical signals,[10] the read/write head for the holographic memories, the system design and stability, etc. In this paper we report our studies on the implementation of a holographic memory for digital data storage. The basic structure of the system is described in Sec. 2. Section 3 describes the coding technique for the optical signals. Experimental results are presented in Sec. 4. Finally, conclusions are presented in Sec. 5.

## 2. Principle of the Digital Holographic Memory System

The basic operation of the holographic memory includes five steps: signal coding, data display, hologram recording, hologram read-out, and decoding, as shown in Fig. 1.

In the coding step, a digital data file is converted into a 2D bright and dark patterns, according to designated coding rules between the bit string of the data file and the pixel brightness of the 2D display device. In the display step, the 2D patterns are displayed on a spatial light modulator (SLM) so that the digital data pattern is imprinted into a light beam. In the hologram recording step, the optical data pages are recorded in a volume holographic material, thus a holographic memory is constructed. In the hologram read-out step, the holographic memory is reconstructed by the illumination of a reference beam. In the decoding step, the reconstructed images are detected and converted into digital signals. Thus, a digital data file is retrieved.

In our studies, frame grabbers are used for the coding and decoding operations. The frame grabber is an image processing board which has 512 by 512 pixels of random access memory. Each pixel has 8 bit resolution, i.e. with gray levels from 0 to 255. For the coding operation, the frame grabber operates in a binary mode,

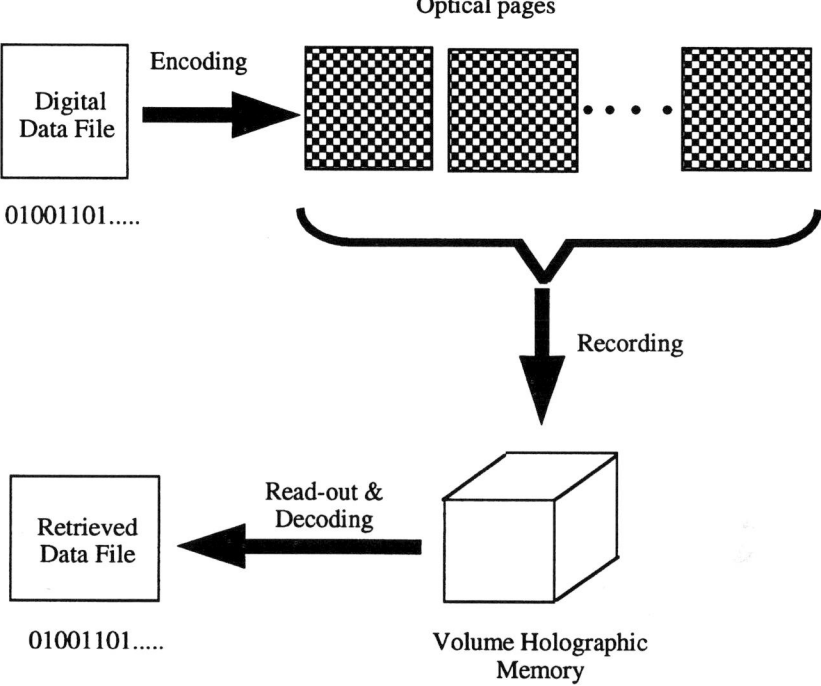

Fig. 1. Basic principle of digital holographic memory.

which means that logic 0 drives the corresponding pixels at the 0 gray level, and logic 1 drives the corresponding pixels at the 255 gray level. Thus in the coding step the 0 and 1 bits of a digital file are converted into a 2D pattern of 0 and 255 gray levels and are stored in the frame grabber. However, the correspondence between the 0 and 1 bits and that of the dark and bright patterns are not so straightforward during the decoding stage. In that step, the input to the frame grabber are optical signals reconstructed from the holograms. Because of the non-uniformities of the devices in the optical system, there is a distribution of brightness for either the 0 bit or the 1 bit pixels. In order to recover the original data file, we need some error correction scheme. The coding and decoding techniques will be described in the next section, and the techniques for improving the memory performance are presented in Sec. 4.

After the coding procedure, the data page of the frame grabber is displayed on a SLM, in our case it is a liquid crystal television (LCTV) panel which is disassembled from an Epson projection TV, VPJ-2000. The dimension of the active area of the LCTV is 2.7 cm (horizontal) by 2.1 cm (vertical), with 480 × 440 pixels. In order to drive the LCTV, only 480 × 440 pixels on the frame grabbers are used. Other pixels of the frame grabber remained in-active. Ideally, one pixel of the liquid crystal (LC) cell can be used to represent one bit information. In practical situations, there is a difficulty in addressing each individual LC pixels. The difficulty arises because the LCTV operates in a way such that there is a transition of gray levels between 0 and 1 pixels on the display. Figure 2 shows one example. Figure 2(a) shows an example of digital data file of the frame grabber while Fig. 2(b) shows the corresponding display on the LCD. It is seen that the difference in brightness between pixels of logic 0 and 1 is very smeared. Figure 2(c) shows a digital data file of alternating blocks of $8 \times 8$ bits of logic 0 and $8 \times 8$ bits of logic 1. Figure 2(d) shows the corresponding optical display on the LCTV panel. It is seen that the boundary lines between the 0 and 1 pixels are also with a gray level. The brightness of the LC pixels of these lines lie between that of the 0 and 1 pixels. Therefore, if one block of $8 \times 8$ LC cells is used to represent one data bit, then it is possible to code the digital data file into an optical display. In optical experiments a low pass filter is used to filter-out the grating structure of the LCTV lines such that the optical signals for each data bit is a single block, as shown in Fig. 2(e). This will increase the signal-to-noise ratio of the detection. In the experiments, we used a block of

```
10101010..........................
01010101..........................
10101010..........................
01010101..........................

..........................
10101010..........................
01010101..........................
```

(a)

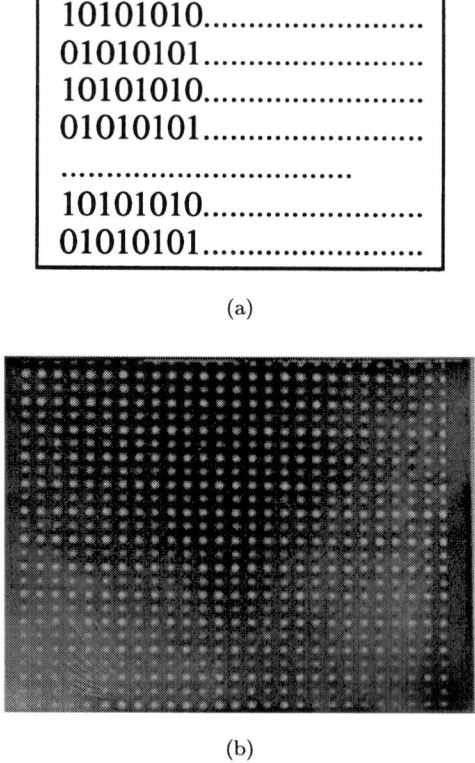

(b)

Fig. 2. Display of digital data file on a LCTV. (a) Data file on a frame grabber, (b) Display of (a) on LCTV, (c) Data file on a frame grabber, (d) Display of (c) on LCTV (e) Lowpass version of (d).

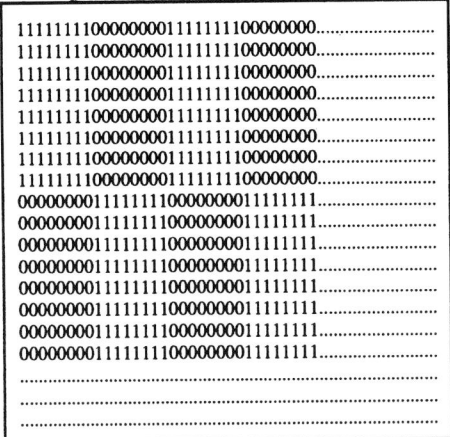

(c)

(d)

(e)

Fig. 2. (*Continued*)

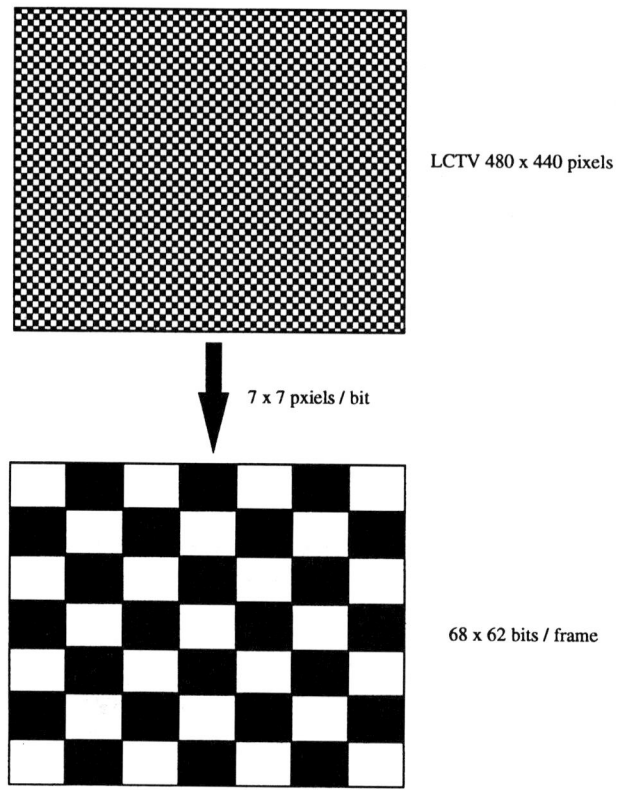

LCTV 480 x 440 pixels

7 x 7 pxiels / bit

68 x 62 bits / frame

Fig. 3. One frame of optical page.

$7 \times 7$ LC pixels to represent one data bit. According to this arrangement, one frame of LCTV display is equivalent to 4,216 bits of data, or 527 bytes. Figure 3 shows the format of an optical page.

The optical pages are recorded in the volume of a hologram recording medium. In our case it is an iron-doped LiNbO$_3$ single crystal. Multiple images are recorded at one recording spot on the crystal using the angle multiplexing technique. Since each recording spot has a diameter of 5 mm, thus, by changing the recording positions on the crystal then many memory spots can be recorded in one crystal.

After the holograms are recorded in the LiNbO$_3$ crystal, the data file can be read out from the holographic memory. When a reading beam illuminates the crystal at an appropriate incident angle which corresponds to the address of a data page, then the data page is reconstructed. The read-out page is imaged onto a CCD array. Our CCD array has $510 \times 492$ pixels. The dimension of the CCD is 8 mm $\times$ 6 mm. Since the dimension as well as the aspect ratio (width to height) of the CCD pixels are different from those of the LCTV pixels, it is difficult to match the CCD pixels with the LCTV pixels simply by optical imaging. We have designed a program that could alleviate this problem. The details of this technique is described in Sec. 4.

## 3. The Encoding Method

This section describes the encoding technique for our holographic memory. There are several coding methods for the digital holographic storage.[11] In our experiment, we used the non-return-zero (NRZ) technique, which means that a bright block ($7 \times 7$ pixels) on LCTV represents one bit of logic 1 and a dark block represents one bit of logic 0. As was described in the previous section, one frame of LCTV is equivalent to 4,216 bits of digital data. On LCTV, the digital data block begins from the left corner to the right corner of the first row, with 68 data blocks in the first row, which represents 68 bits of digital data. Then, data bits from the 69th to the 138th bits are arranged in the second row. It continues in a similar way in the following rows until 4,216 bits are displayed in an optical page. Then, the rest of the data file are displayed in the following pages until the whole data file is encoded.

The optical display of LCTV contains the header bits and the data bits. The first 16 bits of each optical page are the header bits. The rest of the page are the data bits. For the header bits of each page, the first bit is used as the reference. It was always kept bright for two purposes. First, it provides an optical alignment mark for the LCTV and the CCD. Second, its intensity provides a reference for the logic levels of that data page. The next 15 bits of the header bits designate the page number of that page. Under this arrangement, the total number of optical pages can be as many as $2^{15}$. This amounts to 17 Mbytes of digital data. In addition, in order to indicate the size of a particular data file, the next 24 bits (from the 17th to the 40th bits) of the first page of each data file are used to designate the file size. A data file of 16 Mbytes can be designated. Thus, under this arrangement, the first page contains 522 bytes of data, and from the second page onwards, the data size is 525 bytes.

## 4. Optical Experiments

### 4.1. *Experimental setup*

Figure 4 shows the schematic diagram of the experimental setup for the holographic memory. It is a system with the reflection holography structure. The storage medium is an iron-doped LiNbO$_3$ crystal disk with a thickness of 1 cm. The light source is an argon laser with wavelength at 514 nm. A polarization beam splitter is used to split the laser beam into two arms, one is the object beam and the other is the reference beam. A half-wave plate WP1 is used for adjusting the relative intensity between the two beams. In our experiments, the reference beam intensity is at 20 mW/cm$^2$, and the object beam intensity is at 6 mW/cm$^2$, both are measured at the crystal place.

We used the angle-multiplexing technique to record multiple images in the crystal volume. Using this technique, multiple images are recorded at one spot on the crystal simply by changing the angle of incidence of the reference beam for successive recordings. The amount of the angle change between the neighboring recordings should be larger than the Bragg selectivity, in our case the angle of separation was

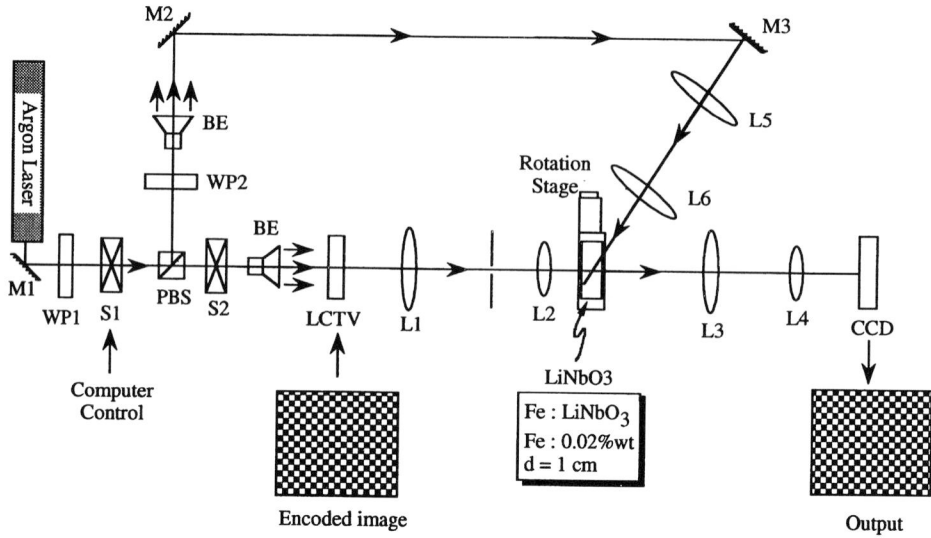

Fig. 4. The setup for optical experiments. M1, M2, M3: mirrors. S1, S2: electronic shutters. WP1, WP2: wave plates. BE: beam splitters. L1, L2, L3, L4, L5, L6: lenses.

set to be 0.08 degrees. The angle change of the reference beam is achieved by rotating mirror M3. Mirror M3 and lenses L5 and L6 form a 4f telescope structure, hence the illuminating position at the $LiNbO_3$ crystal remains unchanged when M3 is rotated. In the optical system the total range of angle rotation of M3 is limited by the F-numbers of lenses L5 and L6. In our system the total range of the angle rotation is 16 degrees. Under this condition, 200 optical pages can be recorded at one recording spot on the crystal. If M3 is rotated outside this range, then lens aberration will be induced and the illuminating spot on the crystal will be moved to different positions, which means that the angle multiplexing scheme can no longer be achieved.

The digital data file to be recorded is stored in the hard disk of a personal computer. During the recording stage, the file is encoded and displayed page by page on LCTV. The optical image on the LCTV is imaged onto the crystal with a spot of 5 mm diameter. For multiple-image storage, shutters S1 and S2 are opened and the exposure schedule is controlled by a personal computer.[4] To reconstruct the holograms, shutter S1 is open and shutter S2 is closed. The reconstructed image is imaged by lenses L3 and L4 onto a CCD camera and is captured by the decoding frame grabber. The decoded data is displayed on a monitor or it can be processed for other applications.

### 4.2. Preliminary setup

Before presenting the operation of the holographic memory system we must describe the preliminary setup. Since the digital data file is to be represented by a spatial distribution of 2D light patterns, it is necessary to see how accurately the optical devices represent the 0 and 1 bit data. The spatial uniformity of two devices has to be considered: CCD array and LCTV. Typically, the uniformity of a CCD array is good within 10%. Thus, with a proper thresholding value, the detected signals can be correctly discriminated to be logic 0 or 1. On the other hand, the uniformity of the LCTV has to be checked carefully.

As was described in Sec. 2, the LCTV panel was divided into 68 × 62 blocks to represent 68 × 62 bits of data, with 7 × 7 pixels of LC cells to represent one bit of data. In order to test the uniformity of the LCD panel, a chess board pattern of 68 × 62 bits is used. The bright bits of this pattern have a gray level of 255 and the dark bits have a gray level of 0. In order to measure the uniformity of the display, the LCTV is imaged onto the CCD array, and the intensity is captured by a frame grabber. Figure 5(a) shows the detected image. Note that the intensity distribution of one horizontal line of the image is superimposed on

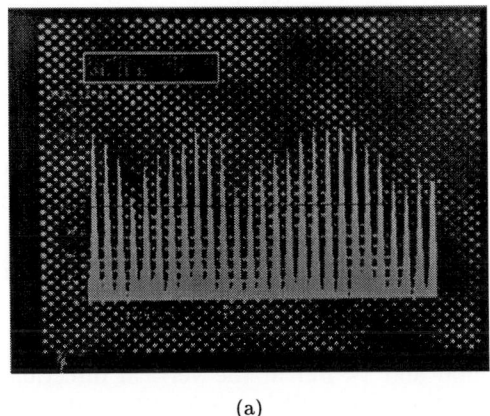

(a)

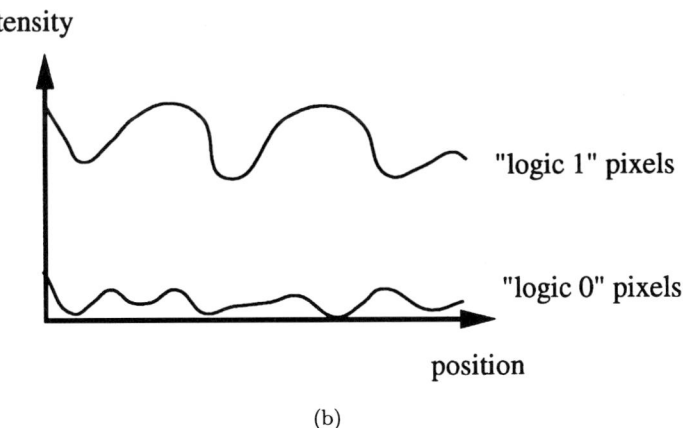

(b)

Fig. 5. Light distribution of LCTV. (a) Intensity distribution of a chess board pattern, (b) Envelopes of the intensity distribution of logic 1 and logic 0 pixels.

the same photo. The envelope of the distributions for bright and dark data points are shown in Fig. 5(b). It is seen that the peak to peak variation in either the dark or bright pixels can be as high as 36%. In the optical memory system, there are other components such as lenses and the photorefractive crystal placed between the LCTV and the CCD, the uniformity of the detected image will be further reduced. If a fixed value is chosen for determining logic 0 or 1 of each bit, then there is a high possibility that an error bit will be produced at the valleys of the bright spots or at the peaks of the dark spots.

In order to alleviate this problem, we have constructed a look-up table to provide the thresholding values for each data bit. This look-up table is constructed in the beginning stage of hologram recording. We first record two holograms of chess board pages. The first optical page is a chess board pattern with alternating bright and dark blocks. The second optical page is another chess board image with a bright and dark patterns which is inverted to that of the first page. Other data files are recorded in the third and the following pages. During the hologram readout stage, these two chess board pages are reconstructed and detected. The average value of the intensity of logic 1 and logic 0 at each position gives the thresholding value for that bit. Thus, a look up table is constructed and is used for the decoding of the following data pages.

Since the optical pages are displayed on LCTV and the holograms are read out and detected by a CCD array, it is important to have perfect imaging between the LCTV and CCD. Ideally, one pixel of the liquid crystal should be imaged into one pixel of the CCD detector. In the practical case, there is a dimensional mismatch between the two devices. The period of the LCTV pixels in the horizontal direction is about 56 $\mu$m and 48 $\mu$m in the vertical direction. For the CCD array, it is about 16 $\mu$m in the horizontal and 12 $\mu$m in the vertical directions. The two devices are not well matched. We resolved this geometrical problem by using a coordinate matching technique, as shown in Fig. 6. In this technique, 510 × 492 pixels of the CCD array are mapped onto the 512 × 512 frame grabber, as indicated by the dotted rectangle in the figure. The optical system is adjusted such that the image of the LCD panel is as large as possible but is maintained within the detection area of the CCD, as indicated by the chess board image in the figure. The coordinates for the corners of the chess board are detected as $(x1, y1), (x2, y1), (x1, y2), (x2, y2)$. This region represents one page of optical data of 68 × 62 bits. Thus, the coordinates of the center of the $(m \times 68 + n)$th bit can be calculated by the expressions:

$$x = x1 + m \times (x2 - x1 + 0.5)/68$$

$$y = y1 + n \times (y2 - y1 + 0.5)/62 \,. \tag{1}$$

In optical experiments, the image of the LCTV is measured and the coordinates of the four corners of the chess board image are determined. Then, the reconstructed images are detected and the optical signal of each bit can be obtained by using Eq. (1).

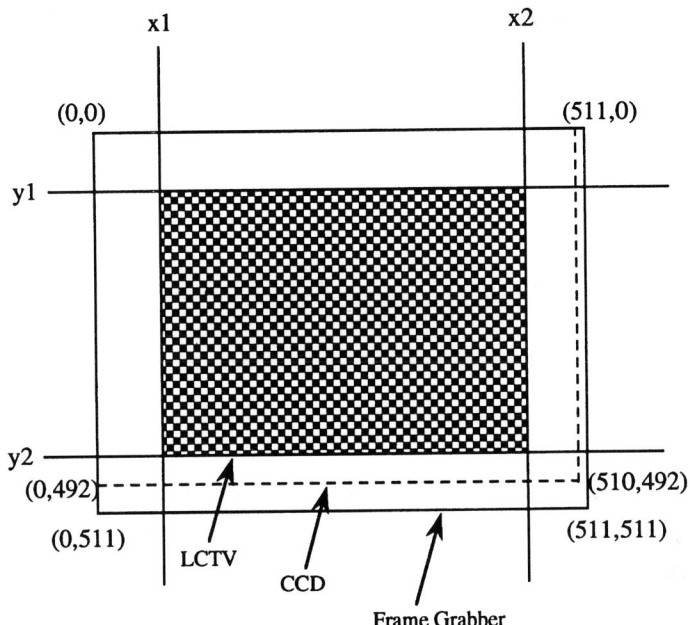

Fig. 6. The coordinate matching between LCTV and CCD.

Since each optical page represents 525 bytes of digital data, thus, a data file which is larger than 525 bytes will be divided into multiple pages. These are stored in the LiNbO$_3$ crystal using the angle multiplexing technique. An exposure schedule for photorefractive holograms was used such that equal diffraction efficiency of the multiple holograms could be obtained. In the practical case, the diffraction efficiencies of each of the readout pages are not equal because of the perturbations to the optical system and the scattering noise in the crystal. Furthermore, if the holograms are not fixed after the recording, then the memory is decayed due to the illumination of the reading beam. Figure 7 shows the distribution of the intensity of the readout pages of 66 holograms. In the figure, the horizontal axis represents the page number, and the vertical axis represents the histogram of the intensity of each page (i.e. the brightness of the vertical axis is proportional to the number of pixels of the corresponding gray level). It is seen from the figure that in the first few pages, the intensity of data bits with logic 1 are close to gray level 255 and that of logic 0 are close to gray level 0. As the page number is increased, the holograms are erased by the reading beam and the intensity of logic 1 is decayed. Finally, the intensity for logic 1 bits is only about 80. On the other hand, the brightness of logic 0 is increased due to the fanning and noise gratings produced in the crystal by the reading beam. Thus the dynamic range of the readout signal is reduced and discrimination between logic 1 and logic 0 is difficult.

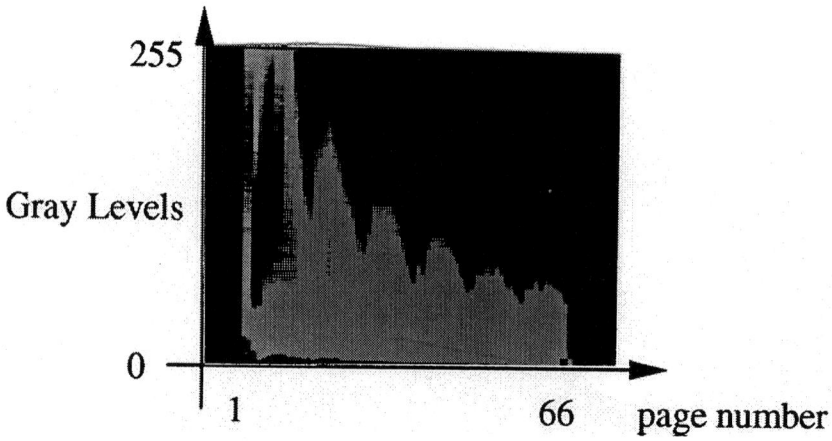

Fig. 7. The gray level histograms of 66 holograms. The brightness of the vertical axis is proportional to the number of pixels at that gray level.

In order to alleviate this problem, we have designed a method to expand the dynamic range of the readout signal. During the decoding stage, the reconstructed image is detected, the histograms of the intensity is calculated, then the dynamic range of each page is expanded such that it covers gray levels from 0 to 255. Figure 8 shows one example. Figure 8(a) shows a intensity histogram of one readout page. The dynamic range of the gray levels is seen to be from zero to 100 and the middle value is at 50. In order to expand the dynamic range, the histogram of this page is shifted so that the middle value is at 128, and the dynamic range is from 78 to 178, as shown in Fig. 8(b). Then, an appropriate regime of the shifted dynamic range is selected and expanded such that it is from 0 to 255. The selection of the regime depends on the characteristics of the readout signals. In the example shown in Fig. 8(c), 30% of the dynamic range is selected for the expansion, thus the expanded gray levels for each bit is given by

$$g = 128 + (x - 128) \times 100/30 . \tag{2}$$

Under this condition, signals with gray levels at or higher than 156 (the shaded region in the right-hand side of Fig. 8(b)) will be saturated at 256, and gray levels at or less than 90 (the shaded region in the left-hand side of Fig. 8(b)) will be set to be 0, as shown by two arrows in Fig. 8(c). Note that the dynamic thresholding, coordinate matching, and dynamic range expansion operations are performed in the computer during the decoding stage of hologram readout. These will increase computing time and thus decrease the decoding speed of the holographic memory. However, using these techniques, the performance of the holographic memory can be greatly improved, as is demonstrated in the experiments.

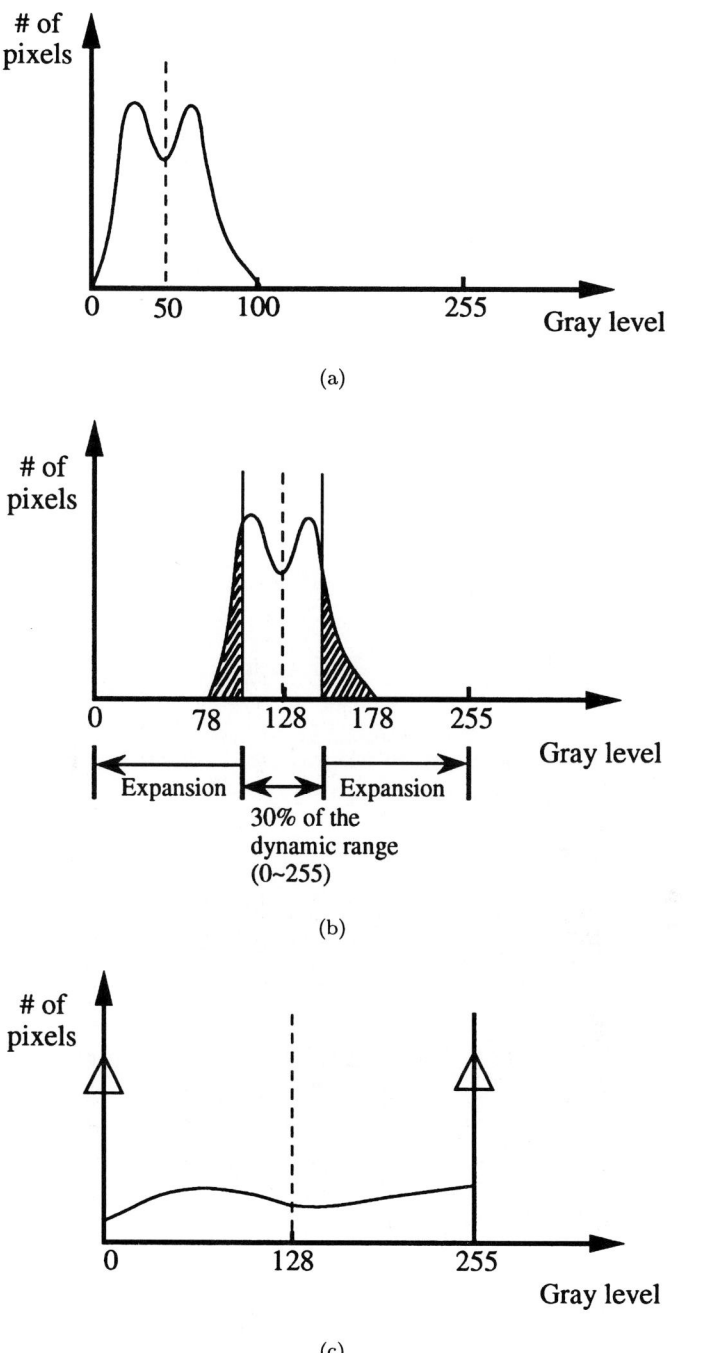

(a)

(b)

(c)

Fig. 8. Expansion of the dynamic range of the detected image. (a) Histogram of the gray levels of the detected image, (b) A shifted version of the histogram, (c) Expansion of the histogram.

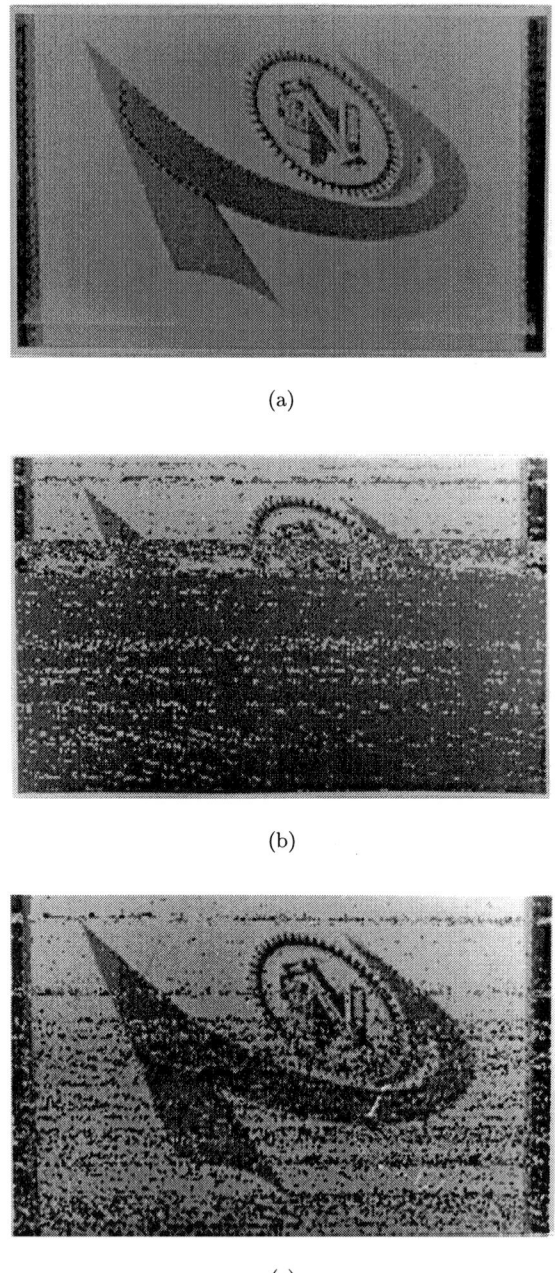

(a)

(b)

(c)

Fig. 9. Experimental result of the digital holographic storage. (a) The original photo, (b) The retrieved photo (with no adjustment on the dynamic range of the reconstructed image), (c) The retrieved photo after 50% expansion of the dynamic range. Note that the original photo is a color printing.

### 4.3. *Experimental results*

In the first experiment, the performance of the optical system with no crystal is tested, i.e. the interface between the optical system and the computer is tested before the holographic memory is made. A random number program is used to generate digital data files for the optical pages. 10,000 optical pages are generated. Each page is displayed on the LCTV, imaged onto the CCD, and is decoded back into digital signals. No any error bit occurred in the retrieved files. If we define the bit error rate (BER) as the number of error bits times the inverse of the total number of data bits, then since each page has 4,216 bits and the BER of the optical system is estimated to be less than $2.38 \times 10^{-8}$.

Next, the $LiNbO_3$ crystal is put into the system. A computer file of a color photo is used for the holographic storage experiment. The data file is 8 Kbytes. According to our encoding method, the digital file is encoded into 16 optical pages. These are recorded in the $LiNbO_3$ crystal by using the angle multiplexing technique. The holographic memory is reconstructed from the crystal, detected by the CCD array, and is decoded. The color photo is retrieved exactly and the decoded file has no error bit. The BER in this case is estimated to be less than $1.48 \times 10^{-5}$. This result shows the feasibility of our holographic memory.

Finally, a color photo of 32 Kbytes is used for the experiment. This data file is encoded into 64 optical pages. In addition, there are two pages of chess board images which are used for the construction of the look up table for dynamic thresholding. Thus, the total number of holograms is 66. The optical pages are recorded into the $LiNbO_3$ crystal to form the holographic memory. In reading the memory, the holograms are reconstructed and the photo is retrieved. The results are shown in Fig. 9. Figure 9(a) shows the original photo while Fig. 9(b) shows the reconstructed photo which is decoded but with no adjustment on the dynamic range of the detected signals. It is seen that the photo was not recovered well. The BER is about 70%. Figure 9(c) is the retrieved photo which is decoded with 50% expansion of the dynamic range. It is seen that the quality of the readout image is greatly improved. The BER is reduced to be 8%. This demonstrates that great improvement can be obtained from the adjustment of the dynamic range, especially for cases of large memories. It should be noted that, no matter how the dynamic range is expanded, there always remained some pixels with gray levels around the middle range, i.e. 128. These pixels are difficult to distinguish between logic 1 and 0. In other words, using the dynamic expansion technique, there is a limit that the BER can be improved. The fundamental method for improving the BER would be to fix the photorefractive holograms so that there will be no memory decay in the readout stage.[12-14]

## 5. Conclusions

We have presented a read-only holographic memory for the storage of digital data files. The holographic memory is recorded in the volume of an iron-doped $LiNbO_3$

photorefractive crystal the using angle-multiplexing technique. The interface techniques between the optical memory and a personal computer, and the coding and decoding methods between the digital data file and the optical memory are described. In addition, we have constructed a dynamic thresholding method to improve the non-uniformity problem of the LCTV, developed a coordinate matching technique for matching the dimensions of LCTV and CCD pixels, and designed a dynamic range expansion method for resolving the hologram decaying problem. By using these techniques, the performance of the holographic memory has been improved greatly. In optical experiments, we have demonstrated a holographic memory for the data file of a 8 KB color photo. The photo is retrieved correctly from the memory without any error bit. The BER is equivalent to be less than $1.48 \times 10^{-5}$. In another memory experiment of a 32 KB color photo, the BER is estimated to be 7%. Further improvement on the BER of large memories can be expected if the hologram fixing techniques have been applied.

## Acknowledgment

This research is supported by the National Science Council, Taiwan, R. O. C. under the contracts: NSC 85-2215-E-009-016, NSC 85-2732-E-009-011, and NSC 86-2215-E-009-009.

## References

1. P. J. van Heerden, "Theory of optical information storage in solids", *Appl. Opt.* **2**, 4 (1963) 393–400.
2. E. N. Leith, A. Kozma, J. Upatnieks, J. Marks, and N. Massey, "Holographic data storage in three-dimensional media", *Appl. Opt.* **5**, 8 (1966) 1303–1311.
3. F. S. Chen, J. T. LaMacchia, and D. B. Fraser, "Holographic storage in lithium niobate", *Appl. Phys. Lett.* **13**, 7 (1968) 223–225.
4. F. H. Mok, "Angle-multiplexed storage of 5,000 holograms in lithium niobate", *Opt. Lett.* **18**, 11 (1993) 915–917.
5. H. Y. Li and D. Psaltis, "Three-dimensional holographic disks", *Appl. Opt.* **33** (1994) 3764–3774.
6. J. F. Heanue, M. C. Bashhaw, and L. Hesselink, "Volume holographic storage and retrieval of digital data", *Science* **265** (1994) 749–752.
7. J. H. Hong, I. McMichael, T. Y. Chang, W. Christian, and E. G. Paek, "Volume holographic memory systems: techniques and architectures", *Opt. Eng.* **34**, 8 (1995) 2193–2203.
8. D. Psaltis and F. H. Mok, "Holographic memories", *Scientific American* **273**, 5 (1995) 70–76.
9. G. T. Sincerbox, (ed.), *Selected Papers on Holographic Storage*, SPIE Milestone Series, **95**, SPIE, Bellingham, Washington (1994).
10. M. A. Neifeld and M. McDonald, "Error correction for increasing the usable capacity of photorefractive memories", *Opt. Lett.* **19** (1994) 1483–1485.
11. J. F. Heanue, M. C. Bashaw, and L. Hesselink, "Channel codes for digital holographic data storage", *J. Opt. Soc. Am. A* **12**, 11 (1995) 2432–2439.

12. J. J. Amodi, "Holographic pattern fixing in electro-optic crystals", *Appl Phys. Lett.* **18**, 12 (1971) 540–542.

13. D. L. Staebler, W. J. Burke, W. Philips, and J. J. Amodi, "Multiple storage and erasure of fixed holograms in Fe-doped LiNbO$_3$", *Appl. Phys. Lett.* **26**, 4 (1975) 182–184.

14. J. F. Heanue, M. G. Bashaw, A. J. Daiber, R. Snyder, and L. Hesselink, "Digital holographic storage system incorporating thermal fixing in lithium niobate", *Opt. Lett.* **21**, 19 (1996) 1615–1617.

International Journal of High Speed Electronics and Systems, Vol. 8, No. 4 (1997) 767–777

# INVESTIGATION OF MULTIWAVELENGTH OPTICAL POWER LIMITING AMPLIFIER AND ITS APPLICATIONS IN HIGH-SPEED SONET WAVELENGTH-DIVISION MULTIPLEXING SELF-HEALING RING NETWORK

YUNG-KUANG CHEN[*], SHIEN-KUEI LIAW[†], and SIEN CHI[†]

*Institute of Electro-Optical Engineering,*
*National Sun Yat-Sen University,*
*P. O. Box 59-83, Kaohsiung,*
*Taiwan 80424, R.O.C.*

†*Institute of Electro-Optical Engineering,*
*National Chiao-Tung University,*
*Taiwan, R.O.C.*

A multiwavelength optical power limiting amplifier (OLA) for high-speed SONET self-healing ring (SHR) networks is reported. Four possible OLA configurations are investigated. We find that the configuration consisting of a high-gain common erbium-doped fiber amplifier (EDFA) followed by a grating-multiplexed multiple-power-EDFA module is the best scheme for multiwavelength power-limiting operation. A constant channel output of $> 11$ dBm, small inter-channel power variation of $\leq 0.5$ dB, and fairly low noise figure are obtained within a large dynamic range of 45 dB. Network application in a SHR network is also demonstrated and the ring size of 150 km served by a single three-WDM-channel OLA at channel rates of 2.488 Gb/s is obtained.

## 1. Introduction

The synchronous optical network (SONET) self-healing ring (SHR) architectures have been increasingly deployed to provide network survivability. Among various architectures, the four-fiber bi-directional SHR one (BSHR/4) has the highest available capacity and can work with today's operation systems with minimum change.[1] It has been shown that the use of optical power limiting amplifiers (OLAs)[2] and associated optical switches in such BSHR/4 networks can reduce the network cost drastically.[3] Limiting-power amplification has been demonstrated using two,[3] three,[2] or composite[4] cascaded erbium-doped fiber amplifiers (EDFAs) which require high pump power and a number of optical components, such as isolators and very narrow-bandwidth optical filters[2,3] or differential lump loss components.[4] However, the indispensable inter-staged narrowband optical filters of the proposed OLAs in Refs. 3 and 2 restrict the wavelength-division-multiplexing (WDM) transmission operation. Furthermore, large inter-channel power variation may be incurred for the proposed OLA in Ref. 4 operated in WDM transmission, which is due to the spectral gain dependence of the EDFA. The multiwavelength WDM SHR architecture[5] makes it easier, more graceful, and less expensive to upgrade the embedded SHR networks without adding more fibers or using high-speed electronics ($\geq$ 10 Gb/s) facilities. Therefore, the multiwavelength OLAs with a large dynamic range are strongly required for the WDM SHR networks.

In this paper, we investigate four possible multiwavelength OLA configurations without using any inter-staged optical bandpass filters. We find that the configuration consisting of a high-gain common erbium-doped fiber amplifier (EDFA) followed by a grating-multiplexed multiple-power-EDFA module is the best scheme for multiwavelength power-limiting operation. It can provide high channel output power and small inter-channel power variations with a fairly low noise figure characteristics. To our knowledge, this is the first multiwavelength OLA with a large dynamic range of 45 dB reported to date. We then apply it in a WDM BSHR/4 interoffice network. The network feasibility was tested by system experiments employing a single three-WDM-channel OLA as a power amplifier and a pre-amplifier for 2.488 Gb/s channel-line-rate transmission.

## 2. Configurations of Multiwavelength OLAs

Four possible configurations (A, B, C, and D) of multiwavelength OLAs are depicted in Fig. 1. Configuration A is formed by cascading two EDFAs directly. Configuration B is constructed with a high-gain EDFA followed by a grating-multiplexed amplifier (GMA) module. The GMA module consists of a pair of diffraction-grating-based demultiplexer (DEMUX) and multiplexer (MUX),[6] and multiple power EDFAs. Configuration C is composed of a GMA module followed by a common power EDFA. Configuration D is formed by cascading two GMA modules. All 980 nm-pumped EDFAs are unidirectional due to the built-in optical isolator at the output port of each EDFA. In each configuration, the EDFA was single-forward-pumped with 50 mW for each first-staged EDFA to offer a sufficient gain, and were dual-pumped with a total of 100 mW for each second-staged power EDFA to offer high saturated output power. The DEMUX and MUX have four channels with same wavelengths of 1547, 1549, 1551, and 1553 nm. The 3 dB and 20 dB down bandwidths of each channel are about 0.4 and 0.9 nm, respectively. The average channel isolation and insertion loss of each MUX and DEMUX are about 35 dB and 3.5 dB, respectively.

The experimental setup for examining the characteristics of the multiwavelength OLA is described in the following. Three DFB lasers at 1547, 1549, and 1553 nm, respectively, were amplified individually by a 980 nm-pumped power EDFA, combined through a MUX and then fed to a variable optical attenuator (VOA1). We changed the attenuator loss to control these channel input signal levels simultaneously, ranging from $-45$ to $+5$ dBm, and then launched these signals into the OLA. A second variable optical attenuator (VOA2) was inserted between the OLA and a DEMUX. Both VOA1 and VOA2 are spectral-flattened optical attenuators.

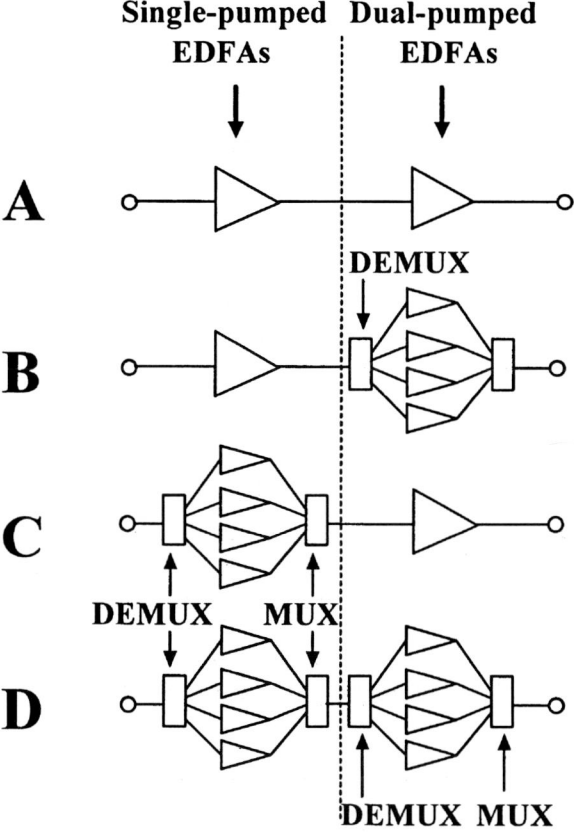

**Fig. 1.** Four possible configurations (A, B, C, and D) for multiwavelength WDM optical power limiting amplifier. EDFA: erbium-doped fiber amplifier, MUX/DEMUX: the wavelength multiplexer/demultiplexer.

## 3. Characteristic Comparison of Multiwavelength OLAs

Figure 2 shows the measured gain versus channel input power at 1553 nm under three-wavelength operation for the first-staged amplifier and the cascaded amplifier (i.e. the multiwavelength OLA) of configurations A, B, and C. For the cascaded amplification, the cascaded gains are all increased for three configurations as compared with the first-staged gains. Configuration B provides the highest cascaded small-signal channel gain of about 55 dB. Configuration A offers the lowest cascaded gain for input channel signals less than −25 dBm. The measured cascaded channel output power versus channel input power for these configurations at 1547 nm and 1553 nm are shown in Fig. 3. Note that configuration B has the smallest inter-channel output power variations of ≤ 0.5 dB, and provides a channel output power of ≥ +11 dBm as the channel input signals varied from −45 dBm to 0 dBm. This is due to the fact that the narrowband channel-filtering of the DEMUX not only

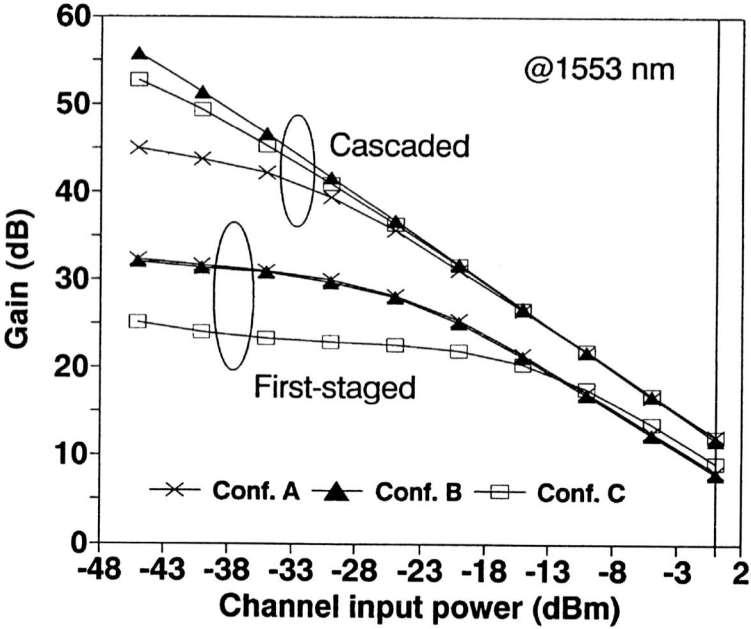

Fig. 2. Measured gain against channel input power at 1553 nm under three-wavelength operation for the first-staged amplifier and the cascaded OLA of configurations A, B, and C.

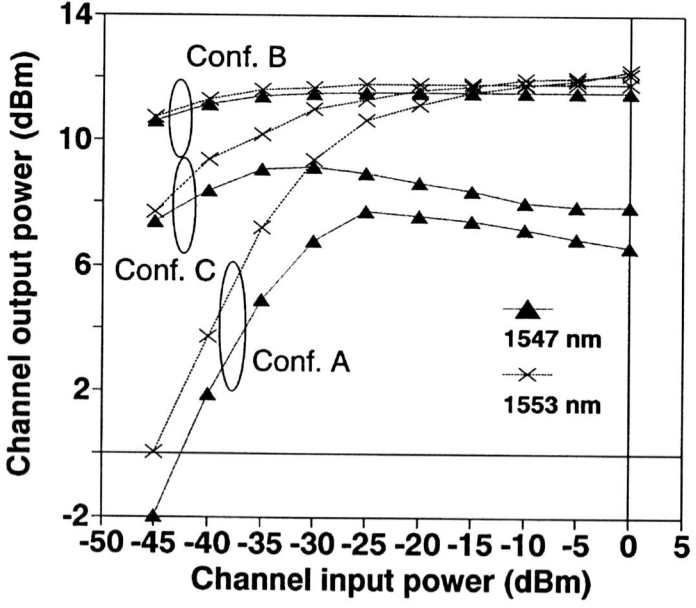

Fig. 3. Measured channel output power against channel input power at 1547 nm and 1553 nm for the cascaded OLA of configurations A, B, and C.

selects the channel signal, but also eliminates most of the amplified spontaneous emission (ASE) noise generated in the first-staged amplifier.

On the contrary, configuration A (where no narrowband optical filter was used) had the worst inter-channel output power variations of 2 to 5 dB within this input signal range, and had the lowest channel output power when input signal level was less than −30 dBm. The low channel output power was due to the depletion of the gain of the second-staged amplifier by the excess ASE noise power generated in the first-staged EDFA. At large signal inputs, only the signal itself plays a role; the ASE of the first-stage has already been suppressed. This is why in Fig. 2, there is no difference among three configurations for large channel input power. The saturation induces strong spectrally dependent loss that generates large inter-channel power variation among WDM channels spanning the spectral region from 1540–1560 nm. This phenomenon is quite serious for the homogeneously broadened three-level erbium-doped alumino-germano-silicate glass system[7,8] used in this work. Configuration C provides modest channel output power due to the fact that most ASE generated in the first-staged GMA module have been eliminated through channel-filtering of the MUX, but with worse inter-channel output power variation (0.5 to 3 dB) due to the same reasoning as that of configuration A.

Figure 4 shows the measured channel output power and noise figure of both the first-staged amplifier and the cascaded OLA for configuration B at 1553 nm.

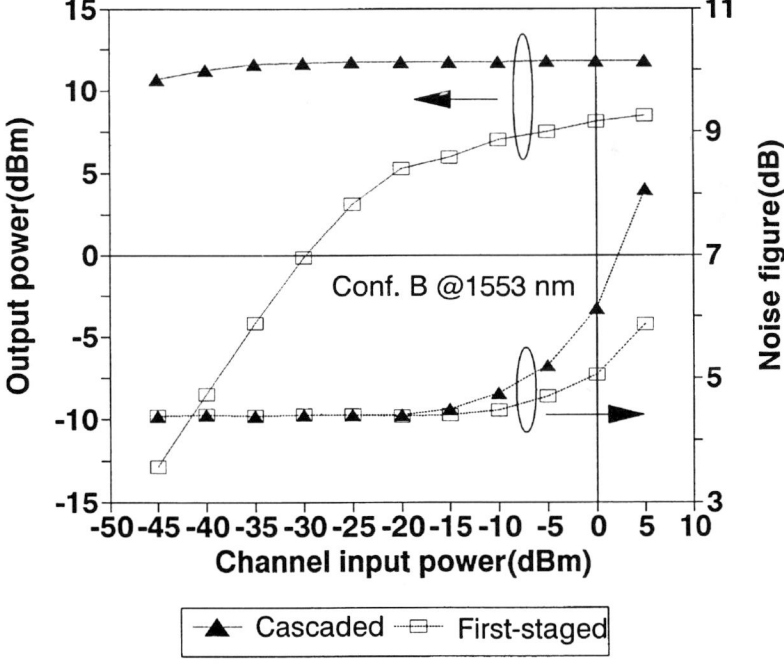

Fig. 4. Measured channel output power and noise figure against channel input power at 1553 nm for the first-staged amplifier and the cascaded OLA of configuration B.

Whereas the channel gain was "soft-limited" in the first-staged EDFA, the OLA channel output power was "hard-limited" at +11.3 dBm. The noise figure measurement technique is the polarization-nulling method.[9] For input power levels lower than −15 dBm, a noise figure of about 4.3 dB was observed in both cases for all configurations. For input power levels higher than −15 dBm, the noise figures increased in both cases. The OLA noise figure characteristics ($NF_{total}$) can be understood from $NF_{total} = NF_1 + (NF_2/G_1)$,[2] where $NF_i$ and $G_i$ ($i = 1, 2$) are the noise figures and gains of the two amplifier stages, respectively. It is clear that in the small signal region where $G_1$ is high, $NF_{total}$ is dominated by $NF_1$. However, as the OLA was operated deeply into gain saturation, these two amplifier gains started to decrease drastically. In addition, $NF_2$ began to increase significantly as the input signal power increased.[10,11] Therefore, the cascaded noise figure became much greater than that of the first-stage when the OLA was operated deeply into saturation, as shown in Fig. 4.

The proposed configuration D, as shown in Fig. 1(d), is only attractive for WDM operation with channels at both 1530 nm and 1550 nm bands simultaneously. This is because power suppression of the channels at the 1530 nm band by the WDM channels at the 1550 nm band will be incurred even for configuration B with large input channel signals operation. However, configuration D is less cost-effective than configuration B due to additional channel EDFAs, DEMUX, and MUX in the first-staged GMA module. Consequently, from the performance and cost-effective points of view, configuration B is the best scheme for multiwavelength power-limiting operation in 1540 to 1560 nm range. Figure 5 shows the measured channel output

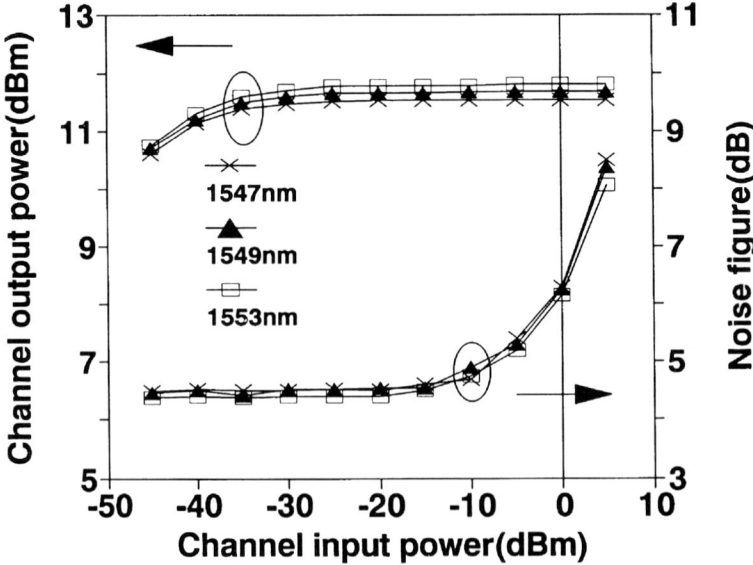

Fig. 5. Channel output power and noise figure curves against channel input power for different channel wavelengths of the configuration B OLA.

power and noise figure versus channel input power of the configuration B OLA for different channel wavelengths. Note that it provided an output power of $\geq +11$ dBm per channel with small inter-channel power variations of $\leq 0.5$ dB as the WDM channel input signals varied from $-45$ dBm to 0 dBm. The noise figure was about 4.3 dB and below 6.3 dB for the channel input power up to $-15$ dBm and 0 dBm, respectively.

Furthermore, both the variable optical attenuators, VOA1 and VOA2, are spectral-flattened devices with the spectral characteristic of attenuation difference of 0.04 dB in the wavelength range from 1547 nm to 1553 nm. Thus, the individual channel fade between 1547 nm and 1553 nm is negligible. The excellent performance of the multiwavelength OLA obtained here may be attributed to the OLA configuration, narrow spectral filtering passband and high channel isolation characteristics of the MUX and DEMUX, and the design of each second-staged power EDFA.

## 4. OLA System Performance and Network Demonstration

To examine the system performance of the configuration B OLA, the experimental setup in Fig. 6 was used. A 2.488 Gb/s pseudorandom $2^{31} - 1$ NRZ signal was used to modulate a chirp-adjustable Ti:LiNbO$_3$ external modulator[12] for the channel at 1549 nm. At the receiving end, the demultiplexed channel signal was detected by an optical PIN-FET receiver and then measured by the bit-error-rate (BER) tester. The receiver sensitivity, $P_r$, at the input port of PIN-FET receiver was $-29.1$ dBm at a BER of $1 \times 10^{-9}$.

To clarify the system experiment and link loss analysis, we define some variables and terminology. The transmitted per-channel power, $P_t$, is the optical power of each wavelength channel signal at the output port of the MUX at the transmitting end (i.e. before the input port of the VOA1). The WDM OLA per-channel input power, $P_{in}$, is the channel power level at the input port of the WDM OLA. The WDM OLA per-channel output power, $P_{out}$, is the channel power level at the output port of the WDM OLA. The received channel power, $P_x$, is the channel power level at the input port of DEMUX at the receiving end. That means $P_x = P_r + 3.5$ dB where 3.5 dB is the averaged channel insertion loss of the DEMUX and $P_r$ ($= -29.1$ dBm) is the receiver sensitivity of the PIN-FET receiver at a BER of $1 \times 10^{-9}$. In consequence, $P_x = -25.6$ dBm. Furthermore, the link-1 loss and link-2 loss as shown in Fig. 6 are the allowable attenuation of the VOA1 and VOA2, respectively, at a BER of $1 \times 10^{-9}$. In other words, the link-1 loss $= P_t - P_{in}$ and the link-2 loss $= P_{out} - P_x$. In evaluating the system performance of WDM OLA, we changed the VOA1 attenuation loss to control $P_{in}$ simultaneously and then adjusted the VOA2 attenuation loss to maintain a received channel power $P_x$ of $-25.6$ dBm (i.e. $P_r = -29.1$ dBm) at a BER of $1 \times 10^{-9}$. Finally, the allowable total link loss is defined as the summation of the link-1 loss and the link-2 loss. The allowable total link loss is the performance index of OLA application as an in-line amplifier in single and cascading operations.

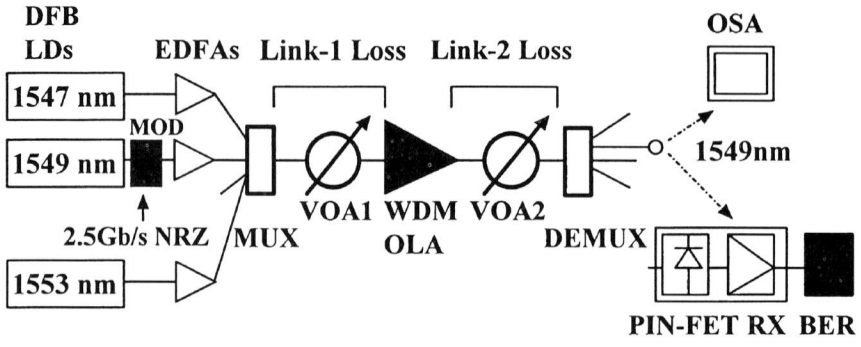

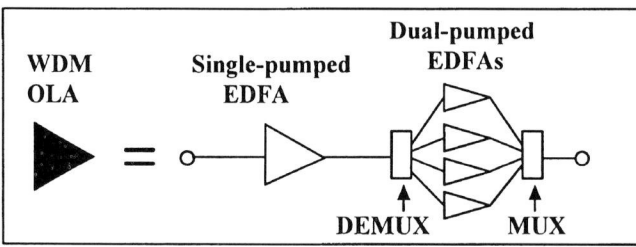

Fig. 6. Experimental setup for evaluating OLA system performance.

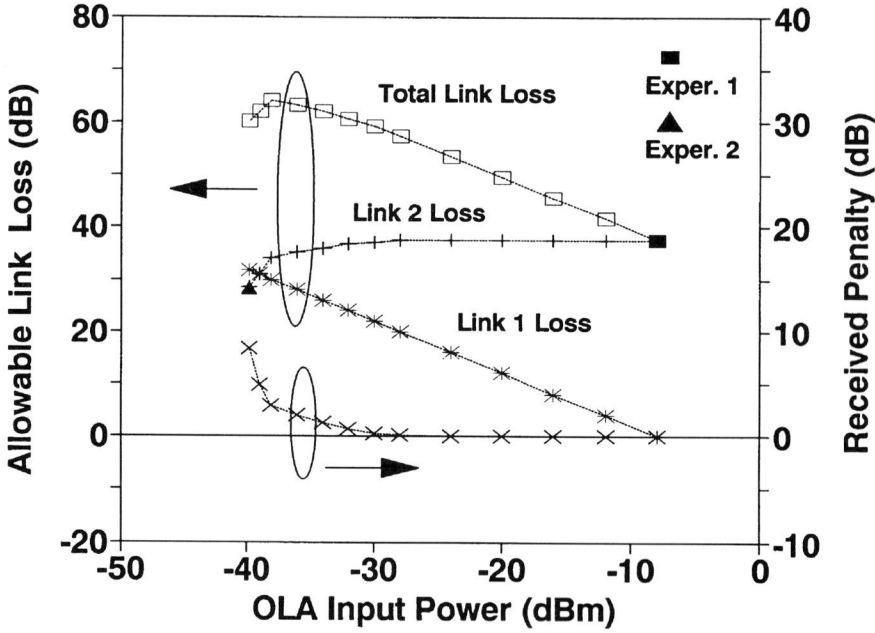

Fig. 7. Allowable link transmission loss and the received power penalty at a BER of $1 \times 10^{-9}$ versus channel input power of configuration B OLA for 2.488 Gb/s NRZ signal.

Figure 7 shows the allowable link transmission loss and the received power penalty at a BER of $1 \times 10^{-9}$ versus the WDM OLA per-channel input power, $P_{in}$, from $-8$ dBm to $-40$ dBm. Although the transmitted per-channel power $P_t$ can be as large as $+5$ dBm, the power level of $P_t$ set at $-8$ dBm is the reasonable transmitted power level after the external modulator and MUX in practical situation. Note that the allowable link-1 loss decreases linearly as $P_{in}$ increases, but the allowable link-2 loss slightly increases from 28.4 dB at $P_{in} = -40$ dBm to 37.6 dB at $P_{in} = -8$ dBm. The power penalty was increased from 0 dB at $P_{in} = -8$ dBm to 7.6 dB at $P_{in} = -40$ dBm, which is because the dominant detected electronic noise is the receiver thermal noise at $P_{in} = -8$ dBm and the signal-spontaneous beat noise becomes comparable with thermal noise at $P_{in} = -40$ dBm.

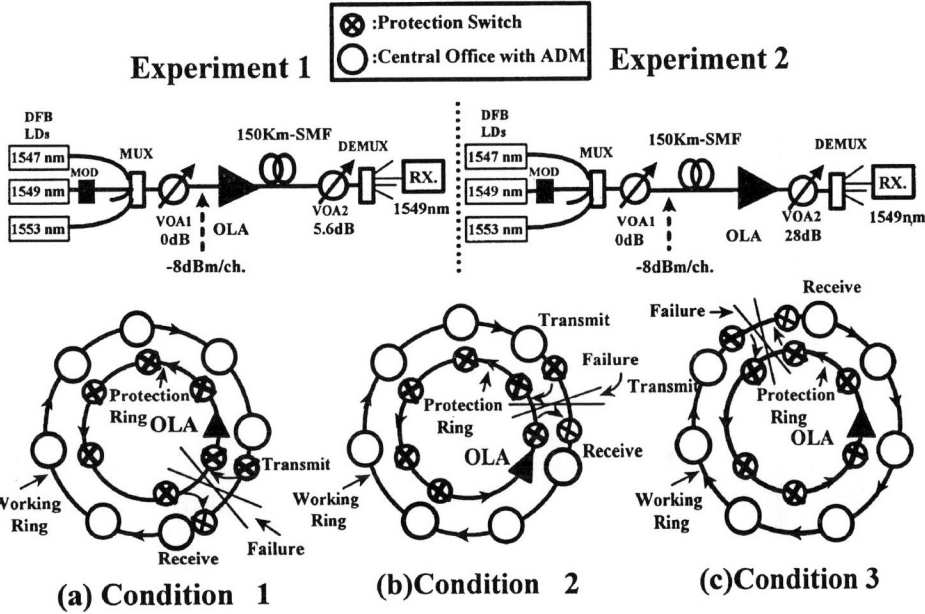

Fig. 8. Three self-healing ring network failure conditions (1)–(3) and the experimental verifications (1) and (2). Bit rate tested at the 1549 nm channel was 2.488 Gb/s.

In a four-fiber BSHR WDM SONET architecture, an OLA is supposed to work as a power, in-line, or a pre-amplifier, depending on the failure location along the ring, as shown by conditions (1) to (3) in Fig. 8 (note that only two of the four fibers are shown). To demonstrate that an OLA can function satisfactorily in these conditions, we carried out two system experiments configured according to condition (1) as a power-amplifier (**Exper. 1**) and condition (2) as a pre-amplifier (**Exper. 2**). We use conventional single-mode fiber (SMF) with a length of 150 km in these system experiments. The transmission loss, including the connection and splice losses, of the 150 km SMF was about 31.6 dB.

The measured results for the two system experiments are also shown in Fig. 7. For both experiments, there was a negligible power penalty induced by the fiber dispersion (17 ps/km/nm) of 150 km SMF due to the use of chirp-adjustable external modulator. That is the reason we used a chirp-adjustable external modulator instead of an ordinary external modulator to eliminate the dispersion penalty in the system transmission. Although a system experiment corresponding to condition (3), as shown in Fig. 8(c), was not carried out, we can easily predict the maximum allowable total link loss at a BER of $1 \times 10^{-9}$ for the in-line OLA operation to be about 64 dB at $P_{in} = -36$ dBm, according to the total link loss in Fig. 7 with negligible dispersion penalty. However, the maximum ring size served by this single OLA is now limited by the pre-amplifier case of 150 km long SMF. If low-noise optical receiver with higher receiver sensitivity and high-power transmitter are used, the system performance and the ring size can be further improved within the full OLA dynamic range.

## 5. Conclusions

In conclusion, we have demonstrated the multiwavelength OLAs with a large dynamic range which can be used in an all-optical protection ring of high-speed SONET interoffice WDM SHR network. We found that the configuration consisting of a high-gain EDFA followed by a grating-multiplexed multiple-power-EDFA module is the best scheme to provide high channel output powers and small inter-channel power variations within a large dynamic range. A fairly-low noise figure of 5.4 dB for channel input power up to $-5$ dBm has been achieved. Network application in a SHR network has also been demonstrated. We have experimentally verified that a single OLA can handle a ring size of 150 km at SONET OC-48 channel rates. The proposed OLA may also find applications in high-speed multiwavelength WDM long-haul transmission, subscriber-loop distribution systems, and switching networks.

## Acknowledgments

The authors would like to thank W. Y. Guo, and the members of Photonics Technology Division in Chung-Hua Telecommunication Laboratories for their technical and facility supports.

## References

1. T. H. Wu and W. I. Way, "A novel passive protected SONET bi-directional ring architecture", *IEEE Military Commun. Conf.*, McLean, VA, Nov. 1991, paper 38.5.
2. W. I. Way, D. Chen, M. A. Saifi, M. J. Andrejco, A. Yi-Yan, A. Von Lehman, and C. Lin, "High gain limiting erbium-doped fibre amplifier with over 30 dB dynamic range", *Electron. Lett.* **27** (1991) 211–213.
3. W. I. Way, T. H. Wu, A. Yi-Yan, M. J. Andrejco, and C. Lin, "Optical power limiting amplifier and its applications in an SONET self-healing ring network", *J. Lightwave Technol.* **10** (1992) 206–214.

4. O. C. Graydon, M. N. Zervas, and R. I. Laming, "Erbium-doped-fibre optical limiting amplifiers", *J. Lightwave Technol.* **13** (1995) 732–739.

5. T. H. Wu, *Fiber Network Service Survivability*, Artech House, New York, 1992.

6. J. P. Laude and J. M. Lerner, "Wavelength division multiplexing/demultiplexing (WDM) using diffraction grating", *Proc. SPIE* **503** (1984) 22–28.

7. R. G. Smart, J. L. Zyskind, J. W. Sulhoff, and D. J. DiGiovanni, "Dependence of performance of saturated in-line erbium-doped fiber amplifiers on pump wavelength around 1480 nm", *IEEE Photon, Technol. Lett.* **5** (1993) 523–525.

8. E. L. Goldstein, V. da Silva, L. Eskildsen, M. Andrejco, and Y. Silberberg, "Inhomogeneously broadened fiber-amplifier cascade for wavelength-multiplexed system", *IEEE Photon. Technol. Lett.* **5** (1993) 543–545.

9. J. Aspell, J. F. Federici, B. M. Nyman, D. L. Wilson, and D. S. Shenkl, "Accurate noise figure measurements of erbium-doped fiber amplifiers under saturation conditions", *Technical Dig. Opt. Fiber Commun. Conf.*, Feb. 1992, paper ThA4.

10. D. N. Payne and R.I. Laming, "Noise characteristics of erbium-doped fiber amplifier pumped at 980 nm", *IEEE Photon. Technol. Lett.* **2** (1990) 418–421.

11. W. I. Way, A. Lehman, J. Aspell Von, M. Andrejco, M. Suisi, and C. Lin, "Noise figure of a gain-saturated erbium-doped fiber amplifier pumped at 980 nm", *Technical Dig. Topical Meeting on Optical Amplifier and their Applications*, 1990, paper TuB3.

12. A. H. Gnauck, S. K. Korotky, J. J. Veselka, J. Nagel, C. T. Kemmerer, W. J. Minford, and D. T. Moser, "Dispersion penalty reduction using an optical modulator with adjustable chirp", *IEEE Photon. Technol. Lett.* **3** (1991) 916–918.